T0160114

THE PRACTICAL ENCYCLOPEDIA OF
WHOLE
FOODS

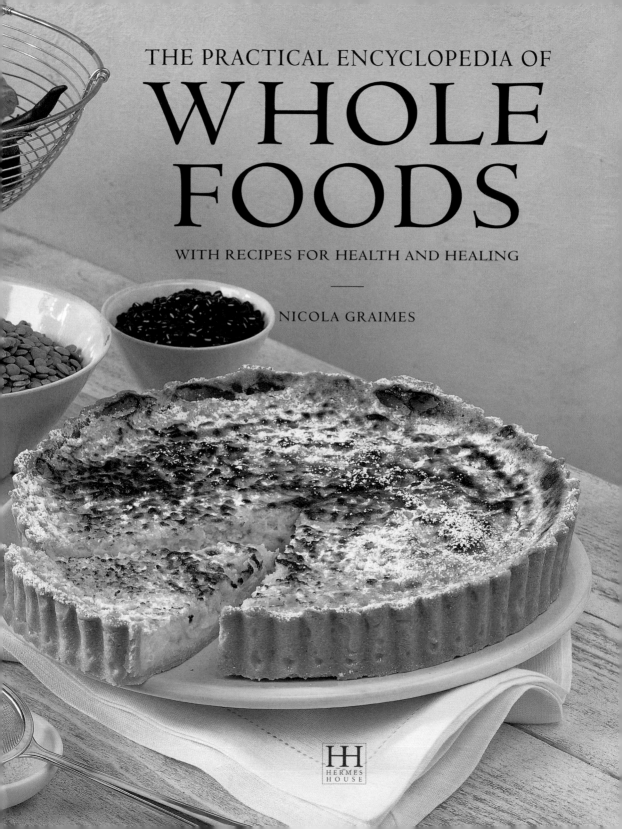

THE PRACTICAL ENCYCLOPEDIA OF
WHOLE
FOODS

WITH RECIPES FOR HEALTH AND HEALING

—

NICOLA GRAIMES

HH
HERMES
HOUSE

This edition is published by Hermes House, an imprint of Anness Publishing Ltd,
Blaby Road, Wigston, Leicestershire LE18 4SE; info@anness.com

www.hermeshouse.com; www.annesspublishing.com

If you like the images in this book and would like to investigate using them for publishing,
promotions or advertising, please visit our website www.practicalpictures.com
for more information.

Publisher: Joanna Lorenz
Editor: Jan Cutler
Designers: Nigel Partridge and Ian Sandom
Photographers: Thomas Odulate (recipes) and Amanda Heywood
Home Economists: Kate Jay and Annabel Ford
Production Controller: Helen Wang

© Anness Publishing Ltd 2012

A CIP catalogue record for this book is available from the British Library.

NOTES
Bracketed terms are intended for American readers.
For all recipes, quantities are given in both metric and imperial measures and, where appropriate,
in standard cups and spoons. Follow one set of measures, but not a mixture,
because they are not interchangeable.
Standard spoon and cup measures are level. 1 tsp = 5ml, 1 tbsp = 15ml, 1 cup = 250ml/8fl oz.
Australian standard tablespoons are 20ml. Australian readers should use 3 tsp
in place of 1 tbsp for measuring small quantities.
American pints are 16fl oz/2 cups. American readers should use 20fl oz/
2.5 cups in place of 1 pint when measuring liquids.
Electric oven temperatures in this book are for conventional ovens. When using a fan oven, the
temperature will probably need to be reduced by about 10–20°C/20–40°F. Since ovens vary,
you should check with your manufacturer's instruction book for guidance.
The nutritional analysis given for each recipe is calculated per portion (i.e. serving or item), unless
otherwise stated. If the recipe gives a range, such as Serves 4–6, then the nutritional analysis will be
for the smaller portion size, i.e. 6 servings. The analysis does not include optional
ingredients, such as salt added to taste.
Medium (US large) eggs are used unless otherwise stated.

PUBLISHER'S NOTE
Although the advice and information in this book are believed to be accurate and true at the time
of going to press, neither the authors nor the publisher can accept any legal responsibility or liability
for any errors or omissions that may have been made nor for any inaccuracies nor for any loss,
harm or injury that comes about from following instructions or advice in this book.

CONTENTS

Introduction

Throughout history, every culture has used food to prevent and treat illness and disease, and promote good health. The Egyptians praised the lentil for its ability to enlighten the mind; the Ancient Greeks and Romans used honey to heal wounds; while in China, sprouted beans and grains were used to treat a wide range of illnesses, from constipation to dropsy.

However, around the time of the industrial revolution, people in Western countries came to disregard the medicinal and therapeutic properties of food, and it is only relatively recently that interest in the healing qualities of food has been revived. This renewed interest, owing to our growing concern about what we eat and drink, and our quest for good health, is spurred on by scientists who have undertaken extensive research into eating habits, and have also investigated the properties of individual foods.

Numerous studies have revealed the positive attributes of a diet that is rich in fruit and vegetables, whole grains, nuts and seeds, and beans, complemented by a moderate amount of dairy foods. Studies have shown that vegetarians suffer less from many diseases, such as obesity, cancer, heart disease, gallstones, diabetes and constipation, that plague modern Western cultures. In fact, every scientific study comparing vegetarians with people eating a typical Western diet has found the former to be healthier and less likely to suffer from illness. Yet, vegetarianism is not just about achieving optimum health, it should also be an enjoyable and delicious way of eating.

WHAT ARE WHOLE FOODS?

Whole foods are foods to which nothing has been added or taken away. They are foods that haven't been unnecessarily altered or subjected to chemical processing, or loaded with harmful additives, colourings, or flavourings. In the narrowest sense, whole foods are specifically unrefined dried ingredients, such as grains, pulses, beans and seeds, but in this book we have taken the liberty to expand the term to include all foods that should be included in a healthy diet. It is important to choose unrefined foods whenever you can, simply because they ensure the greatest intake of vitamins, minerals and fibre. When food is processed, precious nutrients are taken away as a result, although there are various degrees to which this occurs. However, some would argue that a diet consisting entirely of whole foods could be decidedly brown and boring. A healthy whole foods diet should include a wide range of other ingredients to add both variety and

Right: A wide range of organic produce is available in health-food stores.

essential nutrients. Plenty of fruit and vegetables, dairy products, fats and oils, and natural sweeteners are all needed to make whole foods palatable and appealing. And there's no reason why, if you are eating mainly whole foods, that you can't include a few refined foods. A little white flour added to a wholemeal (whole-wheat) cake or pastry, for instance, will give a lighter end result and will only affect the nutritional value marginally. It is not a sin to eat white rice instead of brown, or plain pasta rather than wholemeal occasionally, if the rest of the

Vegetarian Children

Children can thrive on a vegetarian diet as long as it is varied and balanced, and not based on foods such as chips (French fries) and baked beans. Unlike adults, young children do not entirely benefit from a high-fibre, low-fat diet. They need plenty of calories and nutrients and, because they have small stomachs, require regular, small, nutritious meals.

A diet based on low-fat and high-fibre foods can leads to malnutrition in young children because it does not provide sufficient nutrients and calories for growth and development. Reduced-fat foods, such as skimmed milk and low-fat cheeses, lack much-needed calories, and their full-fat equivalents should be given to children under 2 years of age. High-fibre foods, such as brown rice, and wholemeal (whole-wheat) bread and pasta, are too bulky for young children, and they become full before they have eaten enough nutrients. White bread and rice, and ordinary pasta are acceptable alternatives, provided they are eating plenty of fruit and vegetables, potatoes, cereals, beans and lentils.

Children should avoid fizzy, caffeine- and sugar-laden drinks, and drink only small amounts of juices and squashes that contain artificial sweeteners, which can cause diarrhoea if consumed in excess. Children should, instead, be encouraged to drink water, milk and diluted fruit juice.

Above: Try to eat at least five portions of fruits and vegetables a day.

dish or meal is full of nutrient-packed, high-fibre foods.

It may be a cliché, but there is more than a grain of truth in the adage, 'You are what you eat.' Our bodies rely and thrive on a varied nutritious diet. Yet a healthy diet is not just about boosting physical welfare. Our mental and emotional well-being is equally affected by what we put on our plates. The more appetizing and appealing, the better.

ORGANIC FOODS

As food scares continue, many people are increasingly concerned about the type of food that they eat. The growing use of antibiotics, artificial additives and chemicals, as well as the introduction of irradiation and genetically-modified foods, has added fuel to this concern. In 1995, 46 per cent of fruits and vegetables analyzed in a UK study contained pesticide residues. A group of pesticides known as organophosphates have been a particular problem in carrots, while the results for celery are also disturbing.

People are looking for healthier, less processed foods, and the demand for organic foods is growing at a rate of about 30 per cent every year. Organic foods were, until relatively recently, found only in health-food stores, but now there is an expanding range of fresh and packaged organic foods available from supermarkets. Reassuringly, every food that is labelled organic has to fulfil certain strict criteria. No artificial pesticides, fertilizers, or other chemicals can be used in the growing and/or production of organic food, and genetically-modified or irradiated ingredients are not permitted.

Traditional methods of agriculture, such as crop rotation, are used along with natural fertilizers. This preserves wildlife and minimizes pollution. Owing to their shorter shelf-life, organic fruits and vegetables are less likely to have travelled thousands of miles before reaching stores. This could mean that in the future there may be a return to locally produced, seasonal foods. Whether organic food tastes better or is higher in nutrients is open to debate, but the environment and our health will undoubtedly benefit in the long-run.

The Basic Vegetarian Whole Food Diet

We are often told to eat a balanced diet, but in the context of a vegetarian diet what does this mean? The key to good health is to eat a variety of foods that provide the right proportion of protein, carbohydrates, fibre, fat, vitamins and minerals as well as water. The ideal diet features enough calories to provide the body with vital energy, but not an excess, which leads to weight gain. Getting this balance right is crucial to health.

When people opt for a vegetarian diet, it is not simply a matter of swapping meat and fish for cheese and eggs. Vegetarians need to ensure they eat plenty of fruit and vegetables, legumes, nuts, seeds, rice, bread, pasta and potatoes, and some dairy

Wholemeal (whole-wheat) bread (below), whole grain cereals (left), and potatoes in their skins (above) provide more nutrients in this form than if they were refined (or peeled).

foods. They should aim to eat nutrient-rich foods, rather than those that provide plenty of calories but few nutrients, such as cake and crisps. The following may be a useful guide:

WHOLE GRAINS AND POTATOES
Aim for 6–11 servings a day
This group includes cereals, such as oats, wheat, corn, millet, barley, bread, rice,

Above: Butter and margarine provide few nutrients and are laden with calories.

pasta, as well as potatoes. They should form the main part of every meal. Wholemeal (whole-wheat) bread and pasta, brown rice, and potatoes with their skins on contain the most nutrients and provide starchy carbohydrates, fibre, protein, B complex vitamins, and minerals. **A serving equals:** 1 slice of bread, ½ cup of cooked cereal, rice or pasta, or 1 medium potato.

FRUIT AND VEGETABLES
Aim for at least 5 servings a day
Fruit and vegetables provide significant amounts of vitamins, minerals, and fibre and are low in fat and calories. Cruciferous vegetables, such as broccoli, cabbage, sprouts, cauliflower and chard, provide a powerful combination of antioxidants, which are believed to provide protection against certain cancers. Bright orange, yellow, and red fruit and vegetables are rich in the antioxidant beta carotene and vitamin C. **A serving equals:** 1 medium apple, banana or orange, a handful of cherry tomatoes, a

Below: Peas, beans and corn provide fibre.

glass of fresh fruit juice, 2 or more heaped serving spoonfuls of cooked vegetables, or a bowl of salad.

LEGUMES, NUTS, AND SEEDS
2–3 servings a day
Legumes, including beans, peas and lentils, tofu and tempeh, and nuts and seeds provide valuable protein, fibre, iron, calcium, zinc, and vitamins B and E. Legumes are low in fat and provide plenty of fibre. Nuts and seeds are nutritious but are high in fat and should be eaten in moderation. **A serving equals:** a small handful of nuts and seeds, ½ cup cooked beans or 115g/4oz tofu or tempeh.

DAIRY FOODS AND NON-DAIRY ALTERNATIVES
2–3 servings a day
This group includes milk, cheese, and yogurt and provides valuable amounts of protein, calcium, and vitamins B_{12}, A and D. These foods can be high in fat so should be eaten in moderation. Eggs are also included in this group; a maximum of 3–4 are recommended a week. **A serving equals:** 1 egg, a small slice of cheese, a small glass of milk, or a small container of yogurt.

FATS, SWEETS AND SNACKS
Eat sparingly
This diverse group includes chocolate, crisps (US potato chips), cakes and cookies, as well as butter, margarine, and cooking oils. These foods provide few nutrients, but are laden with calories and, if eaten in excess, will lead to weight gain. Too many sugary foods can cause tooth decay.

Below: Tofu and beancurd

The Essentials for Good Health

Along with water, there are six essential components for good health, which if consumed in the correct proportions, will provide the body with both sustained energy and the correct balance of nutrients required.

Below: Soluble fibre found in oats helps reduce blood cholesterol.

Carbohydrates

At one time, carbohydrates, which are made up of starches, fibre and sugars, were considered to be fattening and less valuable than protein-rich foods. However, they are now recognized as the body's major source of energy and carbohydrate-rich foods supply a substantial amount of protein, vitamins, minerals and fibre, with very little fat. About half the food we eat should be unrefined complex carbohydrates, such as wholegrain cereals, wholemeal (whole-wheat) bread and pasta, and brown rice. These high-

Below: Rice is a good source of insoluble fibre.

Fibre

Fruits, vegetables, grains, legumes, nuts and seeds are our main source of fibre, of which there are two types: insoluble and soluble. Insoluble fibre, which is found in whole-wheat, brown rice, bran, and nuts, provides bulk to the diet and helps to combat constipation. Soluble fibre, found in legumes, vegetables and oats, binds with toxins in the gut and promotes their

fibre foods are broken down slowly by the body and provide a steady supply of energy. They are preferable to sugars or simple carbohydrates because these foods are quickly absorbed into the bloodstream and give only a short-term energy boost. When feasible, opt for unrefined carbohydrates, as the refined versions, such as white flour, rice and sugar are stripped of nutrients, including vitamins, minerals, and fibre. It is important to remember that the more carbohydrates that you eat, the more you depend on them for supplying essential nutrients.

excretion, and also helps to reduce blood cholesterol. Both types of fibre reduce the risk of bowel disorders, including diverticulitis, colon and rectal cancer, and irritable bowel syndrome (although bran has been found to aggravate symptoms of IBS). Few people get enough fibre. On average we eat about 12 grams of fibre a day, but we should be consuming about 18 grams. People who want to lose weight will find that a high-fibre diet is beneficial, as it provides bulk and naturally limits the amount of food eaten.

Protein

This macro-nutrient is essential for the maintenance and repair of every cell in the body, and also ensures that enzymes, hormones, and antibodies function properly. Protein is made up of amino acids, of which there are 20, and eight of these need to be supplied by diet. A food containing all eight amino acids is known as a 'complete' or high-quality protein.

Above: Nuts contain fat as well as protein.

For vegetarians, these include eggs and dairy products, as well as soya beans. Protein from plant sources, such as nuts, pasta, potatoes, legumes, cereals and rice, does not usually contain all eight amino acids and is known as 'incomplete' or low-quality protein. We should aim to get 10–15 per cent of calories from protein.

Vegetarians are often asked where they get their protein, and lack of this nutrient can be a concern for those cutting out meat and fish from their diet. Yet in reality

Below: Buckwheat pasta is a 'complete' protein.

most people eat too much protein and deficiency is virtually unheard of, and an excess of protein can be detrimental, rather than beneficial to health. High-protein foods, such as dairy products and nuts, are a source of fat, and have been found to leach calcium from the body, which increases the risk of osteoporosis. It is also a common misconception that vegetarians have to meticulously combine protein foods in every meal to achieve the correct balance of amino acids. Nutritionists now believe that, provided a varied diet of grains, legumes, dairy produce, eggs and vegetables is eaten on a daily basis, intentionally combining proteins is unnecessary.

How to Increase Your Fibre Intake

• Base your diet on wholemeal (whole-wheat) bread and pasta, brown rice, and fruit and vegetables. Refined and processed foods contain less fibre and nutrients.

• Start the day with a wholegrain cereal, such as porridge or bran flakes.

• Eat plenty of dried fruit – add it to breakfast cereals, natural (plain) yogurt or use to make a compote.

• Add beans and lentils to salads and soups to boost their fibre content.

• Avoid peeling fruits and vegetables, if possible, as the skins contain valuable fibre.

Fats

A small amount of fat in the diet is essential for health. Fat not only provides vitamins A, D and E, and essential fatty acids that cannot be made in the body, but also contributes greatly to the taste, texture, and palatability of food. It contains a high number of calories, and should make up no more than 30 per cent of your diet. The type of fat is as crucial as the quantity.

Saturated fat (found mainly in dairy products in the vegetarian diet) has been associated with an increased risk of cancer and coronary heart disease. Eating too much saturated fat can raise blood cholesterol levels and lead to narrowed arteries, more so than eating foods, such as eggs, that are high in cholesterol.

Unsaturated fats, both poly-unsaturated and monounsaturated, can help reduce harmful 'LDL' cholesterol (the type that clogs up arteries) and, importantly, increase the beneficial 'HDL' cholesterol, which is thought to reduce cholesterol levels in the body. Mono-unsaturated fats, such as olive oil, sesame oil and rapeseed oil, are less vulnerable to oxidation than polyunsaturated fats. Polyunsaturated fats provide essential fatty acids, omega-3 and 6. Omega-3 (linolenic acid), which is found in walnuts, soya beans, wheatgerm and rapeseed oil, has been found to reduce the risk of heart disease, while omega-6 (linoleic acid), which is found in nuts, seeds and oils, is thought to reduce levels of blood cholesterol.

Water

The importance of water is often taken for granted, yet although it is possible to survive for weeks without food, we can live for only a few days without water. Water plays a vital role in the body: it transports nutrients, regulates the body temperature, transports waste via the kidneys, and acts as a lubricating fluid. Most people do not drink enough water.

How to Reduce Dietary Fat

While a vegetarian diet is often lower in fat than one based on meat, it is very easy to eat too many dairy products, oil-laden salad dressings and sauces, and high-fat ready-meals. Here are a few simple ways to reduce fat in your diet:
• Use strong, aged cheese, such as Parmesan – only a small amount is needed to add flavour to a dish.

• Try making low-fat salad dressings using miso, orange juice, yogurt, herbs, spices or tomato juice instead of oils.
• Stir-fry foods using only a little oil. For best results make sure the wok/frying pan is very hot before adding the oil.
• Avoid blended oils, as they can contain coconut or palm oil, which are both saturated fats.

• Opt for low-fat cheeses, such as cottage, curd or mozzarella instead of high-fat cheeses, such as Cheddar.
• Use low-fat yogurt instead of cream in cooked recipes. Stir in a spoonful of cornflour (cornstarch) (mixed to a paste with a little water) to prevent the yogurt from curdling when heated.
• Choose complex carbohydrates, including potatoes, pasta, brown rice and beans, instead of high-fat protein foods.

Above: Use naturally low-fat cheeses, such as cottage cheese, curd cheese, ricotta and quark.

it is thought that an adult requires around 2.5 litres/4 pints per day. A shortage of water can cause headaches and loss of concentration. Fizzy drinks (sodas), tea and coffee all act as diuretics and speed up the loss of water, which causes further dehydration.

Vitamins and Minerals

These nutrients are vital for good health and the functioning of our bodies, and with a few exceptions, must be supplied by diet. The levels our bodies require vary depending on health, lifestyle and age, as well as whether or not a female is pregnant. Contrary to popular belief,

Above: Eggs contain all eight essential amino acids, and are a good source of vitamin B_{12}.

vitamins and minerals do not provide energy, but assist in the release of energy provided by carbohydrates, fat and protein.

Vitamins are either water-soluble or fat-soluble. Fat-soluble vitamins A, D, E and K are stored in the liver for some time. Water-soluble vitamins, B complex and C, cannot be stored and must be replaced on a daily basis. If you drink alcohol or smoke, increase your intake of vitamin B-

Below: Oranges are rich in vitamin C.

How to Preserve Nutrients

The nutrients in food, particularly fruits and vegetables, are unstable and are diminished by time, preparation methods and cooking. Leave a piece of cut fruit or a sliced potato exposed to air or soaking in water and its vitamin and mineral levels plummet. Old, wilted, or damaged produce also have reduced levels of vitamins and minerals. The following tips will ensure that you get the most from your fruit and vegetables:
• Buy fruits and vegetables that are as fresh as possible, and avoid those that have been stored under fluorescent light, as this can set off a chemical reaction that depletes nutrients.
• Buy loose fresh produce, which is much easier to check for quality than pre-packed foods.
• Buy fruit and vegetables in small quantities, do not keep them for too long, and remove them from plastic bags as soon as possible.

• Depending on the type of fruit or vegetable, store in a cool larder (pantry) or in the bottom of the refrigerator.
• Avoid peeling fruits and vegetables, if possible, and do not prepare them too far in advance of cooking, as nutrients such as vitamin C will be destroyed.
• Eat fruits and vegetables raw, when they are at their most nutritious.
• Avoid boiling vegetables because this method of cooking destroys water-soluble vitamins, such as thiamine and vitamins B and C. If you must boil vegetables, use as little water as possible and do not overcook them. The cooking water can also be kept and used as stock for soup.

It is not just fruit and vegetables that benefit from careful storage and handling – nuts, seeds, legumes and grains will also be fresher and have a higher nutrient content if stored and cooked correctly.

Right: Miso contains a good amount of the water-soluble vitamin B_{12}.

and C-rich foods. Of the B-complex vitamins, vegetarians should make sure they get enough B_{12}, although this shouldn't be difficult as it is needed only in tiny amounts. It is found in dairy products, fortified breakfast cereals, yeast extract, miso and eggs.

There are 16 essential minerals; some, such as calcium, are needed in relatively large amounts, while trace elements, such as selenium and magnesium, are needed in tiny quantities. Minerals have various functions, but predominantly regulate and balance the body and maintain a healthy immune system. A deficiency of iron affects one-fifth of the world's population, and vegetarians need to make a point of eating iron-rich foods.

Essential Vitamins and Minerals

VITAMIN	BEST VEGETARIAN SOURCES	ROLE IN HEALTH	DEFICIENCY
A (retinol in animal foods, beta carotene in plant foods)	*animal sources:* milk, butter, cheese, egg yolks and margarine *plant sources:* carrots, apricots, squash, red (bell) peppers, broccoli, green leafy vegetables, mango and sweet potatoes	Essential for vision, bone growth, and skin and tissue repair. Beta carotene acts as an antioxidant and protects the immune system	Deficiency is characterized by poor night vision, dry skin and lower resistance to infection, especially respiratory disorders
B_1 (thiamin)	Wholegrain cereals, brewer's yeast, potatoes, nuts, pulses and milk	Essential for energy production, the nervous system, muscles, and heart. Promotes growth and boosts mental ability	Deficiency is characterized by depression, irritability, nervous disorders, loss of memory. Common among alcoholics
B_2 (riboflavin)	Cheese, eggs, milk, yogurt, fortified breakfast cereals, yeast extract, almonds and pumpkin seeds	Essential for energy production and for the functioning of vitamin B6 and niacin, as well as tissue repair	Deficiency is characterized by lack of energy, dry cracked lips, numbness and itchy eyes
Niacin (part of B complex)	Pulses, potatoes, fortified breakfast cereals, wheatgerm, peanuts, milk, cheese, eggs, peas, mushrooms, green leafy vegetables, figs and prunes	Essential for healthy digestive system, skin and circulation. It is also needed for the release of energy	Deficiency is unusual, but characterized by lack of energy, depression and scaly skin
B_6 (piridoxine)	Eggs, wholemeal (whole-wheat) bread, breakfast cereals, nuts, bananas, and cruciferous vegetables, such as broccoli, cabbage and cauliflower	Essential for assimilating protein and fat, to make red blood cells, and a healthy immune system	Deficiency is characterized by anaemia, dermatitis and depression
B_{12} (cyanocobalamin)	Milk, eggs, fortified breakfast cereals, cheese and yeast extract	Essential for formation of red blood cells, maintaining a healthy nervous system and increasing energy levels	Deficiency is characterized by fatigue, increased risk of infection, and anaemia
Folate (folic acid)	Green leafy vegetables, fortified breakfast cereals, bread, nuts, pulses, bananas and yeast extract	Essential for cell division; makes genetic material (DNA) for every cell. Extra is needed pre-conception and during pregnancy to protect a foetus against neural tube defects	Deficiency is characterized by anaemia and appetite loss. Linked with neural defects in babies
C (ascorbic acid)	Citrus fruit, melons, strawberries, tomatoes, broccoli, potatoes, (bell) peppers and green vegetables	Essential for the absorption of iron, healthy skin, teeth, and bones. An antioxidant that strengthens the immune system and helps fight infection	Deficiency is characterized by increased susceptibility to infection, fatigue, poor sleep and depression
D (calciferol)	Sunlight, margarine, vegetable oils, eggs, cereals and butter	Essential for bone and teeth formation; helps the body to absorb calcium and phosphorus	Deficiency is characterized by softening of the bones, muscle weakness and anaemia. Long-term shortage in children results in rickets
E (tocopherol)	Seeds, nuts, vegetable oils, eggs, wholemeal (whole-wheat) bread, green leafy vegetables, oats and cereals	Essential for healthy skin, circulation, and maintaining cells. It is a powerful antioxidant	Deficiency is characterized by increased risk of heart attack, strokes and certain cancers

MINERAL	BEST VEGETARIAN SOURCES	ROLE IN HEALTH	DEFICIENCY
Calcium	Milk, cheese, yogurt, green leafy vegetables, sesame seeds, broccoli, dried figs, pulses, almonds, spinach and watercress	Essential for building and maintaining bones and teeth, muscle function and the nervous system	Deficiency is characterized by soft and brittle bones, osteoporosis, fractures and muscle weakness
Iron	Egg yolks, fortified breakfast cereals, green leafy vegetables, dried apricots, prunes, pulses, whole grains and tofu	Essential for healthy blood and muscles	Deficiency is characterized by anaemia, fatigue and low resistance to infection
Zinc	Peanuts, cheese, whole grains, sunflower and pumpkin seeds, pulses, milk, hard cheese and yogurt	Essential for a healthy immune system, tissue formation, normal growth, wound healing and reproduction	Deficiency is characterized by impaired growth and development, slow wound healing, and loss of taste and smell
Sodium	Most salt comes from processed foods, such as crisps (US potato chips), cheese and canned foods. It is also found naturally in most foods	Essential for nerve and muscle function and the regulation of body fluid	Deficiency is unlikely but can lead to dehydration, cramps and muscle weakness
Potassium	Bananas, milk, beans, peas, lentils, nuts, seeds, whole grains, potatoes, fruits and vegetables	Essential for water balance, normal blood pressure and nerve transmission	Deficiency is characterized by weakness, thirst, fatigue, mental confusion and raised blood pressure
Magnesium	Nuts, seeds, whole grains, beans, peas, lentils, tofu, dried figs and apricots, and green vegetables	Essential for healthy muscles, bones and teeth, normal growth, and nerves	Deficiency is characterized by lethargy, weak bones and muscles, depression and irritability
Phosphorus	Milk, cheese, yogurt, eggs, nuts, seeds, beans, peas, lentils and whole grains	Essential for healthy bones and teeth, energy production and the assimilation of nutrients, particularly calcium	Deficiency is rare
Selenium	Avocados, lentils, milk, cheese, butter, Brazil nuts and seaweed	Essential for protecting against free radical damage and may protect against cancer – an antioxidant	Deficiency is characterized by reduced antioxidant protection
Iodine	Seaweed and iodized salt	Aids the production of hormones released by the thyroid gland	Deficiency can lead to the formation of a goitre and a sluggish metabolism and apathy, as well as dry skin and hair
Chloride	Table salt and foods that contain table salt	Regulates and maintains the balance of fluids in the body	Deficiency is rare
Manganese	Nuts, whole grains, beans, peas, lentils, tofu and tea	Essential component of various enzymes that are involved in energy production	Deficiency is not characterized by any specific symptoms

The Whole Food Kitchen

This fascinating guide includes every kind of natural food, from fruit and vegetables to grains, and from dairy foods to herbs and spices. It includes essential facts about key health benefits and traditional healing qualities, as well as information on buying and storing, preparing and cooking whole foods. It is an inspiration to anyone interested in finding out more about foods that can make you live, look and feel better.

Fruit

Perhaps the ultimate convenience food, most fruits can be simply washed and eaten and, because the nutrients are concentrated just below the skin, it is best to avoid peeling. Cooking fruit reduces valuable vitamins and minerals, so, if you can, eat it raw. Fruit is an excellent source of energy and provides valuable fibre and antioxidants, which are said to reduce the risk of heart disease and certain cancers. Thanks to modern farming methods and efficient transportation, most fruit is available all year round, although it is generally best when home-grown, organically produced and in season.

Orchard Fruits

These fruits have a long history, spanning thousands of years and offer an incredible range of colours and flavours. This group includes many favourites, from crisp, juicy apples, which are available all year round, to luscious, fragrant peaches – a popular summer fruit.

Apricots

APPLES

There are thousands of varieties of apple, although the choice in stores is often restricted to a mere few. Some of the most well-liked eating varieties are Cox's Orange Pippin, Granny Smith, Gala, Braeburn, and Golden and Red Delicious.

The Bramley Seedling, with its thick, shiny, green skin and tart flesh, is the most familiar cooking apple and is perfect for baking, or as the basis of apple sauce. Some less well-known varieties, many of which have a short season, are often available from farm stores. Home-grown apples bought out of season may have spent several months in cold storage, where ripening and maturation are artificially halted. When they are taken out of storage, the apples deteriorate quickly.

Apples are delicious when they are eaten raw with their skin on. However, this versatile fruit is often used in breakfast dishes, main meals, salads, desserts, pies and even soups. Large cooking apples are ideal puréed, stewed and baked, but their tartness means that sugar has to be added. Some varieties of eating apple are just as good cooked and don't need any added sugar.

To preserve the maximum amount of vitamins and minerals, cook apples over a low heat with little or no water. Most of the insecticides that are used on apples collect in the apple core and seeds, so, unless the apples are organic, these should be removed before cooking.

Buying and Storing: When buying apples, choose bright, firm fruits without any bruises. Organic apples

An Apple a Day

Numerous studies have shown that eating apples regularly could reduce harmful LDL cholesterol in the body. In France, 30 middle-aged men and women were asked to add 2–3 apples a day to their diet for a month. By the end of the month, 80 per cent of the group showed reduced cholesterol levels, and in half of the group the drop was more than 10 per cent. Additionally, the level of good HDL cholesterol went up. Pectin, a soluble fibre found particularly in apples, is believed to be the magic ingredient.

*Large cooking apples (left)
and eating apples*

Baked Apples

Baking is a simple and nutritious way of cooking this orchard fruit. Use cooking apples such as Bramley.

1 Preheat the oven to 180°C/350°F/ Gas 4. Remove the core of the apples, then score the skin around the circumference to prevent the skin bursting. Place the apples in a baking dish with a little water.

2 Fill the cavity of the apples with a mixture of soft dark brown sugar, dried fruit and nuts. Top each with a knob (pat) of butter and bake for about 40 minutes or until the apples are soft.

are more prone to blemishes than non-organic ones, and the fruits can look a little tatty but the taste will often be superior. Smaller apples tend to have a better flavour and texture than larger specimens. Store apples in a cool place, away from direct sunlight.

Health Benefits: The cleansing and blood-purifying qualities of apples are highly valued in natural medicine. Apples aid digestion and can remove impurities in the liver. They are a good source of vitamin C and fibre, if you eat the skin. Although low in calories, apples contain fructose, a simple sugar that is released slowly to supply the body with energy and balance blood sugar levels. Skin problems and arthritis are said to benefit from eating apples regularly.

APRICOTS

The best apricots are sunshine gold in colour and full of juice. They are delicious baked or used raw in salads.

Buying and Storing: An apricot is at its best when truly ripe. Immature fruits are hard and tasteless and never seem to attain the right level of sweetness.

Health Benefits: Extremely rich in beta carotene, minerals and vitamin A, apricots are a valuable source of fibre.

CHERRIES

There are two types: sweet and sour. Some are best eaten raw like the popular Bing, while others, such as Morello, are best cooked.

Buying and Storing: Choose firm, bright, glossy fruits that have fresh, green stems. Discard any that are soft, or have split or damaged skin.

Glossy, red, sweet cherries

Health Benefits: Cherries stimulate and cleanse the system, removing toxins from the kidneys. They are a remedy for gout and arthritis. Cherries also contain iron, potassium, vitamins C and B, as well as beta carotene.

NECTARINES
Like a peach without the fuzzy skin, this sweet juicy fruit is named after the drink of the gods – nectar – and is delicious baked or used raw in salads.

Buying and Storing: see Peaches.

Health Benefits: When eaten raw, nectarines are especially rich in vitamin C. They aid the digestion, effectively reduce high blood pressure and cleanse the body.

PEACHES
These summer fruits are prized for their perfume and luscious juiciness. Peaches range in colour from gold to deep red and the flesh can be orange or white.

Buying and Storing: Avoid overly soft fruit. Peaches and nectarines are extremely fragile and bruise easily, so buy when

Nectarines and peaches

slightly under-ripe. To ripen them quickly, place in a brown paper bag with an already ripened fruit. Store ripe nectarines and peaches in the refrigerator but bring back to room temperature before eating.

Health Benefits: Much of the vitamin C content of a peach lies in and just under its delicate skin, so eat the fruit unpeeled. Peaches are an excellent source of the antioxidant beta carotene, which is said to lower the risk of heart disease and some forms of cancer.

PEARS
Pears have been popular for thousands of years and were extensively cultivated by both the Greeks and the Romans. Pears come into their own in the late summer and autumn with the arrival of the new season's crops. Particular favourites are green and brown-skinned Conference; Williams, with its thin, yellow skin and sweet, soft flesh; plump

Comice, which has a pale yellow skin with a green tinge; and Packham, an excellent cooking pear.

Like certain apples, some types of pear are good for cooking, others are best eaten raw, and a few varieties fit happily into both camps.

Pears can be used in both sweet and savoury dishes; they are excellent in salads, and can be baked, poached in syrup, and used in pies and tarts. Pears are unlikely to cause any allergic reactions, so they make perfect weaning food when cooked and puréed.

Buying and Storing: Choose firm, plump fruit that are just slightly under-ripe. Pears can ripen in a day or so and then they pass their peak very quickly and become woolly or squashy. To tell if a pear is ripe, feel around the base of the stalk, where it should give slightly when gently pressed, but the pear itself should be firm.

Health Benefits: Despite their high water content, pears contain useful amounts of vitamin C, fibre and potassium. In natural medicine, they are used as a diuretic and laxative. Rich in pectin and soluble fibre, pears could also be valuable in lowering harmful cholesterol levels in the body. Eating pears regularly is said to result in a clear, healthy complexion and glossy hair.

PLUMS
Ranging in colour from pale yellow to dark, rich purple, plums come in many different varieties, although only a few are available in stores. They can be sweet and juicy or slightly tart; the latter are best cooked in pies and cakes, or made into a delicious jam. Sweet plums can be eaten as they are, and are good in fruit salads, or they can be puréed and combined with custard or yogurt to make a delicious fruit fool.

From left, Conference, Comice and Williams pears

Plums

QUINCE
Fragrant, with a thin, yellow or green skin. These knobbly fruits, which can be either apple- or pear-shaped, are always cooked. Their high pectin content means that they are good for jellies and, in Spain and France, quinces are used to make a fruit paste that is served with soft cheeses.

Buying and Storing: Look for smooth ripe fruits that are not too soft. Quinces keep well and can be stored in a bowl in your kitchen or living room. They will fill the room with their delicious scent.

Health Benefits: Quinces are rich in soluble fibre and pectin. They also calm the stomach and allay sickness.

Plums should be just firm, and not too soft, with shiny, smooth skin that has a slight 'bloom'. Store ripe plums in the refrigerator. Unripe fruits can be kept at room temperature for a few days to ripen. Plums relieve constipation and are thought to stimulate the nerves.

Yellow, pear-shaped quince

Dried Fruit
A useful source of energy, dried fruit is higher in calories than fresh fruit, and packed with vitamins and minerals. The drying process boosts the levels of vitamin C, beta carotene, potassium and iron. Apricots and prunes are the most popular types, but dried apple rings, cherries and peaches are also available. Sulphur, often used as a preservative in dried fruits, is best avoided, especially by people who suffer from asthma. Look for unsulphured fruit.

Stoning Fruit

To remove the stone (pit) from peaches, apricots or plums, cut around the middle of the fruit down to the stone with a paring knife. Twist each half of the fruit in opposite directions.

2 Prize out the stone using the tip of the knife and discard. Rub the cut flesh with lemon juice.

Citrus Fruits

Juicy and brightly coloured, citrus fruits such as oranges, grapefruit, lemons and limes are best known for their sweet, slightly sour juice, which is rich in vitamin C. They are invaluable in the kitchen, adding an aromatic acidity to many dishes, from soups and sauces to desserts and pies. Buy organic fruit when you can, and eat within a week or two.

ORANGES

Best eaten as soon as they are peeled, oranges start to lose vitamin C from the moment they are cut. Thin-skinned oranges tend to be the juiciest.

Popular varieties include the Navel (named after the belly button-type spot at the flower end), which contains no pips and so is good for slicing; sweet, juicy Jaffa and Valencia; and Seville, a sour orange used to make marmalade.

The outermost layer of the orange rind can be removed using a vegetable peeler or paring knife. This thin rind contains aromatic oils, which give a delightful perfumed flavour to both savoury and sweet dishes.

Oranges

GRAPEFRUIT

The flesh of the grapefruit ranges in colour from vivid pink and ruby red to white; the pink and red varieties are sweeter. Heavier fruits are likely to be juicier. Served juiced, halved or cut into slices, grapefruit can provide a refreshing start to the day. The fruit also adds a zesty tang to salads or a contrast to rich foods. Cooking or grilling (broiling) mellows the tartness, but keep cooking times brief to preserve the nutrients. A glass of grapefruit juice before bed is said to promote sleep.

LEMONS

Both the juice and rind of this essential cooking ingredient can be used to enliven salad dressings, vegetables, marinades, sauces and cookies. Lemon juice can also be used to prevent some fsruits and vegetables from discolouring when cut. Lemons should be deep yellow in colour, firm and heavy for their size, with no hint of green in the skin as this is a sign of immaturity, while a thin, smooth skin is a sign of juicy flesh. A slice of lemon in hot water cleanses the system and invigorates the whole body.

Citrus Nutrients

Eating an orange a day will generally supply an adult's requirement for vitamin C, but citrus fruits also contain phosphorus, potassium, calcium, beta carotene and fibre. Pectin, a soluble fibre that is found in the flesh and particularly in the membranes of citrus fruit, has been shown to reduce cholesterol levels. The membranes also contain bioflavonoids, which have powerful antioxidant properties. Drink fresh fruit juice when you can, as bottled, canned and concentrated citrus juices have reduced levels of vitamin C.

Grapefruit

Lemons

With a spoonful of honey added, a hot lemon drink is an old and trusted remedy for alleviating colds and flu.

LIMES

Once considered to be rather exotic, limes are now widely available. Avoid fruits with a yellowing skin as this is a sign of deterioration. The juice has a sharper flavour than that of lemons and if you substitute limes for lemons in a recipe, you will need to use less juice. Limes are used a great deal in Asian cooking and the rind can be used to flavour curries, dips and marinades. Coriander (cilantro), chillies, garlic and ginger are all natural partners.

The Powers of Vitamin C

Citrus fruit is best known for its generous vitamin C content, which is found predominantly in the flesh. An antioxidant, vitamin C has been found to thwart many forms of cancer (particularly cancer of the stomach and oesophagus) by defending body cells against harmful free radicals. Free radicals attack DNA – the cell's genetic material – causing them to mutate and possibly become cancerous.

Numerous population studies have also demonstrated that a high dietary intake of vitamin C significantly reduces the risk of death from the world's greatest killers: the heart attack and stroke. It has been found both to lower harmful LDL cholesterol in the body and to raise beneficial HDL cholesterol. It does this by converting LDL cholesterol into bile acids, which are normally excreted. If vitamin C is in short supply, LDL cholesterol accumulates in the body.

The ability of vitamin C to boost the immune system by helping to fight viruses is well documented. It can be particularly beneficial for infections of the urinary tract and the herpes simplex virus. Researchers are in two minds as to whether vitamin C actually prevents colds but they certainly agree that it can lessen the severity and length of colds and flu. It also boosts the body's ability to absorb iron from food.

Vitamin C is destroyed by heat as well as being water soluble, and is therefore easily lost in cooking. If fruits are cut some time before eating, much of their vitamin C content will also be lost.

Limes are a good source of vitamin C.

Grating Citrus Rind

1 To remove long, thin shreds of rind, use a zester. Scrape it along the surface of the fruit, applying firm pressure.

2 For finer shreds, use a grater. Rub the fruit over the fine cutters to remove the rind without any of the white pith.

Cutting Fine Strips or Julienne

1 Using a vegetable peeler, remove strips of orange rind making sure the white pith is left behind on the fruit.

2 Stack several strips of citrus rind and, using a sharp knife, cut them into fine strips or julienne.

Buying and Storing: Look for plump, firm citrus fruit that feels heavy for its size, and has a smooth thin skin; this indicates that the flesh is juicy. Fruits with bruises, brown spots, green patches (or yellow patches on limes) and soft, squashy skin should be avoided, as should dry, wrinkled specimens. Citrus fruits can be kept at room temperature for a few days but if you want to keep them longer, they are best stored in the refrigerator and eaten within two weeks. Most citrus fruits are waxed or sprayed with fungicides so scrub them thoroughly to remove any residues. If you can, buy organic or unwaxed fruit.

COOK'S TIPS

• *Rolling citrus fruit firmly over a work surface or in the palms of your hands will help you extract the maximum amount of juice from the fruit.*

• *Limes and lemons will yield more juice if cut lengthways, rather than horizontally.*

Berries and Currants

These baubles of vivid red, purple and black are the epitome of summer and autumn, although they are now likely to be found all year round. Despite their distinctive appearance and flavour, berries and currants are interchangeable in their uses – jams, jellies, pies and tarts are the obvious choices. Interestingly, they also share health-giving qualities, including the ability to treat stomach problems and cleanse the blood, and therefore play a part in natural medicine.

STRAWBERRIES

These are the favourite summer fruits and do not need any embellishment. Serve ripe (avoid those with white or green tips) and raw, on their own, or with a little cream or natural (plain) yogurt. Wash only if absolutely necessary and just before serving.

Strawberries

Health Benefits: Strawberries are rich in B complex vitamins and vitamin C. They contain significant amounts of potassium, and have good skin-cleansing properties.

RASPBERRIES

Soft and fragrant, raspberries are best served simply and unadulterated – maybe with a spoonful of natural yogurt. Those grown in Scotland are regarded as the best in the world. Raspberries are very fragile and require the minimum of handling, so wash only if really necessary. They are best eaten raw as cooking spoils their flavour and vitamin C content.

Raspberries

Health Benefits: Raspberries are a rich source of vitamin C. They are effective in treating menstrual cramps, as well as cleansing the body and removing toxins. Raspberry leaf tea is often drunk in the last few weeks of pregnancy, as it prepares the uterus for labour.

BLUEBERRIES

Dark purple in colour, blueberries are very popular in the USA. When ripe, the berries are plump and slightly firm, with a natural 'bloom'. Avoid any that are soft and dull-skinned, and wash and dry carefully to avoid bruising. Cultivated blueberries are larger than the wild variety. Both types are sweet enough to be eaten raw, but are also good cooked in pies and muffins, used for jellies and jams, or made into a sauce to serve with nut or vegetable roasts. Unwashed blueberries will keep for up to a week in the refrigerator.

Health Benefits: Numerous studies show that eating blueberries regularly can improve night vision as well as protect against the onset of cataracts and glaucoma. Blueberries are also effective in treating urinary tract infections and can improve poor circulation.

BLACKBERRIES

These are a familiar sight in early autumn, growing wild in hedgerows. Cultivated blackberries have a slightly longer season and are generally much larger than the wild fruits. Juicy and plump, blackberries can vary in sweetness, which is why they are so often cooked. Wash them carefully to prevent bruising the fruits, then pat dry with kitchen paper. Use in pies and tarts, or make into jams and jellies. The berries can also be lightly cooked, then puréed and sieved to make a sauce to serve with other fruits or ice cream. Blackberries make an ideal partner to apples and pears.

Blackberries

Cranberry Cure

A recent study reported in the Journal of the American Medical Research Association supports the long-held belief that cranberries combat cystitis and other infections of the urinary tract. It found that drinking cranberry juice reduces levels of bacteria not only in the urinary tract but also in the bladder and kidneys.

Blueberries

Blackberries are high in fibre and contain a wealth of minerals, including magnesium, iron and calcium. They are rich in vitamin C, and are one of the best low-fat sources of vitamin E. In natural medicine, blackberries are used to cleanse the blood and they have a tonic effect. They are also used to ease stomach complaints and to treat menstrual problems. Blackberries are rich in bioflavonoids, which act as antioxidants, inhibiting the growth of cancer cells and protecting against cell damage by carcinogens.

GOOSEBERRIES

A favourite fruit of Northern Europe, gooseberries are relatively rare in other parts of the world. They range from the hard and sour green type to the sweeter, softer purple variety. The skin can vary from smooth and silky to fuzzy and spiky. Slightly unripe, tart gooseberries make wonderful pies, crumbles, jams and jellies. Ripe, softer fruits can be puréed and mixed with cream, yogurt or custard, to make a delicious fruit fool.

Health Benefits: Rich in vitamin C, gooseberries also contain beta carotene, potassium and fibre.

Blackcurrants

BLACKCURRANTS, REDCURRANTS AND WHITECURRANTS

These pretty, delicate fruits are usually sold in bunches on the stem. To remove the currants from the stalk, run the prongs of a fork down through the clusters, taking care not to damage the fruit. Wash the fruits carefully, then pat dry. Raw blackcurrants are quite

Whitecurrants

tart, but this makes them ideal for cooking in sweet pies. They make delicious jams and jellies, and are especially good in summer pudding when they are partnered by other berries. Sweeter whitecurrants make a delightful addition to fruit salads.

Health Benefits: The nutritional value of currants has long been recognized. They are high in antioxidants, vitamins C and E, and carotenes. They also contain significant amounts of fibre, calcium, iron and magnesium. In natural medicine, blackcurrants are often used to settle stomach upsets.

Buying and Storing: Look for firm, glossy berries and currants. Make sure that they are not squashed or mouldy. Ripe fruits do not keep well and are best eaten on the day of purchase – store in the refrigerator. Unripe fruits can be kept for longer. Raspberries, blueberries, blackberries and currants all freeze well.

Gooseberries

Fruit Purée

Soft berries are perfect for making uncooked fruit purées or coulis. Sweeten if the fruit is tart and add a splash of lemon juice to bring out the flavour.

1 To make raspberry purée, place some raspberries, with lemon juice and icing (confectioners') sugar to taste, in a food processor and process until smooth.

2 Press through a nylon sieve. Store in the refrigerator for up to two days.

Redcurrants

Grapes, Melons, Dates and Figs

These fruits were some of the first ever to be cultivated and are therefore steeped in history. They are available in an immense variety of shapes, colours and sizes, and with the exception of melons, they can also be bought dried. As well as being a good source of nutrients, these fruits are high in soluble fibre.

GRAPES

There are many varieties of grape, each with its own particular flavour and character. Most are grown for wine production. Grapes for eating are less acidic and have a thinner skin than those used for wine-making. Seedless grapes are easier to eat and contain less tannin than the seeded fruit. Grapes range in colour from deep purple to pale red, and from bright green to almost white. The finest eating grapes are Muscat grapes, which have a wonderful, perfumed flavour. They may be pale

Red and green grapes

green or golden, or black or red. Italia grapes, another popular eating variety, have a luscious musky flavour and may be green or black. Unless they are organic, grapes should be thoroughly washed before eating as they are routinely sprayed with pesticides and fungicides.

Serve grapes with cheese, in salads or as a topping for a tart. Before cooking them, remove the skin by blanching the grapes in boiling water for a few seconds, then peel with a small knife.

A Glass of Red Wine

According to a recent American study, phenolic is just one of the compounds found in red wine that may delay the onset of cancer. This news comes following research that wine – particularly red wine – may reduce the risk of heart disease. Nutritionally, wine is virtually worthless and should be drunk in moderation, although it may increase the absorption of iron if drunk with a meal.

Buying and Storing: Buy grapes that are plump, and fairly firm. They should be evenly coloured and firmly attached to the stalk. Unwashed fruit may be stored in the refrigerator for up to five days.

Health Benefits: Grapes contain iron, potassium and fibre. They are powerful detoxifiers and can improve the condition of the skin, and treat gout, liver and kidney disorders. Research has revealed that resveratrol, a natural substance produced by grapes, can help inhibit the formation

Galia melons (front left and back), Cantaloupe melons (centre), and Watermelon (right)

of tumours and that purple grape juice may be even more effective than aspirin in reducing the risk of heart attacks.

MELONS

Watermelons are very low in calories because of their high water content, which is around 90 per cent. They contain less vitamin C than the fragrant, orange-fleshed varieties, such as the Cantaloupe and Charentais. Avoid buying ready-cut melons, because most of the vitamins will have been lost.

Buying and Storing: Look for melons that feel heavy for their size and yield to gentle pressure at the stem end.

Health Benefits: When they are eaten on their own, melons are easy to digest, and pass quickly through the system. But, when they are consumed with other foods requiring a more complex digestive process, they may actually inhibit the absorption of nutrients.

Figs

FIGS

These delicate, thin-skinned fruits may be purple, brown or greenish-gold. Delicious raw, figs can also be poached or baked. Choose unbruised, ripe fruits that yield to gentle pressure and eat on the day of purchase. If they are not too ripe they can be kept in the refrigerator for a day or two, but bring to room temperature if eating raw. Figs are a well-known laxative and a good source of calcium.

DATES

Like figs, dates are one of the oldest cultivated fruits, possibly dating back as far as 50,000BC. Fresh dates are sweet and soft and make a good natural sweetener: purée the cooked fruit, then add to cake or bread mixtures, or simply mix into natural (plain) yogurt to make a quick dessert. Dates should be plump and glossy. Medjool dates from Egypt and California have a wrinkly skin, but most other varieties are smooth. They can be stored in the refrigerator for up to a week. Dates are high in vitamin C and a good source of potassium and soluble fibre.

Fresh dates

Dried Vine Fruits

Currants, sultanas (golden raisins) and raisins are the most popular dried fruits. Traditionally, they are used for fruit cakes and breads, but currants and raisins are also good in savoury dishes. In Indian and North African cookery they are frequently used for their sweetness. Figs and dates are also popular – chopped or puréed – as an ingredient in cakes, teabreads and pastries.

It takes about 1.75–2.25kg/4–5lb fresh grapes to produce 450g/1lb sultanas, raisins or currants, while 1.5kg/3lb fresh figs and dates produces just 450g/1lb dried fruit. Although high in natural sugars, which can damage teeth if eaten to excess between meals, dried fruit is a concentrated source of nutrients, including iron, potassium, calcium, phosphorus, vitamin C, beta carotene and some B vitamins.

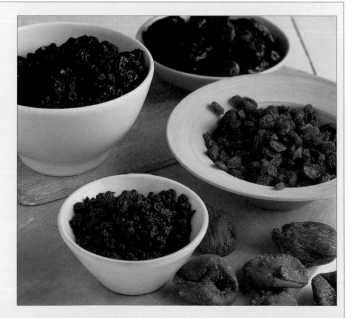

Tropical Fruit

This exotic collection of fruits ranges from the familiar bananas and pineapples to the more unusual papayas and passion fruit. The diversity in colours, shapes and flavours is sure to excite the tastebuds.

PINEAPPLES

These distinctive-looking fruits have a sweet, exceedingly juicy and golden flesh. Unlike most other fruits, pineapples do not ripen after picking, although leaving a slightly unripe fruit for a few days at room temperature may reduce its acidity.

Buying and Storing: Choose pineapples that have green spiky leaves, are heavy for their size, and are slightly soft to the touch. Store in the refrigerator when ripe.

Mangoes

Health Benefits: Pineapple contains an antibacterial enzyme called bromelain, which has anti-inflammatory properties and should help arthritis sufferers. It also aids digestion.

PAPAYA

Also known as pawpaw, these pear-shaped fruits come from South America. When ripe, the green skin turns a speckled yellow and the pulp is a glorious orange-pink colour. The numerous edible, small black seeds taste peppery when dried. Peel off the skin using a sharp knife or a vegetable peeler before enjoying the creamy flesh, which has a lovely perfumed aroma and sweet flavour. Ripe papaya is best eaten raw, while unripe green fruit can be used in cooking.

Health Benefits: Papaya contains an enzyme called papain, which aids the digestion,

although levels of this enzyme diminish with ripening. Skin, hair and nails all benefit from the generous amounts of vitamin C and beta carotene found in papaya. Iron, potassium and calcium are also present.

MANGO

The skin of these luscious, fragrant fruits can range in colour from green to yellow, orange or red. Their shape varies tremendously, too. An entirely green skin is a sign of an unripe fruit, although in Asia, these are often used in salads. Ripe fruit should yield to gentle pressure and, when cut, it should reveal a juicy, orange flesh. Preparing a mango can be fiddly (see opposite). Serve sliced, or purée and use as a base for ice creams and sorbets.

Health Benefits: Rich in vitamin C and beta carotene, mangoes are also reputed to cleanse the blood.

Large and baby pineapples

Other Tropical Fruit

Kiwi fruit, which is also known as the Chinese gooseberry, has a brown, downy skin and vivid green flesh that is peppered with tiny black seeds. It is extremely rich in vitamin C.

Passion fruit is a dark purple, wrinkly, egg-shaped fruit, which hides a pulpy, golden flesh with edible black seeds. Cut in half and scoop out the inside with a spoon. Passion fruit is rich in vitamins A and C.

Preparing Mango

Mangoes can be fiddly to prepare because they have a large, flat stone (pit) that is slightly off-centre. The method below produces cubed fruit. Alternatively, the mango can be peeled with a peeler and sliced around the central stone.

1 Hold the fruit with one hand and cut vertically down one side of the stone. Repeat on the opposite side. Cut away any remaining flesh around the stone.

2 Taking the two large slices, and using a sharp knife, cut the flesh into a criss-cross pattern down to the skin. Holding the mango skin-side down, press it inside out, then cut the mango cubes away from the skin.

COOK'S TIP

To ripen fruit, place it in a paper bag with an already ripened fruit and leave at room temperature or in a warm place.

Papaya

BANANAS

A concentrated bundle of energy, bananas are also full of valuable nutrients. The soft and creamy flesh can be blended into smooth, sweet drinks, mashed and mixed with yogurt, or the fruits can be baked and barbecued whole. Bananas also make an ideal weaning food for babies as they rarely cause an allergic reaction.

Health Benefits: Bananas are rich in dietary fibre, vitamins and minerals, especially potassium, which is important for the functioning of cells, nerves and muscles, and can relieve high blood pressure. Ripe bananas soothe the stomach and are believed to strengthen the stomach lining against acid and ulcers. Their high starch content makes them a good source of sustained energy, and they are also an effective laxative. Bananas are rich in the amino acid tryptophan, which is known to lift the spirits and aid sleep.

Buying and Storing: When buying, look for fruit that is heavy for its size. Mangoes and papayas should yield to gentle pressure. Avoid overly soft or bruised fruit, or those with any hard spots. Ripe mangoes and papayas are best kept in the refrigerator. If you wish to buy ripe bananas, choose yellow (or red) fruit that are patched with brown. Bananas with patches of green can be ripened at room temperature. Don't buy completely green bananas as these rarely ripen properly. Store bananas at cool room temperature.

Sweet, red-skinned bananas and the more familiar large and small yellow-skinned varieties

Vegetables

Vegetables offer an infinite number of culinary possibilities to the cook. The choice is immense and the growing demand for organic produce has meant that pesticide-free vegetables are now increasingly available. Vegetables are an essential component of a healthy diet and have countless nutritional benefits. They are at their best when freshly picked.

Roots and Tubers

Vegetables such as carrots, swedes (rutabagas), parsnips and potatoes, are a comforting and nourishing food, and it is not surprising that they are popular in the winter. Their sweet, dense flesh provides sustained energy, valuable fibre, vitamins and minerals.

Fresh carrots with their green, feathery tops

CARROTS

The best carrots are not restricted to the cold winter months. Summer welcomes the slender sweet new crop, often sold with their green, feathery tops. (These are best removed after buying as they rob the root of moisture and nutrients.)

Buy organic carrots if you can because high pesticide residues have been found in non-organic ones. As an added bonus, organic carrots do not need peeling.

Look for firm, smooth carrots – the smaller they are, the sweeter they are. Carrots should be prepared just before use to preserve their valuable nutrients. They are delicious raw, and can be steamed, stir-fried, roasted or puréed.

Health Benefits: A single carrot will supply enough vitamin A for an entire day and is reputed to cut the risk of lung cancer by half, even among ex-smokers. According to one American doctor, eating an extra carrot a day could prevent 20,000 lung cancer deaths each year in the USA.

> **Brightly Coloured Vegetables**
> Ensure there is colour in your diet. Beta carotene is just one of the carotenoids found in green, yellow, orange and red vegetables (as well as fruit). Most carotenoids are antioxidants, which slow down or prevent cell damage from free radical oxidation in the body. Vitamins C and E are other carotenoids, along with bioflavonoids. These help to enhance the immune system, which protects us against viral and bacterial infections and boosts the body's ability to fight cancer and heart disease.

BEETROOT (BEET)

Deep, ruby-red in colour, beetroot adds a vibrant hue and flavour to dishes. It is often pickled in vinegar, but is much better roasted, as this emphasizes its sweet earthy flavour. Raw beetroot can be grated into salads or used to make relishes. It can also be added to risottos or made into delicious soups. If cooking beetroot whole, wash carefully, taking care not to damage the skin or the nutrients and colour will leach out. Trim the stalks to about 2.5cm/1in above the root. Small beetroots are sweeter and more tender than larger ones.

Health Benefits: Beetroot has long been considered medicinally beneficial and is recommended as a general tonic. It can be used to help disorders of the blood, including anaemia, it is an effective detoxifier and, because of its high fibre content, is recommended to relieve constipation. Beetroot contains calcium, iron and vitamins A and C – all at their highest levels when it is eaten raw.

Beetroot (beet)

This may be due to the high level of the antioxidant beta carotene that carrots contain, especially raw ones. Beta carotene may also reduce the risk of prostate cancer in men.

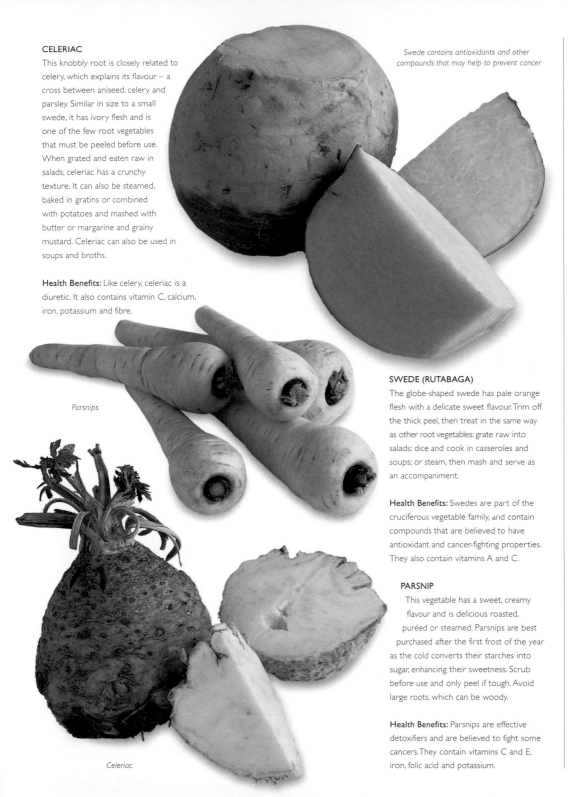

CELERIAC

This knobbly root is closely related to celery, which explains its flavour – a cross between aniseed, celery and parsley. Similar in size to a small swede, it has ivory flesh and is one of the few root vegetables that must be peeled before use. When grated and eaten raw in salads, celeriac has a crunchy texture. It can also be steamed, baked in gratins or combined with potatoes and mashed with butter or margarine and grainy mustard. Celeriac can also be used in soups and broths.

Health Benefits: Like celery, celeriac is a diuretic. It also contains vitamin C, calcium, iron, potassium and fibre.

Swede contains antioxidants and other compounds that may help to prevent cancer

Parsnips

Celeriac

SWEDE (RUTABAGA)

The globe-shaped swede has pale orange flesh with a delicate sweet flavour. Trim off the thick peel, then treat in the same way as other root vegetables: grate raw into salads; dice and cook in casseroles and soups; or steam, then mash and serve as an accompaniment.

Health Benefits: Swedes are part of the cruciferous vegetable family, and contain compounds that are believed to have antioxidant and cancer-fighting properties. They also contain vitamins A and C.

PARSNIP

This vegetable has a sweet, creamy flavour and is delicious roasted, puréed or steamed. Parsnips are best purchased after the first frost of the year as the cold converts their starches into sugar, enhancing their sweetness. Scrub before use and only peel if tough. Avoid large roots, which can be woody.

Health Benefits: Parsnips are effective detoxifiers and are believed to fight some cancers. They contain vitamins C and E, iron, folic acid and potassium.

TURNIPS

This humble root vegetable has many health-giving qualities, and small turnips with their green tops intact are especially nutritious. Their crisp, ivory flesh, which is enclosed in white, green and pink-tinged skin, has a pleasant, slightly peppery flavour, the intensity of which depends on their size and the time of harvesting. Small turnips can be eaten raw. Alternatively, steam, bake or use in casseroles and soups.

Health Benefits: This cruciferous vegetable is said to halt the onset of certain cancers, particularly rectal cancer. It is also a digestive and maintains bowel regularity. The green tops are rich in beta carotene and vitamin C.

POTATOES

There are thousands of potato varieties, and many lend themselves to particular cooking methods. Small potatoes, such as Pink Fir Apple and Charlotte, and new potatoes, such as Jersey Royals, are best steamed. They have a waxy texture, which retains its shape after cooking, making them ideal for salads. Main crop potatoes, such as Estima and Maris Piper, are more suited to roasting, baking or mashing, and can be used to make chips (French fries).

Baby turnips

Discard any potatoes with green patches as these indicate the presence of toxic alkaloids called solanines.

Vitamins and minerals are stored in, or just below, the skin, so it is best to use potatoes unpeeled.

New potatoes and special salad potatoes need only be scrubbed.

Potatoes are not in themselves fattening – it is added ingredients such as cheese and the cooking method that can bump up the calories. Steam rather than boil, and bake instead of frying to retain valuable nutrients and to keep fat levels down.

Health Benefits: Potatoes are high in complex carbohydrates, and include both protein and fibre. They provide plenty of sustained energy, plus vitamins B and C, iron and potassium.

JERUSALEM ARTICHOKES

This small knobbly tuber has a sweet, nutty flavour. Peeling can be fiddly, although scrubbing and trimming is usually sufficient. Store in the refrigerator for up to one week. Use in the same way as potatoes – they make good creamy soups.

Health Benefits: Jerusalem artichokes contain vitamin C and fibre.

COOK'S TIP

To prevent root vegetables and tubers discolouring after preparation, immerse them in a bowl of acidulated water – water containing 15ml/1 tbsp lemon juice. Don't soak them for long, because water-soluble vitamins will leach out into the water.

Potatoes

RADISHES

There are several types of this peppery-flavoured vegetable, which is a member of the cruciferous family. The round ruby red variety is most familiar; the longer, white-tipped type has a milder taste. Mooli or daikon radishes are white and very long; they can weigh up to several kilos or pounds. Radishes can be used to add flavour and a crunchy texture to salads and stir-fries. A renowned diuretic, radishes also contain vitamin C.

Jerusalem artichokes

HORSERADISH

This pungent root is never eaten as a vegetable. It is usually grated and mixed with cream or oil and vinegar, and served as a culinary accompaniment. It is effective in clearing blocked sinuses.

Buying and Storing: Seek out bright, firm, unwrinkled root vegetables and tubers, which do not have soft patches. When possible, choose organically grown produce, and buy in small quantities to ensure freshness. Store root vegetables in a cool, dark place.

Horseradish

Radishes

Mooli

Basic Vegetable Stock

Stock is easy to make at home and is a healthier option than store-bought stock. It can be stored in the refrigerator for up to four days. Alternatively, it can be prepared in large quantities and frozen.

INGREDIENTS

15ml/1 tbsp olive oil
1 potato, chopped
1 carrot, chopped
1 onion, chopped
1 celery stick, chopped
2 garlic cloves, peeled
1 sprig of thyme
1 bay leaf
a few stalks of parsley
600ml/1 pint/2 1/2 cups water
salt and freshly ground black pepper

1 Heat the oil in a large pan. Add the vegetables and cook, covered, for 10 minutes or until softened, stirring occasionally. Stir in the garlic and herbs.

2 Pour the water into the pan and bring to the boil and simmer, partially covered, for 40 minutes. Strain, season and use as required.

Top Tuber

There are two types of this highly nutritious tuber; one has cream flesh, the other orange. The orange-fleshed variety has a higher nutritional content because it is richer in the antioxidant beta carotene, but both types contain potassium, fibre and vitamin C, as well as providing plenty of sustained energy. Sweet potatoes are thought to cleanse and detoxify the body and can boost poor circulation. When cooked, the cream-fleshed variety has a drier texture. Both are suited to mashing, baking and roasting.

Brassicas and Green Leafy Vegetables

This large group of vegetables boasts an extraordinary number of health-giving properties. Brassicas range from the crinkly-leafed Savoy cabbage to the walnut-sized Brussels sprout. Green, leafy vegetables include spinach, spring greens (collards) and Swiss chard.

Broccoli

BROCCOLI

This nutritious vegetable should be a regular part of everyone's diet. Two types are commonly available: purple-sprouting, which has fine, leafy stems and a delicate head, and calabrese, the more substantial variety with a tightly budded top and thick stalk. Choose broccoli that has bright, compact florets. Yellowing florets, a limp woody stalk and a pungent smell are an indication of overmaturity. Trim stalks before cooking, though young stems can be eaten, too. Serve raw in salads or with a dip. If you cook broccoli, steam or stir-fry it to preserve the nutrients and keep the cooking time brief to retain the vivid green colour and crisp texture.

Health Benefits: Broccoli is a member of the cruciferous family, which studies have shown to be particularly effective in fighting cancer of the lung, colon and breast. Sulphur compounds, found in broccoli, stimulate the production of anti-cancer enzymes, which prevent the growth of tumours and inhibit the spread of existing tumours. Raw broccoli contains almost as much calcium as milk and also provides plenty of B vitamins, vitamin C, iron, folate, zinc and potassium.

CAULIFLOWER

The cream-coloured compact florets should be encased in large, bright green leaves. To get the most nutrients from a cauliflower, eat it raw, or bake or steam lightly. Cauliflower has a mild flavour and is delicious tossed in a vinaigrette dressing or combined with tomatoes and spices. Overcooked cauliflower is unpleasant and has a sulphurous taste.

Health Benefits: This creamy white cruciferous vegetable has many cancer-fighting qualities particularly against cancer of the lung and colon. Cauliflower also contains vitamin C, folate and potassium and is used in natural medicine as a blood purifier and laxative.

Preparing Broccoli

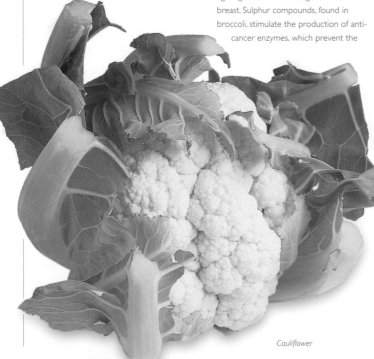

Trim the stalks from broccoli and divide it into florets before using. The stems of young broccoli can be sliced and eaten, too.

Cauliflower

The Crucial Role of Phytochemicals

Cruciferous vegetables, such as broccoli, cabbages, kohlrabi, radishes, cauliflowers, Brussels sprouts, watercress, turnips, kale, pak choi (bok choy), mustard greens, spring greens (collards), chard and swede, are all packed with phytochemicals, which numerous studies have shown can fight off various forms of cancer. Phytochemicals are a group of compounds found in varying amounts in all fruit and vegetables, but particularly in cruciferous vegetables. Phytochemicals are believed to provide an anticarcinogenic cocktail, which plays a crucial role in fighting disease by stimulating the body's enzyme defences against cancer-inducing substances. Eating cruciferous vegetables on a regular basis – at least three or four times a week – may halve the risk of lung, colon, breast, ovary, uterus or prostate cancer.

According to a senior British researcher, phytochemicals may be found to be as important as antioxidants in fighting disease. Phytochemicals include compounds such as carotenoids, selenium, fibre, isothiocyanates, indoles, phenols, tocopherols, bioflavonoids and protease inhibitors.

Kohlrabi (below left); Chinese cabbages and cavalo nero (below); and cauliflower, Savoy cabbage, Brussels sprouts, spinach, broccoli and kale (right) are packed with phytochemicals

CABBAGE

Frequently overcooked, cabbage is best eaten raw, or cooked until only just tender. There are several different varieties: Savoy cabbage has substantial, crinkly leaves with a strong flavour and is perfect for stuffing; firm white and red cabbages can be shredded and used raw in salads (as can Chinese leaves); while pak choi (bok choy) is best cooked in stir-fries or with noodles.

Health Benefits: Studies show that eating cabbage more than once a week can reduce the likelihood of colon cancer in men by about 65 per cent. Raw or juiced cabbage is particularly potent and has antiviral and antibacterial qualities as well. Cabbage is thought to speed up the metabolism of oestrogen in women and this may provide protection against cancer of the breast and womb. It is a valuable source of vitamins C and E, beta carotene, folate, potassium, thiamine and fibre.

Cabbage

Mixed Cabbage Stir-fry

Stir-frying is a quick method of cooking that retains much of the vitamins and minerals that are lost during boiling. When cabbage is cooked in this way, it remains crisp and keeps its vivid colour.

INGREDIENTS

15ml/1 tbsp groundnut or
   sunflower oil
1 large garlic clove, chopped
2.5cm/1 in piece fresh root ginger, chopped
450g/1lb/5 cups mixed cabbage leaves,
   such as Savoy, white, cavalo nero or
   pak choi (bok choy), finely shredded
10ml/2 tsp soy sauce
5ml/1 tsp runny honey
5ml/1 tsp toasted sesame oil (optional)
15ml/1 tbsp sesame seeds, toasted

1 Heat the oil in a wok or large, deep frying pan, then sauté the garlic and ginger for about 30 seconds. Add the cabbage and stir-fry for 3–5 minutes until tender, tossing frequently.

2 Stir in the soy sauce, honey and sesame oil and cook for 1 minute. Sprinkle with sesame seeds and serve.

Health Benefits: Brussels sprouts contain significant amounts of vitamin C, folate, iron, potassium and some B vitamins. Because they are a cruciferous vegetable, sprouts can help prevent certain cancers.

Buying and Storing: Seek out bright, firm brassicas with no signs of discoloration or wilting. Avoid cauliflowers that have black spots or yellowing leaves. Ensure cabbages have a heavy heart. Chinese cabbages should be heavy for their size with bright, undamaged leaves. Choose small Brussels sprouts with tightly packed leaves. Store cabbages and Brussels sprouts in a cool, dark place for up to a week. Broccoli and cauliflower should be stored in the refrigerator for only 2–3 days. Chinese leaves and pak choi (bok choy) don't keep well. Store in the salad drawer of the refrigerator and use within 1–2 days.

Preparing Brussels Sprouts

1 Peel off any outer damaged leaves from the Brussels sprouts.

2 Before cooking, cut a cross in the base of each sprout, so that they cook quickly and evenly.

BRUSSELS SPROUTS

These are basically miniature cabbages that grow on a long tough stalk. They have a strong nutty flavour. The best are small with tightly packed leaves – avoid any that are very large or turning yellow or brown. Sprouts are sweeter when picked after the first frost. They are best cooked very lightly, so either steam or, better still, stir-fry to keep their green colour and crisp texture, as well as to retain the vitamins and minerals.

Brussels sprouts

GREEN LEAFY VEGETABLES

For years we have been told to eat up our greens and now we are beginning to learn why. Research into their health benefits has indicated that eating dark green leafy vegetables, such as spinach, spring greens (collards), chard and kale, on a regular basis may protect us against certain forms of cancer.

Spinach

This dark, green leaf is a superb source of cancer-fighting antioxidants. It contains about four times more beta carotene than broccoli. It is also rich in fibre, which can help to lower harmful levels of LDL cholesterol in the body, reducing the risk of heart disease and stroke. Spinach does contain iron but not in such rich supply as was once thought. Furthermore, spinach contains oxalic acid, which inhibits the absorption of iron and calcium in the body. However, eating spinach with a vitamin C-rich food will increase absorption. Spinach also contains vitamins C and B_6, calcium, potassium, folate, thiamine and zinc. Nutritionally, it is most beneficial when eaten raw in a salad, but it is also good lightly steamed, then chopped and added to omelettes or pasta and rice dishes, such as rissotto.

Kale

Spinach

Mixed Swiss chard

Spinach beet

Swiss chard

A member of the beet family, Swiss chard has large, dark leaves and thick, white, orange or red edible ribs. It can be used in the same way as spinach, or the stems may be cooked on their own. Swiss chard is rich in vitamins and minerals although, like spinach, it contains oxalic acid.

Spinach beet

Similar to Swiss chard, this form of the beet plant is grown only for its leaves and has a sweet, mild flavour. Use in the same way as spinach.

Spring greens (collards)

These leafy, dark green young cabbages are full of flavour. Rich in vitamin C and beta carotene, spring greens contain indoles, one of the phytochemicals that are thought to protect the body against breast and ovarian cancer.

Buying and Storing: Green, leafy vegetables do not keep well – up to 2 or 3 days at most. Eat soon after purchase to enjoy them at their best. Look for brightly coloured, undamaged leaves that are not showing any signs of yellowing or wilting. Wash the leaves thoroughly in cold water before use and eat them raw, or cook lightly, either by steaming or stir-frying to preserve their valuable nutrients.

Spring greens (collards)

Pumpkins and Squashes

Widely popular in the USA, Africa, Australia and the Caribbean, pumpkins and squashes come in a tremendous range of shapes, colours and sizes. Squashes are broadly divided into summer and winter types: cucumbers, courgettes and marrows fall into the summer category, while pumpkins, butternut and acorn squashes are winter varieties.

Pumpkins

WINTER SQUASHES

These have tough inedible skins, dense, fibrous flesh and large seeds. Most winter squashes can be used in both sweet and savoury dishes.

Acorn squash

This small to medium-size squash has an attractive, fluted shape and looks rather like a large acorn – hence its name. The orange flesh has a sweet flavour and slightly dry texture, and the skin colour ranges from golden to dark green. Its large seed cavity is perfect for stuffing.

Butternut squash

A large, pear-shaped squash with a golden brown skin and vibrant orange flesh. The skin is inedible and should be removed along with the seeds. Roast, bake, mash or use in soups or casseroles. The flesh has a rich, sweet, creamy flavour when cooked and makes a good substitute for pumpkin.

Pumpkins

These are native to America, where they are synonymous with Thanksgiving. Small pumpkins have sweeter, less fibrous flesh than the larger ones, which are perhaps best kept for making into lanterns. Deep orange in colour, pumpkin can be used in both sweet and savoury dishes, such as pies, soups, casseroles, soufflés and even ice cream. Avoid boiling pumpkin as it can become waterlogged and soggy. The seeds are edible and highly nutritious.

SUMMER SQUASHES

Picked when still young, summer squash have thin edible skins and tender, edible seeds. Their delicate flesh cooks quickly.

Pattypan squash

These pretty, baby squash resemble mini flying saucers. They are similar in taste to a courgette (zucchini) and are best steamed or roasted. They may be yellow or bright green, and although they can be expensive to buy, there is no waste. It will only keep for a few days in the refrigerator.

Courgettes (zucchini)

The most widely available summer squash, courgettes have the most flavour when they are small and young; the flavour diminishes when they are old and the seeds toughen. Young courgettes have a glossy, bright green skin and creamy coloured flesh. Extremely versatile, they can be steamed, grated raw into salads, stir-fried, griddled, puréed or used in soups and casseroles. Their deep yellow flowers are a delicacy and are perfect for stuffing.

Acorn, pattypan and butternut squashes

Courgettes (zucchini)

Marrows (large zucchini)

The grown-up equivalent of courgettes, marrows have a pleasant, mild flavour and are best baked either plain or with a stuffing. Spices, chillies and tomatoes are particularly good flavourings.

Cucumbers

Probably cultivated as long ago as 10,000BC, cucumbers were popular vegetables with the Greeks and the Romans. The long, thin, smooth-skinned variety is most familiar. Their refreshing, mild flavour makes cucumbers perfect

Marrows (large zucchini)

to use raw in salads or thinly sliced as a sandwich filling. However, they can also be pickled and cooked in other ways, such as steaming, baking or stir-frying.

Buying and Storing: Look for firm, bright, unblemished vegetables that are heavy for their size. Winter squash can be kept for several weeks if stored whole in a cool, dry place. Once cut, they should be kept in the refrigerator and eaten as soon as possible. Summer squash don't keep well and should be stored in the refrigerator for only a few days.

Health Benefits: Summer squash are effective diuretics and their potassium content means they are beneficial for those with high blood pressure. Pumpkins are also a diuretic, as well as a laxative, and like other winter squash contain high amounts of vitamin E, beta carotene and potassium. Beta carotene and vitamin E are antioxidants and are believed to reduce the risk of certain cancers. Summer squash contain smaller amounts of beta carotene. Because of their high water content, all squash are low in calories.

Peeling Pumpkin

1 Cut the pumpkin in half using a large sharp knife and scoop out the seeds and fibrous parts with a spoon.

2 Cut the pumpkin into large chunks, then cut the skin using a sharp knife.

Roasting Squash

1 Preheat the oven to 200°C/100°F/ Gas 6. Cut the squash in half, scoop out the seeds and place the squash cut-side down on an oiled baking tray.

2 Bake for 30 minutes or until the flesh is soft. Serve in the skin, or remove the flesh and mash with butter.

Cucumber

Shoot Vegetables

This highly prized collection of vegetables, each honoured with a distinctive flavour and appearance, ranges from the aristocratic asparagus to the flowerbud-like globe artichoke.

FENNEL

Florence fennel is closely related to the herb and spice of the same name. The short, fat bulbs have a similar texture to celery and are topped with edible feathery fronds. Fennel has a mild aniseed flavour, which is most potent when eaten raw. Cooking tempers the flavour, giving it a delicious sweetness. When using fennel raw, slice it thinly or chop roughly and add to salads. Alternatively, slice or cut into wedges and steam, or brush with olive oil and roast or cook on a griddle. Fennel is at its best when it is fresh and should be eaten as soon as possible. It can, however, be stored in the refrigerator for a few days.

Asparagus

Health Benefits: Fennel is a diuretic and also has a calming and toning effect on the stomach. It is low in calories and contains beta carotene and folate, which is known to reduce the risk of spina bifida in the unborn child. Fennel seeds are good for the digestion.

ASPARAGUS

Highly valued since Roman times, asparagus has been cultivated commercially since the 17th century. There are two main types: white asparagus is picked just before it sprouts above the surface of the soil; while green-tipped asparagus is cut above the ground and develops its colour when it comes into contact with sunlight. It takes three years to grow a crop from seed, which may account for its expense. Before use, scrape the lower half of the stalk with a peeler, then trim off the woody end. Briefly poach spears in a frying pan containing a little boiling salted water, or tie the spears in a bundle and boil upright in a tall pan. Asparagus is delicious served with melted butter, or dipped into mayonnaise or vinaigrette. It can also be roasted in a little olive oil and served with a sprinkling of sea salt to bring out the flavour.

Health Benefits: Asparagus was used as a medicine long before it was eaten as a food. It is a rich source of vitamin C and also has diuretic and laxative properties. It contains the antioxidant glutathione, which has been found to prevent the formation of cataracts in the eyes.

White and red chicory

Preparing Fennel

Cut the fennel bulb in half lengthways, then either cut into quarters or slice thinly.

CHICORY

This shoot has long, tightly packed leaves. There are two kinds, white and red. Red chicory has a more pronounced flavour, while the white variety has crisper leaves. The crisp texture and slightly bitter flavour means that chicory is particularly good in salads. Chicory can also be steamed or braised, although in cooking, sadly, the

Fennel

Health Benefits: Globe artichokes are a good source of vitamins A and C, fibre, iron, calcium and potassium. In natural medicine, they are used to treat high blood pressure.

Buying and Storing: When buying shoot vegetables, always choose the freshest-looking specimens. Asparagus spears should have firm stalks. Chicory should be neither withered nor brown at the edges – the best white chicory is sold wrapped in blue paper to keep out the sunlight and to stop it turning green and bitter. Fennel bulbs should be crisp and white, and have plenty of fresh fronds. Globe artichokes should have tightly closed, stiff leaves and still have the stalk attached.

Store all these vegetables in the salad drawer of the refrigerator. Asparagus, chicory and fennel should be eaten within 2–3 days; globe artichokes will keep for up to a week; and celery will keep for about 2 weeks if very fresh when purchased.

Left: Globe artichokes, celery, and chicory

red-leafed variety fades to brown. Before use, remove the outer leaves and wash thoroughly, then trim the base. In natural medicine, chicory is sometimes used to treat gout and rheumatism. It is also a digestive and liver stimulant, and good for a spring tonic.

CELERY

Like asparagus, celery was once grown primarily for medicinal reasons. Serve raw, steam or braise. Celery leaves have a tangy taste and are also useful for adding flavour to stocks. Low in calories, but rich in vitamin C and potassium, celery is a recognized diuretic and sedative.

GLOBE ARTICHOKES

Once cooked, the purple-tinged leaves of globe artichokes have an exquisite flavour. They are eaten with the fingers by dipping each leaf into garlic butter or vinaigrette dressing, then drawing each leaf through the teeth and eating the fleshy part. The heart is then dipped in the butter or dressing and eaten with a knife and fork.

Preparing Globe Artichokes

1 Hold the top of the artichoke firmly and using a sharp knife, remove the stalk and trim the base so that the artichoke sits flat.

2 Using a sharp knife or scissors, trim off and discard the tops of the leaves and cut off the pointed top.

3 Cook the artichokes in a pan of boiling lightly salted water for 35–45 minutes until a leaf can be pulled out easily. Drain the artichokes upside down.

4 Pull out the central leaves then scoop out the hairy choke with a teaspoon and discard.

Vegetable Fruits

By cultivation and use, tomatoes, aubergines and peppers are all vegetables, but botanically they are classified as fruit. Part of the nightshade family, they have only relatively recently become appreciated for their health-giving qualities.

Tomatoes

TOMATOES

There are dozens of varieties to choose from, which vary in colour, shape and size. The egg-shaped plum tomato is perfect for cooking as it has a rich flavour and a high proportion of flesh to seeds – but it must be used when fully ripe. Too often, store-bought tomatoes are bland and tasteless because they have been picked too young. Vine-ripened and cherry tomatoes are sweet and juicy and are good in salads or uncooked sauces. Large beefsteak tomatoes have a good flavour and are also excellent for salads. Sun-dried tomatoes add a rich intensity to sauces, soups and stews. Genetically engineered tomatoes are now sold in some countries, but at present they are only sold canned as a concentrated purée. Check the label before buying.

AUBERGINES (EGGPLANTS)

The dark-purple, glossy-skinned aubergine is the most familiar variety, although it is the small, ivory-white egg-shaped variety that has inspired the name 'eggplant' in the USA. There is also the pea aubergine that is used in Asian cooking, and a pale-purple Chinese aubergine. Known in the Middle East as 'poor man's caviar', aubergines give substance and flavour to spicy casseroles and tomato-based bakes and are delicious roasted,

Buying and Storing: Look for deep-red fruit with a firm, yielding flesh. Tomatoes that are grown and sold locally will have the best flavour. To improve the flavour of a slightly hard tomato, leave it to ripen fully at room temperature. Avoid refrigeration because this stops the ripening process and adversely affects the taste and texture of the tomato.

Health Benefits: Vine-ripened tomatoes are higher in vitamin C than those picked when they are still green. They are also a good source of vitamin E, beta carotene, magnesium, calcium and phosphorus. Tomatoes contain the bioflavonoid lycopene, which is believed to prevent some forms of cancer by reducing the harmful effects of free radicals.

Aubergines (eggplants)

Peeling and Seeding Tomatoes

Tomato seeds can give sauces a bitter flavour. Removing them and the tomato skins will also give a smoother end result.

2 Lift out the tomatoes with a slotted spoon, rinse in cold water to cool slightly, and peel off the skin.

1 Immerse the tomatoes in boiling water and leave for about 30 seconds – the base of each tomato can be slashed to make peeling easier.

3 Cut the tomatoes in half, then scoop out the seeds and remove the hard core. Dice or roughly chop the flesh according to the recipe.

griddled and puréed into garlic-laden dips. It is not essential to salt aubergines to remove any bitterness; however, this method prevents the absorption of excessive amounts of oil during frying.

Buying and Storing: When buying, look for small to medium-size aubergines, which have sweet, tender flesh. Large specimens with a shrivelled skin are overmature and are likely to be bitter and tough. Store in the refrigerator for up to two weeks.

Health Benefits: An excellent source of vitamin C, aubergines also contain moderate amounts of iron and potassium, calcium and B vitamins. They also contain bioflavonoids, which help prevent strokes and reduce the risk of certain cancers.

Bird's eye chillies

Serrano chillies

Habanero chillies

CHILLIES

Native to America, this member of the capsicum family now forms an important part of many cuisines, including Indian, Thai, Mexican, South American and African. There are more than 200 different types of chilli, ranging from the long, narrow Anaheim to the lantern-shaped and incredibly hot Habanero. Red chillies are not necessarily hotter than green ones – but they will probably have ripened for longer in the sun. The heat in chillies comes from capsaicin, a compound found in the seeds, white membranes and, to a lesser extent, in the flesh. Chillies range in potency from the mild and flavourful to the blisteringly hot. Dried chillies tend to be hotter than fresh. Smaller chillies, such as Bird's eye chillies, contain proportionately more seeds and membrane, which makes them more potent than larger ones. It is very important to take care when using chillies

Red and green chillies

Jalapeño chillies

and to wash your hands afterwards as they can irritate the skin and eyes.

Buying and Storing: Choose unwrinkled bright, firm chillies and store in the refrigerator.

Health Benefits: Chillies contain more vitamin C than an orange and are a good source of beta carotene, folate, potassium and vitamin E. They stimulate the release of endorphins, the body's 'feel-good' chemicals and are a powerful decongestant, helping to open sinuses and air passages. Chillies stimulate the body and improve circulation, but if eaten to excess, or if they are especially hot, can irritate the stomach.

> ### Chilli Boost
>
> For an instant uplift, sprinkle some dried crushed chilli on your food. The chilli will stimulate the release of endorphins, which are the body's 'feel-good' chemicals.
>
>
>
> Handle chillies with care as they can irritate the skin and eyes. It is advisable to wear gloves when preparing chillies.

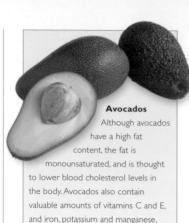

Avocados

Although avocados have a high fat content, the fat is monounsaturated, and is thought to lower blood cholesterol levels in the body. Avocados also contain valuable amounts of vitamins C and E, and iron, potassium and manganese. They are said to improve the condition of the skin and hair.

Once cut, avocados should be brushed with lemon or lime juice to prevent discoloration. They are usually eaten raw. Avocado halves can be dressed with a vinaigrette, or filled with sour cream sprinkled with cayenne pepper, or hummus. Slices or chunks of avocado are delicious in salads. In Mexico, where they grow in abundance, there are countless dishes based on avocados. Guacamole is the best known, but they are also used in soups and stews.

(BELL) PEPPERS

Like chillies, sweet peppers are also members of the capsicum family. They range in colour from green through to orange, yellow, red and even purple. Green peppers are fully developed but not completely ripe, which can make them difficult to digest. They have refreshing, juicy flesh with a crisp texture. Other colours of peppers are more mature, have sweeter flesh, and are more digestible than less ripe green peppers. Roasting or chargrilling peppers will enhance their sweetness. They can also be stuffed, sliced into salads or steamed.

Buying and Storing: Choose peppers that are firm and glossy with an unblemished skin. Store in the refrigerator for up to a week.

Health Benefits: Sweet peppers contain significant amounts of vitamin C, as well as beta carotene, some B complex vitamins, calcium, phosphorus and iron.

Peeling Peppers

1 Roast the peppers under a hot grill (broiler) for 12–15 minutes, turning regularly, until the skin is charred.

2 Alternatively, place on a baking tray and roast in an oven preheated to 200°C/400°F/Gas 6 for 20–30 minutes until blackened and blistered.

3 Put the peppers in a plastic bag and leave until cool – the steam will encourage the skin to peel away easily.

4 Peel off the skin, then slice in half. Remove the core and scrape out any remaining seeds. Slice or chop according to the recipe.

(Bell) peppers

Pods and Seeds

While most of these vegetables are delicious eaten fresh, many of them – peas, corn and broad (fava) and fresh beans, for example – can also be bought frozen. High in nutritional value, these popular vegetables can be enjoyed all year. Other types of pea include mangetouts and sugar snap peas, which can be eaten whole – pod and all.

Above: Clockwise from top left, runner beans, fine green beans, mangetouts, broad (fava) beans, peas and (centre) baby corn cobs.

PEAS

Peas are one of the few vegetables that taste just as good when frozen. Because freezing takes place soon after picking, frozen peas often have a higher nutritional value than fresh. Another advantage is that frozen peas are readily available all year round. Peas in the pod have a restricted availability and their taste diminishes if not absolutely fresh, because their sugars rapidly turn to starch. However, when they are at the peak of freshness, peas are delicious and have a delicate, sweet flavour. Pop them from the pod and serve raw in salads or steam lightly. Delicious cooked with fresh mint, peas also make satisfying purées and soups, and can be added to risottos and other rice dishes.

BROAD (FAVA) BEANS

When young and fresh these beans are a delight to eat. Tiny pods can be eaten whole; simply top and tail, and then slice. Usually, however, you will need to shell the beans as their skins can become tough. Elderly beans are often better skinned after they are cooked. Broad beans can be eaten raw or lightly cooked.

GREEN BEANS

French, runner and dwarf beans are eaten pod and all. They should be bright green and crisp-textured. Simply top and tail and lightly cook or steam them. Serve green beans hot, or leave to cool slightly and serve as a warm salad with a squeeze of fresh lemon juice or a vinaigrette dressing.

Buying and Storing: Look for bright-green, smooth, plump pods and keep in the refrigerator for no more than a day or two.

Health Benefits: Peas and beans are a good source of protein and fibre. They are rich in vitamin C, iron, thiamine, folate, phosphorous and potassium.

CORN

Corn cobs are best eaten soon after picking, before their natural sugars start to convert into starch when the flavour fades and the kernels toughen. Remove the green outer leaves and cook whole or slice off the kernels with a sharp knife. Baby corn cobs can be eaten raw, and are good in stir-fries.

Buying and Storing: Look out for very fresh, plump kernels that show no signs of discoloration, wrinkling or drying and eat soon after purchase. If you do not intend to eat them immediately, store in the coolest part of the refrigerator.

Health Benefits: Corn is a good carbohydrate food and is rich in vitamins A, B and C, and fibre. It contains useful amounts of iron, magnesium, phosphorus and potassium. Baby corn is high in folate, which is essential for maintaining the immune system.

Corn

The Onion Family

Onions and garlic are highly prized as two of the oldest remedies known to man. Both contain allicin, which has been found to stimulate the body's antioxidant mechanisms, raising levels of beneficial HDL cholesterol and combating the formation of clogged arteries. Additionally, these vegetables are indispensable in cooking. The wide variety of onions can be enjoyed raw or cooked and, with garlic, add flavour to a huge range of savoury dishes.

ONIONS

Every cuisine in the world includes onions in one form or another. They are an essential flavouring, offering a range of taste sensations, from the sweet and juicy red onion and powerfully pungent white onion to the light and fresh spring onion (scallion). Tiny pearl onions are generally pickled, while little shallots are delicious roasted with their skins on, when they develop a caramel sweetness. Yellow onions are most common and are highly versatile.

Buying and Storing: When buying, choose onions that have dry, papery skins and are heavy for their size. They will keep for 1–2 months when stored in a cool, dark place.

Health Benefits: Numerous studies highlight the healing powers of the onion. It is a rich source of quercetin, a potent antioxidant that has been linked to preventing stomach cancer. Eating half a raw onion a day is said to thin the blood, lower the LDL cholesterol and raise beneficial HDL cholesterol by about 30 per cent. This means that cholesterol is transported away from the arteries, reducing the risk of heart disease and stroke. Whether raw or cooked, onions are antibacterial and antiviral, helping to fight off colds, relieve bronchial congestion, asthma and hay fever. They are also good for arthritis, rheumatism and gout.

GARLIC

For centuries, this wonder food has been the focus of much attention, and is praised for its medicinal powers, which range from curing toothache to warding off evil demons. The flavour of garlic is milder when whole or sliced; crushing or chopping releases the oils making the flavour stronger. Slow-cooking also tames the pungency of garlic, although it still affects the breath.

Onion and Garlic Cures

Onions have been used in all kinds of traditional remedies.

• In the past, babies would often be given a teaspoonful of onion infusion for colic: a slice of onion would be infused in hot water for a few minutes, and the water left to cool.

• Raw garlic can relieve symptoms of food poisoning. It has been shown to kill bacteria, even those that are resistant to antibiotics. Some people say that garlic keeps old age at bay.

Buying and Storing: Most garlic is semi-dried to prolong its shelf life, yet the cloves should still be moist and juicy. Young garlic, which is available in early summer, has a long green stem and soft white bulb. It has a fresher flavour than semi-dried garlic, but can be used in the same ways. Pungency varies, but the general rule when buying garlic is: the smaller the bulb, the more potent the flavour. If stored in a cool, dry place and not in

Above: Spring onions (scallions), red onions, shallots and white onions

Leeks

the refrigerator, garlic will keep for up to about eight weeks. If the air is damp garlic will sprout, and if it is too warm the garlic cloves will eventually turn to grey powder.

Health Benefits: Garlic tops the American National Cancer Institute's list as a potential cancer-preventative food. Although the antiviral, antibacterial and antifungal qualities of garlic are most potent when eaten raw, cooking does not inhibit its anti-cancer, blood-thinning and decongestant capabilities. Studies show that eating 2–3 garlic cloves a day reduces by half the probability of a subsequent heart attack in previous heart patients. Garlic has also been found to lower blood cholesterol, reduce high blood pressure, boost the immune system, act as an anti-inflammatory, lift mood and have a calming effect. It should be eaten on a daily basis.

Below: Garlic bulbs and cloves

LEEKS

Like onions and garlic, leeks have a very long history. They grow in all sorts of climates and are known to have been eaten and enjoyed by the ancient Egyptians, Greeks and Romans. Leeks are very versatile, having their own distinct, subtle flavour. They are less pungent than onions but are still therapeutically beneficial. Excellent in soups and casseroles, leeks can also be used as a pie filling or in flans, or simply steamed and served hot with a light, creamy sauce, or cooled slightly and dressed with a vinaigrette. They are also delicious sliced or shredded and then stir-fried with a little garlic and ginger.

Commercially grown leeks are usually about 25cm/10in long, but you may occasionally see baby leeks, which are very tender and are best steamed.

Buying and Storing: Choose firm leeks with bright-green leaves. Avoid those without their roots as they deteriorate quickly. Leeks will keep for up to a week in the salad drawer of the refrigerator.

Health Benefits: Leeks have the same active constituents as onions, but in smaller amounts. They also contain vitamins C and E, iron, folate and potassium.

Cleaning Leeks

Leeks need meticulous cleaning to remove any grit and earth that may hide between the layers of leaves. This method will ensure that the very last tiny piece of grit will be washed away.

1 Trim off the root, then trim the top of the green part and discard. Remove any tough or damaged outer leaves.

2 Slash the top green part of the leek into quarters and rinse the leek well under cold running water, separating the layers to remove any hidden dirt. Slice or leave whole, depending on the recipe.

Mushrooms

Thanks to their rich earthiness, mushrooms add substance and flavour dishes. There are more than 2,000 edible varieties but only a tiny proportion are available. These fall into three camps: common cultivated mushrooms, like the button; wild varieties that are now cultivated, such as the shiitake; and the truly wild types that have escaped cultivation, such as the morel.

Cultivated mushrooms come in a wide variety of sizes

Chanterelles

BUTTON (WHITE), CAP AND FLAT MUSHROOMS

The most common cultivated variety of mushrooms, these are actually one type in various stages of maturity. The button mushroom is the youngest and has a tight, white cap and a mild flavour, and can be eaten raw in salads. Cap mushrooms are slightly more mature and larger in size, while the flat mushroom is the largest and has dark, open gills. Flat mushrooms have the most prominent flavour and are good grilled (broiled) or baked on their own, or stuffed.

Below: Field blewitts

Below: Chestnut (left) and portobello mushrooms

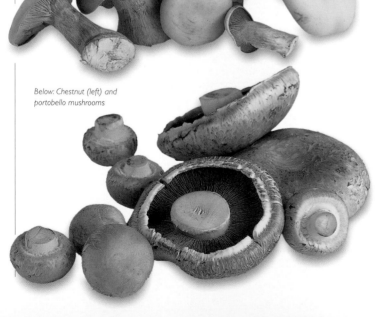

CHESTNUT MUSHROOMS

The brown-capped chestnut mushroom looks similar to the cultivated button but has a more assertive, nutty flavour.

PORTOBELLO MUSHROOMS

Similar in appearance to the cultivated flat mushroom, the portobello is simply a large chestnut mushroom. It has a rich flavour and a meaty texture and is good grilled.

FIELD (PORTOBELLO) MUSHROOMS

This wild mushroom has an intense, rich flavour. It is ideal for grilling and stuffing.

CHANTERELLES

This egg-yolk-coloured mushroom has a pretty, funnel shape and a fragrant but delicate flavour. Also known as the girolle, it is sold fresh in season and dried all year round. If buying fresh, eat as soon as possible and wipe rather than wash as the skin is very porous. Sauté, bake or add to sauces.

FIELD BLEWITTS

This wild mushroom is now widely cultivated in caves in Britain, Switzerland and France. It has a thick, lilac-blue stem,

Dried and fresh ceps

which is topped
with a smooth, whitish
cap. When cooked, field blewitts
have a dense, meaty texture.

CEPS

This wild mushroom, which is also known
by its Italian name, porcini, has a tender,
meaty texture and woody flavour. Dried
ceps are used for their rich flavour.

MORELS

Slightly sweet-flavoured mushrooms with
a distinctive, pointed, honeycomb cap and
a hollow stalk. They can be fiddly to clean.
Morels are costly to buy fresh because
they have a short season, but they can be
bought dried.

ENOKI MUSHROOMS

These Japanese mushrooms have a pretty,
tiny cap on an elegant, long stalk. Sold in
clusters, enoki have a
slightly lemony flavour.
Use in stir-fries or eat
raw in salads.

Morels

OYSTER MUSHROOMS

Now widely available, oyster mushrooms
have a shell-shaped cap and thick stalk.
They are usually pale, grey-brown, although
yellow and pink varieties are also available.

Buying and Storing: Buy mushrooms that
smell and look fresh. Avoid ones with
damp, slimy patches and any that are
discoloured. Store in a paper bag in
the refrigerator for up
to 4 days.

Dried Mushrooms

These are a useful stand-by and have
a rich, intense flavour. To reconstitute
dried mushrooms, soak them in
boiling water for 20–30 minutes,
depending on the variety and size of
mushroom, until tender. Drain and
rinse well to remove any grit
and dirt. Dried mushrooms
often require longer cooking than
fresh ones.

Health Benefits: Mushrooms do not
contain a wealth of nutrients but they are
a useful source of vitamins B_1 and B_2,
potassium, iron and niacin.

Cleaning Mushrooms: Before use, wipe
mushrooms with damp kitchen paper and
trim the stem. Wild mushrooms often
harbour grit and dirt and may need to be
rinsed briefly under cold running water,
but dry thoroughly. Never soak
mushrooms or they will become soggy.
Peeling is not usually necessary.

Oyster mushrooms

Salad Leaves

It is only a few years since the most exotic lettuce available was the crisp-textured iceberg. Today, salad leaves come in a huge variety of shapes, sizes, colours and flavours, from bitter-tasting endive to peppery rocket and red-leafed lollo rosso. Making a mixed leaf salad has never been so easy, or the result so delicious.

Left, clockwise from left: frisée, oak leaf, cos, round (butterhead) and iceberg lettuces

LETTUCES

Cultivated for thousands of years, lettuces were probably first eaten as a salad vegetable during Roman times. Nutritionally, lettuce is best eaten raw, but it can be braised, steamed or made into a soup. Large-leafed varieties can be used to wrap around a filling.

Round (butterhead) lettuce

This soft-leafed lettuce has an unassuming flavour and is good as a sandwich-filler.

Cos lettuce

Known since Roman times, the cos lettuce has long, sturdy leaves and a strong flavour. Little Gem (Bibb) is a baby version of cos and has firm, densely packed leaves.

Iceberg lettuce

This lettuce has a round, firm head of pale-green leaves with a crisp texture. Like the round lettuce, it has a mild, slightly bitter flavour and is best used as a garnish.

It is reputed to be one of the most highly chemically treated crops, so choose organic iceberg lettuces if you can.

Oak leaf

This attractive lettuce has red-tinged, soft-textured leaves with a slightly bitter flavour. In salads, combine with green lettuces for a contrast of tastes and textures.

Lollo rosso

The pretty, frilly leaves of lollo rosso are green at the base and a deep, autumn-red around the edge. Its imposing shape means it is best mixed with other leaves if used in a salad or as a base for roasted vegetables. Lollo biondo is a pale-green version.

Frisée

Also known as curly endive, frisée has spiky, ragged leaves that are dark green on the outside and fade to an attractive pale yellow-green towards its centre. It has a distinctive bitter flavour that is enhanced by a robust dressing.

Radicchio

Lamb's lettuce

Lamb's lettuce

This tiny lettuce has a cluster of small,
rounded, velvety leaves with a delicate
flavour. Serve on its own or mix with
other leaves.

SALAD LEAVES

There is a great variety of different salad
leaves that are now readily available.

Radicchio

A member of the chicory family, radicchio
has deep-red, tightly packed leaves that
have a bitter peppery flavour. It is good in
salads and can be sautéed or roasted.

Rocket (arugula)

Classified as a herb, rocket is a popular
addition to salads, or it can be served as a
starter with thin shavings of Parmesan
cheese. It has a strong, peppery flavour,
which is more robust when wild. Lightly
steamed rocket has a milder flavour than
the raw leaves but it is equally delicious.

Sorrel

Rocket (arugula)

Sorrel

The long
pointed leaves
of sorrel have a
refreshing, sharp flavour that is best
when mixed with milder tasting leaves. It
contains oxalic acid which, when cooked,
inhibits the absorption of iron. Sorrel is an
effective diuretic.

Watercress

The hot, peppery
flavour of
watercress
complements
milder tasting
leaves and is
classically
combined
with
fresh
orange.
It does

Watercress

not keep well and is best used within two
days of purchase. Watercress is a member
of the cruciferous family and shares its
cancer-fighting properties.

Buying and Storing: Salad leaves are best
when they are very fresh and do not keep
well. Avoid leaves that are wilted,
discoloured or shrivelled. Store in the
refrigeratror, unwashed, for
between two days
and one week,
depending on the variety.
As salad leaves are routinely
sprayed with pesticides, they should be
washed thoroughly, but gently, to avoid
damaging the leaves, and then dried in a
dish cloth. Better still, choose organically
grown produce.

Health Benefits: Although all types of
salad leaves are about 90 per cent water,
they contain useful amounts of vitamins
and minerals, particularly folate, iron and
the antioxidants, vitamin C and beta
carotene. The outer, darker leaves tend to
be more nutritious than the paler leaves in
the centre. More importantly, like other
green, leafy vegetables, their antioxidant
content has been found to guard against
the risk of many cancers. Salad leaves are
usually eaten raw when the nutrients are
at their strongest. Lettuce is reputed to
have a calming, sedative effect.

Herbs

Herbs have been highly prized by natural practitioners for centuries because, in spite of their low nutritional value, they possess many reputed healing qualities. In cooking, herbs can make a significant difference to the flavour and aroma of a dish and they have the ability to enliven the simplest of meals. Fresh herbs can easily be grown at home in the garden, or in a pot or window box.

Chives and bay leaves

BASIL

This delicate aromatic herb is widely used in Italian and Thai cooking. The leaves bruise easily, so are best used whole or torn, rather than cut with a knife. Basil is said to have a calming effect on the stomach, easing constipation, sickness and cramps, and aiding digestion.

BAY LEAVES

These dark-green, glossy leaves are best left to dry for a few days before use. They have a robust, spicy flavour and are an essential ingredient in bouquet garni. Studies show that bay has a restorative effect on the digestive system.

CHIVES

A member of the onion family, chives have a milder flavour and are best used as a garnish, snipped over egg or potato dishes, or added to salads or flans. Like onions, chives are an antiseptic and act as a digestive.

CORIANDER (CILANTRO)

Warm and spicy, coriander is popular in Indian and Thai curries, stir-fries and salads. It looks similar to flat leaf parsley but its taste is completely different. It is often sold with its root intact. The root has a more intense flavour than the leaves and can be used in curry pastes. Coriander is

Using Dried Herbs

Although fresh herbs have the best flavour and appearance, dried herbs can be a convenient and useful alternative, especially in the winter months when some fresh herbs are not available.

• A few dried herbs such as basil, dill, mint and parsley do not dry well, losing most of their flavour.

• Oregano, thyme, marjoram and bay retain their flavour when dried and are useful substitutes for fresh.

• Dried herbs have a more concentrated flavour than fresh, so much less is required – usually a third to a half as much as fresh.

• When using dried herbs in cooking, always allow sufficient time for them to rehydrate and soften.

• Dried herbs do little for uncooked dishes, but are useful for flavouring marinades, and are good in slow-cooked stews and soups.

• When buying dried herbs, they should look bright, not faded and, because light spoils their flavour and shortens shelf-life, store in sealed, airtight jars in a cool, dark place.

Basil

Coriander
(cilantro)

partner for mustard. An attractive herb with delicate, wispy leaves, add to dishes just prior to serving as its mild flavour diminishes with cooking. Dill is a popular herb for settling the stomach and is thought to reduce flatulence. It is also said to be mildly soporific and, in the form of gripe water, is sometimes given to babies to relieve wind and colic.

an effective digestive, easing indigestion and nausea. It is also said to act as a tonic for the heart.

DILL

The mild aniseed flavour of dill goes well with potatoes, courgettes (zucchini) and cucumber. It makes a good addition to creamy sauces and can be added to egg dishes. It can also be used as a flavouring for dressings and marinades and is a good

Dill

Pesto

Freshly made pesto, spooned over warm pasta or spread over bread and topped with a round of goat's cheese, makes a perfect quick supper. It is usually made with basil, but other herbs, such as rocket (arugula), coriander (cilantro) or parsley, can be substituted. The pine nuts can also be replaced with walnuts, cashew nuts or pistachio nuts.

INGREDIENTS

50g/2oz/1 cup fresh basil leaves
2 garlic cloves, crushed
40g/1 1/2oz/1/2 cups pine nuts
120ml/4fl oz/1/2 cup olive oil, plus extra
  for drizzling
60ml/4 tbsp freshly grated
  Parmesan cheese
salt and freshly ground black pepper

1 Place the basil, garlic and pine nuts in a food processor or blender and process until finely chopped.

2 Gradually add the olive oil and then the Parmesan and blend to a coarse purée. Season to taste. Spoon into a lidded jar, then pour over the extra olive oil to cover. Use at once, or store in the refrigerator.

Freezing Herbs

This is an excellent method of preserving fresh delicate herbs such as basil, chives, dill, tarragon, coriander and parsley. The herbs will lose their fresh appearance and texture when frozen, but are still suitable for use in cooking. They will keep for up to 3 months in the freezer.

• Half-fill ice-cube trays with chopped herbs and top up with water. Freeze, then place the cubes in freezer-bags. The frozen cubes can be added to soups, stews and stocks, and heated until they melt.

• Place whole sprigs or leaves, or chopped herbs in freezer bags, expel any air and tightly seal.

• Freeze herb sprigs or leaves on trays. When the herbs are frozen, transfer them carefully to freezer-bags, expel any air, seal tightly and return to the freezer.

• Pack chopped fresh herbs in plastic pots and freeze. Scatter into soups and stews straight from the freezer.

Kaffir lime leaves

KAFFIR LIME LEAVES

These attractive glossy, green leaves are commonly used in Asian cuisines, lending a tantalizing citrus aroma and flavour to a wide variety of dishes. They are available fresh from Asian stores, or dried from large supermarkets. The fruit resembles a knobbly lime and its rind, which is rich in vitamin C, is used grated in Thai and Indonesian curries. The leaves can be used as a digestive.

LEMON BALM

This herb makes a refreshing tea and is good in any sweet or savoury dish that uses lemon juice. It has antibacterial, antiviral and antidepressant qualities. The calming and sedative attributes of lemon balm are beneficial for those suffering from stress or nervous exhaustion.

MARJORAM

Closely related to oregano, marjoram has a slightly sweeter flavour. It goes well in Mediterranean-style vegetable dishes, such as ratatouille, or in casseroles and tomato sauces, but should be added at the last minute as its flavour diminishes when heated. It also makes a good addition to a marinade. Majoram improves the circulation and relieves stomach pains.

MINT

The most familiar types are spearmint and peppermint, but there are other distinctly flavoured varieties, such as apple, lemon and pineapple mint, which are worth looking out for, and make a refreshing drink when infused in boiling water. Mint is used as a flavouring in a wide variety of dishes, from stuffings to fruit salads. It is a vital ingredient in the Middle Eastern salad, tabbouleh, and is also mixed with natural (plain) yogurt to make raita, a soothing accompaniment to hot curries. It is a traditional cure for nausea and indigestion and is also effective in stimulating and cleansing the system.

Lemon balm, marjoram, mint and oregano

OREGANO

This is a wild variety of marjoram but has a more robust flavour that goes well with tomato-based dishes. Oregano can relieve digestive problems.

PARSLEY

There are two types of parsley: flat leaf and curly. Both taste relatively similiar, but the flat leaf variety is preferable in cooked dishes. Parsley is an excellent source of vitamin C, iron and calcium. Chewing parsley after eating garlic or onions can neutralize the smell and freshen breath.

Parsley

ROSEMARY

Wonderfully aromatic, rosemary is traditionally used in meat dishes, but it can also add a smoky flavour to hearty bean and vegetable dishes. Rosemary has a reputation for invigorating the circulation, and for relieving headaches and respiratory problems.

Rosemary and sage

SAGE

The leaves of this herb, which may be silver-grey or purple, have a potent aroma and only a small amount is needed. Sage is commonly added to meat dishes but, if used discreetly, it is delicious with beans, cheese, lentils and in stuffings. Sage was used medicinally before it found its way into the kitchen and is regarded as a tonic for the stomach, kidneys and liver.

Thyme

THYME

This robustly flavoured aromatic herb is good in tomato-based recipes, and with roasted vegetables, lentils and beans. It is also an essential ingredient in a bouquet garni. Thyme aids the digestion of fatty foods and works as a powerful antiseptic.

TARRAGON

A popular herb in French cooking, tarragon has an affinity with all egg- and cheese-based dishes. The short slender-leafed French variety has a warm, aniseed flavour and is considered to be superior to Russian tarragon. Tarragon has diuretic properties and can relieve indigestion. Infused in a herbal tisane, it can soothe sore throats and promote restful sleep.

Buying and Storing: Fresh herbs are sold loose, in packets or growing in pots. The packets do not keep for as long and should be stored in the refrigerator. Place stems of fresh herbs in a half-filled jar of water and cover with a plastic bag. Sealed with an elastic band, the herbs should keep in the refrigerator for a week. Growing herbs should be kept on a sunny windowsill. If watered regularly, and not cut too often, they will keep for months.

Drying Herbs

Bay, rosemary, sage, thyme and marjoram all dry well. However, other more delicate herbs, such as basil, coriander (cilantro) and parsley, are better used fresh. Pick herbs before they flower, preferably on a sunny morning after the dew has dried. Avoid washing them – instead brush with a pastry brush or wipe with a dry cloth. Tie the herbs in bunches and hang them upside down in a warm, dark place. The leaves should be dry and crisp after a week. Leave in bundles or strip the leaves from the stems and store in airtight jars.

Making Herbal Infusions

Infusions, or tisanes, are made from steeping fresh herbs in boiling water. They can be used as a medicinal gargle or refreshing healthy drink. Peppermint tea is an excellent remedy for indigestion or irritable bowel syndrome and is best drunk after a meal.

To make peppermint tea: pour boiling water over fresh peppermint leaves. Cover the bowl and leave to stand for about 10 minutes, then strain the liquid into a cup and drink.

Tarragon

Sprouted Seeds, Beans, Peas and Lentils

Sprouts are quite remarkable in terms of nutritional content. Once the seed (or pulse or grain) has germinated, the nutritional value rises dramatically. There are almost 30 per cent more B vitamins and 60 per cent more vitamin C in the sprout than in the original seed, pulse or grain. Supermarkets and health food stores sell a variety of sprouts, but it is easy to grow them at home – all you need is a jar, some muslin and an elastic band.

Alfalfa sprouts

MUNG BEANSPROUTS

The most commonly available beansprouts, these are popular in Chinese and Asian cooking, where they are used in soups, salads and stir-fries. They are fairly large, with a crunchy texture and a delicate flavour.

ALFALFA SPROUTS

These tiny, wispy white sprouts have a mild, nutty flavour. They are best eaten raw to retain their crunchy texture.

WHEAT BERRY SPROUTS

Sprouts grown from wheat berries have a crunchy texture and sweet flavour and are excellent in breads. If they are left to grow, the sprouts will become wheatgrass, a powerful detoxifier that is is usually made into a juice.

CHICKPEA SPROUTS

Sprouts grown from chickpeas have a nutty flavour and add substance to dishes.

LENTIL SPROUTS

These sprouts have a slightly spicy, peppery flavour and thin, white shoots. Use only whole lentils: split ones won't sprout.

ADUKI BEANSPROUTS

These fine wispy sprouts have a sweet nutty taste. Use in salads and stir-fries.

Sprouting Seeds, Beans, Peas and Grains

Larger peas, such as chickpeas, take longer to sprout than small beans, but they are all easy to grow and are usually ready to eat in three or four days. Store sprouts in a covered container in the refrigerator for 2–3 days.

2 The next day, pour off the water through the muslin and fill the jar again with water. Shake gently, then turn the jar upside down and drain thoroughly. Leave the jar on its side in a warm place, away from direct sunlight.

1 Wash 45ml/3 tbsp seeds, beans, peas or grains thoroughly in water, then place in a large jar. Fill the jar with lukewarm water, cover with a piece of muslin (cheesecloth) and fasten securely with an elastic band. Leave in a warm place to stand overnight.

3 Rinse the seeds, beans, peas or grains three times a day, until they have grown to the desired size. Make sure they are drained thoroughly to prevent them turning rancid. Remove from the jar, rinse well and remove any ungerminated beans.

How to Use Beansprouts

• Sprouted lentils, peas and beans have a denser more fibrous texture, while sprouts grown from seeds are lighter. Use a mixture of the three for a variety of tastes and textures.
• Mung beansprouts are often used in Oriental food, particularly stir-fries, and require little cooking.
• Alfalfa sprouts are good as part of a sandwich filling as well as in salads. They are not suited to cooking.
• Sprouted grains are good in breads, adding a pleasant crunchy texture. Knead them in after the first rising, before shaping the loaf.
• Use chickpea and lentil sprouts in casseroles and bakes.

Wheat berry sprouts

Chickpea sprouts

Lentil sprouts

Aduki beansprouts

Buying and Storing: If you can, choose fresh, crisp sprouts with the seed or bean still attached. Avoid any that are slimy or musty-looking. Sprouts are best eaten on the day they are bought but, if fresh, they will keep, wrapped in a plastic bag, in the refrigerator for 2–3 days. Rinse and pat dry before use.

Health Benefits: Sprouted seeds, beans, peas, lentils and grains supply rich amounts of protein, B vitamins and vitamins C and E, potassium and phosphorus which, due to the sprouting process, are in an easily digestible form. In Chinese medicine, sprouts are highly valued for their ability to cleanse and rejuvenate the system.

Tips on Sprouting

• Use whole seeds and beans as split ones will not germinate.
• Regular rinsing with fresh water and draining is essential when sprouting to prevent the beans from turning rancid and mouldy.
• Cover the sprouting jar with muslin (cheesecloth) to allow air to circulate and water in and out.
• After two or three days, the jar can be placed in sunlight to encourage the green pigment chlorophyll and increase the sprout's magnesium and fibre content.
• Soya beans and chickpea sprouts need to be rinsed four times a day.
• Keen sprouters may wish to invest in a special sprouting container that comes with draining trays.

Sprouting container

Sea Vegetables

The West has only relatively recently acknowledged the extraordinary variety and remarkable health benefits of sea vegetables, which have been an essential part of the Asian diet for centuries. Sea vegetables are highly versatile and can be used as the main component of a dish, to add texture and substance, or as a seasoning. Some sea vegetables, such as wakame, hijiki and kombu (or kelp) can be used in soups, stews and stir-fries, while others, such as agar-agar and carrageen, are used as a setting agent in jellies, mousses and cheesecakes.

Laver

Toasting Nori

Nori can be toasted, over either an electric hob (stovetop) or a gas burner until it is very crisp. The sheets can then be crumbled and used as a garnish for soups, salads or stir-fries. Take care when toasting the nori sheets that you do not scorch them – or your fingers.

1 Hold a sheet of nori with a pair of tongs about 5cm/2in above an electric or gas hob for about 1 minute, moving it around so it toasts evenly and turns bright green and crisp.

NORI

This useful sea vegetable has a delicate texture and mild flavour. It is sold in thin purple-black sheets, which turn a pretty, translucent green when toasted or cooked. It is one of the few sea vegetables that does not require soaking. Nori is processed by being chopped, flattened and dried on frames, like paper. In Japanese cooking, the sheets are used to wrap delicate, small parcels of vinegared rice and vegetables that are eaten as sushi. Once toasted and crisp, nori is crumbled and used as a garnish.

particularly in Wales, Scotland and Ireland. It is cooked into a thick dark purée, which can be spread on hot toast or mixed with oatmeal to make the Welsh delicacy, laverbread. It can also be added to sauces and stuffings. Available ready-cooked in cans from health food stores, laver has a stronger flavour than nori and a higher concentration of vitamins and minerals.

LAVER

A relation of nori, which grows outside Japan, laver is commonly found around the shores of Britain. Unlike Japanese nori, it is not cultivated. Laver is used in traditional regional cooking –

Nori sheets and flakes

2 Leave the nori sheet to cool for a few moments, then crumble. Sprinkle over salad, or use to garnish soups or stir-fries.

Arame

ARAME

Sold in delicate, black strips, arame has a mild, slightly sweet flavour and, if you haven't tried sea vegetables before, it is a good one to try. It needs to be soaked before using in stir-fries or salads, but if using in moist or slow-cooked dishes, such as noodles and soups, it can be added straight from the packet. Arame has been used to treat female disorders and is recommended for high blood pressure. It is rich in iodine, calcium and iron.

Preparing Arame

Soaking and cooking times vary depending on how the arame is to be used.

1 Rinse the arame in a sieve (strainer) under cold, running water, then place in a bowl and cover with cold water. Leave to soak for 5 minutes – it should double in volume. Drain and place in a pan.

2 Add fresh water and bring to the boil. Simmer for 20 minutes until tender.

WAKAME

This sea vegetable is often confused with its relative, kombu, because it looks very similar until it is soaked, when it changes colour from brown to a delicate green. Wakame has a mild flavour and is one of the most versatile sea vegetables. Soak briefly and use in salads and soups or toast, crumble and use as a condiment. It is rich in calcium and vitamins B and C.

KOMBU

Known as kelp in the West, kombu is now farmed in Britain. It is a brown sea vegetable and is usually sold dried in strips, although in Japan it is available in a multitude of forms. It has a very strong flavour and is used in slowly cooked dishes, soups and stocks – it is an essential ingredient in the Japanese stock, dashi. A small strip of kombu added to beans while they are cooking will soften them and increase their digestibility as well as their nutritional value. Kombu is richer in iodine than other sea vegetables, and also contains calcium, potassium and iron.

Kombu or kelp

Wakame

Hijiki

HIJIKI

This sea vegetable looks similar to arame but is thicker and has a slightly stronger flavour. Once soaked, hijiki can be sautéed or added to soups and salads, but it does require longer cooking than most sea vegetables. It expands considerably during soaking, so only a small amount is needed. It is particularly rich in calcium and iron.

Using Agar-agar to Make Jelly

Agar-agar can be used in place of gelatine; 10g/¼oz agar-agar flakes will set about 600ml/1 pint/2½ cups liquid.

1 Place 10g/¼oz agar-agar flakes in a pan with 300ml/½ pint/1¼ cups cold water; leave to soak for 15 minutes.

2 Bring to the boil, then simmer for a few minutes until the flakes dissolve. Stir in 300ml/½ pint/1¼ cups fresh orange juice. Pour into a jelly mould and leave to cool, then chill until set.

DULSE

A purple-red sea vegetable, dulse has flat fronds, which have a chewy texture and spicy flavour when cooked. For hundreds of years, dulse was popular in North America and northern Europe and was traded on both sides of the Atlantic. It needs to be soaked until soft before adding to salads, noodle dishes, soups and vegetable dishes. It can also be toasted and crumbled to make a

nourishing garnish. Dulse is rich in several minerals — potassium, iodine, phosphorus, iron and manganese.

AGAR-AGAR

The vegetarian equivalent to the animal-derived gelatine, agar-agar can be used as a setting agent in both sweet and savoury dishes. Known as kanten in Japan, it can be bought as flakes or strands, both of which need to be dissolved in water before use. Agar-agar has a neutral taste and its gelling abilities vary according to the other ingredients in a dish, so you may need to experiment, if substituting it for gelatine in a recipe, to achieve the best results. It is more effective than gelatine, so only a small amount is needed. It is said to be an effective laxative.

Dulse

Carrageen (left) and agar-agar flakes

CARRAGEEN

This fern-like seaweed, also known as Irish moss, is found along the Atlantic coasts of America and Europe. Like agar-agar, it has gelling properties but produces a softer set, making it useful for jellies and mousses and as a thickener in soups and stews. It is used for treating colds and bronchial problems as well as digestive disorders.

Buying and Storing: Sea vegetables are usually sold dried and will keep for months. Once the packet is opened, transfer the sea vegetables to an airtight jar. Fresh sea vegetables may be stored in the refrigerator, but will only remain fresh for 1–2 days. Rinse well before use.

Health Benefits: The health benefits of sea vegetables have been recognized for centuries and range from improving the lustre of hair and clarity of the skin to reducing cholesterol levels in the body. Sea vegetables are particularly rich in the antioxidant beta carotene. They contain some of the B complex vitamins, and significant amounts of the major minerals, such as calcium, magnesium, potassium, phosphorus and iron, as well as useful amounts of trace elements, such as selenium, zinc and iodine.

The rich mineral content of sea vegetables benefits the nervous system, helping to reduce stress. It also boosts the immune system, aiding the metabolism, while the iodine content prevents goitre and helps thyroid function. Research shows that alginic acid found in some seaweeds, notably kombu, arame, hijiki and wakame, binds with heavy metals, such as cadmium, lead, mercury and radium, in our intestines and helps to eliminate them.

COOK'S TIP

Some sea vegetables simply need washing and soaking for a few minutes before serving or adding to dishes; others require prolonged soaking and cooking before they are tender enough to eat. Most expand considerably after soaking, so only a small amount is required.

Rolled Sushi with Mixed Filling

INGREDIENTS

320g/11½ oz/1½ cups sushi rice
4 sheets nori seaweed, for rolling
soy sauce and gari (ginger pickles),
*   to serve*

FOR THE MIXED VINEGAR
40ml/8 tsp rice vinegar
22.5ml/4½ tsp sugar
3ml/⅔ tsp sea salt

FOR THE FILLING
4 large dried shiitake mushrooms
37.5ml/7½ tsp soy sauce
15ml/1 tbsp each of mirin, sake or dry
*   white wine and sugar*
1 small carrot, quartered lengthways
½ cucumber, quartered lengthways,
*   seeds removed*

Makes 32 pieces

1 Cook the rice in salted boiling water, then drain. Meanwhile, heat the ingredients for the mixed vinegar. Leave the vinegar to cool, then add to the hot cooked rice. Stir well with a spatula, fanning the rice constantly – this gives the rice an attractive glaze. Cover with a damp cloth and leave to cool. Do not put in the refrigerator, as this will make the rice harden.

2 To make the filling, soak the shiitake mushrooms in 200ml/7fl oz/scant 1 cup water for 30 minutes; drain, reserving the soaking water, and remove their stems. Pour the reserved soaking water into a pan and add the remaining filling ingredients (except the cucumber), then simmer for 4–5 minutes. Remove the carrot and set aside. Continue cooking until all the liquid has evaporated, then thinly slice the shiitake mushrooms and set aside for the filling.

3 Place a bamboo mat (makisu) on a chopping board. Lay a sheet of nori, shiny side down on the mat.

4 Spread a quarter of the prepared, dressed rice over the nori, using your fingers to press it down evenly. Leave a 1cm/½ in space at the top and bottom. Place a quarter of each of the filling ingredients – the sliced mushrooms, carrot and cucumber – across the middle of the layer of rice.

5 Carefully hold the nearest edge of the nori and the mat, then roll up the nori using the mat as a guide to make a neat tube of rice with the filling ingredients in the middle. Roll the rice tightly to ensure that the grains stick together and to keep the filling in place. Roll the sushi off the mat and make three more rolls in the same way.

6 Using a wet knife, cut each roll into eight pieces and stand them upright on a platter. Wipe the blade and rinse it under cold water between cuts to prevent the rice from sticking. Serve soy sauce and gari with the sushi.

Cereal Grains

Grains have been cultivated throughout the world for centuries. The seeds of cereal grasses, they are packed with concentrated goodness and are an important source of complex carbohydrates, protein, vitamins and minerals.

The most popular types of grain, such as wheat, rice, oats, barley and maize, come in various forms, from whole grains to flours. Inexpensive and readily available, grains are incredibly versatile and should form a major part of our diet.

Wheat

Wheat is the largest and most important grain crop in the world and has been cultivated since 7,000BC.

The wheat kernel comprises three parts: bran, germ and endosperm. Wheat bran is the outer husk, while wheat germ is the nutritious seed from which the plant grows. Sprouted wheat is an excellent food, highly recommended in cancer prevention diets. The endosperm, the inner part of the kernel, is full of starch and protein and forms the basis of wheat flour. In addition to flour, wheat comes in various other forms.

Whole-wheat berries

Wheatgrass

WHEAT BERRIES
These are whole wheat grains with the husks removed and they can be bought in health food stores.

Wheat berries may be used to add a sweet, nutty flavour and chewy texture to breads, soups and stews, or can be combined with rice or other grains. Wheat berries must be soaked overnight, then cooked in boiling salted water until tender. If they are left to germinate, the berries sprout into wheatgrass, a powerful detoxifier and cleanser (see below).

WHEAT BRAN
Wheat bran is the outer husk of the wheat kernel and is a by-product of white flour production. It is very high in soluble dietary fibre, which makes it nature's most effective laxative. Wheat bran makes a healthy addition to bread doughs, breakfast cereals, cakes, muffins and cookies, and it can also be used to add substance to stews and bakes.

Wheatgrass – a Natural Healer
Grown from the whole-wheat grain, wheatgrass has been recognized for centuries for its general healing qualities. When juiced, it is a powerful detoxifier and cleanser and is a rich source of B vitamins and vitamins A, C and E, as well as all the known minerals.

Its vibrant green colour comes from chlorophyll (known as 'nature's healer'), which works directly on the liver to eliminate harmful toxins. It is also reputed to have anti-ageing capabilities.

Once it is juiced, wheatgrass must be consumed within 15 minutes, preferably on an empty stomach. Some people may experience nausea or dizziness when drinking the juice for the first time, but this will soon disappear.

Wheat germ

Wheat flakes

Bulgur wheat

way as wheat berries (although it cooks in less time), or as an alternative to rice and other grains. When cooked, it has a slightly sticky texture and pleasant crunchiness. Serve it as an accompaniment, or use in salads and pilaffs.

BULGUR WHEAT

Unlike cracked wheat, this grain is made from cooked wheat berries, which have the bran removed, and are then dried and crushed. This light, nutty grain is simply soaked in water for 20 minutes, then drained – some manufacturers specify cold water but boiling water produces a softer grain. It can also be cooked in boiling water until tender. Bulgur wheat is the main ingredient in the Middle Eastern salad, tabbouleh, where it is combined with chopped parsley, mint, tomatoes, cucumber and onion, and dressed with lemon juice and olive oil.

Cooking Wheat Berries

Wheat berries make a delicious addition to salads, and they can also be used to add texture to breads and stews.

1 Place the wheat berries in a bowl and cover with cold water. Soak overnight, then rinse thoroughly and drain.

2 Place the wheat berries in a pan with water. Bring to the boil, then cover and simmer for 1–2 hours until tender, replenishing with water when necessary.

WHEAT FLAKES

Steamed and softened berries that have been rolled and pressed are known as wheat flakes or rolled wheat. They are best used on their own or mixed with other flaked grains in porridge, as a base for muesli (granola), or to add nutrients and substance to breads and cakes.

WHEAT GERM

The nutritious heart of the whole wheat berry, wheat germ is a rich source of protein, vitamins B and E, and iron. It is used in much the same way as wheat bran and lends a pleasant, nutty flavour to breakfast cereals and porridge. It is available toasted or untoasted. Store wheat germ in an airtight container in the refrigerator as it can become rancid if kept at room temperature.

CRACKED WHEAT

This is made from crushed wheat berries and retains all the nutrients of whole-wheat. Often confused with bulgur wheat, cracked wheat can be used in the same

SEMOLINA

Made from the endosperm of durum wheat, semolina can be used to make a hot milk dessert or it can be added to cakes, cookies and breads to give them a pleasant grainy texture.

COUSCOUS

Although this looks like a grain, couscous is a form of pasta made by steaming and drying cracked durum wheat. Couscous is popular in north Africa, where it forms the basis of a national dish of the same name. Individual grains are moistened by hand, passed through a sieve (strainer) and steamed in a couscousière, suspended over a bubbling vegetable stew, until light

Semolina

Cooking Couscous

Traditionally, the preparation of couscous is a time-consuming business, requiring lengthy steaming. The couscous found in most stores nowadays, however, is pre-cooked, which cuts the preparation time drastically.

1 Place the couscous in a large bowl, add enough boiling water to cover and leave for 10 minutes or until all the water has been absorbed. Separate the grains, season and mix in a knob (pat) of butter.

2 Alternatively, moisten the grains and place in a muslin-lined (cheesecloth-lined) steamer. Steam for 15 minutes or until the grains are tender and fluffy.

and fluffy. Nowadays, the couscous that is generally available is the quick-cooking variety, which simply needs soaking, although it can also be steamed or baked. Couscous has a fairly bland flavour, which makes it a good foil for spicy dishes.

WHEAT FLOUR

This is ground from the whole grain and may be wholemeal (whole-wheat) or white, depending on the degree of processing. Hard, or strong flour is high in the protein gluten, which makes it ideal for bread-making, while soft flour is lower in gluten but higher in starch and is better for light

cakes and pastries. Durum wheat flour comes from one of the hardest varieties of wheat and is used to make pasta. Most commercial white flour is a combination of soft and hard wheat, which produces an 'all-purpose' flour.

Because the refining process robs many commercial flours of most of their nutrients, the lost vitamins and minerals are synthetically replaced. When buying flour, look for brands that are unbleached and organically produced as these have fewer chemical additives. Nutritionally, stoneground whole-wheat flour is the best buy because it is largely unprocessed and

Couscous

Wheat flour (left) and malted brown flour, which contains flour from malted wheat grains. Stoneground versions are available

Coeliac Disease

This is caused by an allergy to gluten, a substance found in bread, cakes, pastries and cereals. It is estimated that millions of people suffer from the disease, many without diagnosis. Symptoms may include anaemia, weight loss, fatigue, depression and diarrhoea. Wheat, rye, barley and oats are the main culprits and sufferers
are usually advised to remove these completely from their diet. Rice, soya, buckwheat, quinoa, millet and corn are gluten-free substitutes.

retains all the valuable nutrients. It produces slightly heavier breads, cakes and pastries than white flour, but can be combined with white flour to make lighter versions, although, of course, the nutritional value will not be as high.

SEITAN

Used as a meat replacement, seitan is made from wheat gluten and has a firm, chewy texture. It can be found in the chiller cabinet of health food stores. Seitan has a neutral flavour that benefits from marinating. Slice or cut into chunks and stir-fry, or add

to stews and pasta sauces during the last few minutes of cooking time. Seitan does not need to be cooked for long, just heated through.

Buying and Storing: Buy wheat-based foods from stores with a high turnover of stock. Wheat berries can be kept for around 6 months, but whole-wheat flour should be used within 3 months, as its oils turn rancid. Always decant grains into airtight containers and store in a cool, dark place. Wheat germ deteriorates very quickly at room temperature and should be stored in an airtight container in the refrigerator for no more than a month.

Health Benefits: Wheat is most nutritious when it is unprocessed and in its whole form. (When milled into white flour, wheat loses a staggering 80 per cent of its nutrients.) Wheat is an excellent source of dietary fibre, the B vitamins and vitamin E, as well as iron, selenium and zinc. Fibre is the most discussed virtue of whole wheat and most of this is concentrated in the bran. Eating one or more spoonfuls of bran a day is recommended to relieve constipation. Numerous studies show fibre to be effective in inhibiting colon and rectal cancer, varicose veins, haemorrhoids and obesity. Phytoestrogens found in wholegrains may also ward off breast cancer. On the negative side, wheat is also a well-known allergen and triggers coeliac disease, a gluten intolerance.

Seitan

Rice

Throughout Asia, a meal is considered incomplete without rice. It is a staple food for over half the world's population, and almost every culture has its own repertoire of rice dishes, ranging from risottos to pilaffs. What's more, this valuable food provides a good source of vitamins and minerals, as well as a steady supply of energy.

White and brown long grain rice

Jasmine fragrant rice

LONG GRAIN RICE

The most widely used type of rice is long grain rice, where the grain is five times as long as it is wide. Long grain brown rice has had its outer husk removed, leaving the bran and germ intact, which gives it a chewy nutty flavour. It takes longer to cook than white rice but contains more fibre, vitamins and minerals. Long grain white rice has had its husk, bran and germ removed, taking most of the nutrients with them and leaving a bland-flavoured rice that is light and fluffy when cooked. It is often whitened with chalk, talc or other preservatives, so rinsing is essential. Easy-cook long grain white rice, sometimes called parboiled or converted rice, has been steamed under pressure. This process hardens the grain and makes it difficult to overcook, and some nutrients are transferred from the bran and germ into the kernel during this process. Easy-cook brown rice cooks more quickly than normal brown rice.

JASMINE RICE

This rice has a soft, sticky texture and a delicious, mildly perfumed flavour – which accounts for its other name, fragrant rice. It is a long grain rice that is widely used in Thai cooking, where its delicate flavour tempers strongly spiced food.

Cooking Long Grain Brown Rice

There are many methods and opinions on how to cook rice. The absorption method is one of the simplest and retains valuable nutrients, which would otherwise be lost in cooking water that is drained away.

Different types of rice have different powers of absorption, however the general rule of thumb for long grain rice is to use double the quantity of water to rice. For example, use 1 cup of rice to 2 cups of water. 200g/7oz/1 cup long grain rice is sufficient for about four people as a side dish.

1 Rinse the rice in a sieve (strainer) under cold, running water. Place in a heavy pan and add the measured cold water. Bring to the boil, uncovered, then reduce the heat and stir the rice. Add salt, to taste, if you wish.

2 Cover the pan with a tight-fitting lid. Simmer for 25–35 minutes, without removing the lid, until the water is absorbed and the rice tender. Remove from the heat and leave to stand, covered, for 5 minutes before serving.

Red rice

Wild rice

RED RICE

This rice comes from the Camargue in France and has a distinctive chewy texture and a nutty flavour. It is an unusually hard grain, which although it takes about an hour to cook, retains its shape. Cooking intensifies its red colour, making it a distinctive addition to salads and stuffings.

WILD RICE

This is not a true rice but an aquatic grass grown in North America. It has dramatic, long, slender brown-black grains that have a nutty flavour and chewy texture. It takes longer to cook than most types of rice – from 35–60 minutes, depending on whether you like it chewy or tender – but you can reduce the cooking time by soaking it in water overnight. Wild rice is extremely nutritious. It contains all eight essential amino acids and is particularly rich in lysine. It is a good source of fibre, low in calories and gluten free. Use in stuffings, serve plain or mix with other rices in pilaffs and rice salads.

BASMATI RICE

This is a slender, long grain rice, which is grown in the foothills of the Himalayas. It is aged for a year after harvest, giving it a characteristic light, fluffy texture and aromatic flavour. Its name means 'fragrant'.

Both white and brown types of basmati rice are available. Brown basmati contains more nutrients, and has a slightly nuttier flavour than the white variety. Widely used in Indian cooking, basmati rice has a cooling effect on hot and spicy curries. It is also excellent for biryanis and for rice salads, when you want very light, fluffy separate grains.

White and brown basmati rice

Quick Ways to Flavour Rice

• Cook brown rice in vegetable stock with sliced dried apricots. Sauté an onion in a little oil and add ground cumin, coriander and fresh chopped chilli, then mix in the cooked rice.

• Add raisins and toasted almonds to saffron-infused rice.

Valencia rice

Quick Ways to Flavour Risotto

• When making risotto, replace a quarter of the vegetable stock with red or white wine.

• Add a bay leaf, the juice and zest of a lemon, or a lemon grass stalk and cardamom pods to the cooking water.
• Saffron adds a yellow colour to risotto rice. Add a few strands to the vegetable stock.

VALENCIA RICE

Traditionally used for making Spanish paella, this short grain rice is not as sturdy as risotto rice and needs to be handled with care because it breaks down easily. The best way of cooking paella is to leave the rice unstirred once all the ingredients are in the pan.

RISOTTO RICE

To make Italian risotto, it is essential that you use a special, fat, short grain rice. Arborio rice, which originates from the Po Valley region in Italy, is the most widely sold variety of risotto rice, but you may also find varieties such as Carnaroli and Vialone Nano in specialist stores. When cooked, most rice absorbs around three times its weight in water, but risotto rice can absorb nearly five times its weight, and the result is a creamy grain that still retains a slight bite.

Above: Clockwise from left, arborio, carnaroli and vialone nano risotto rice

Making a Simple Risotto

A good risotto, which is creamy and moist with tender grains that retain a slight bite, is easy to make. The secrets are to use the correct type of rice (arborio, carnaroli, or vialone nano); to add the cooking liquid gradually – it should be completely absorbed by the rice before the next ladleful is added; and to stir the risotto frequently to prevent the grains sticking to the pan.

INGREDIENTS

15ml/1 tbsp olive oil
small knob (pat) of butter
1 onion, finely chopped
350g/12oz/1¾ cups risotto rice
1.2 litres/2 pints/5 cups hot vegetable stock
50g/2oz/⅔ cup freshly grated Parmesan cheese
salt and freshly ground black pepper

SERVES 4

Variations

• Add finely chopped cooked (not pickled) beetroot (beet) towards the end of the cooking time to give the rice a vibrant pink colour and slight sweetness.
• To make mushroom and broccoli risotto, sauté 175g/6oz/2 cups sliced or chopped flat mushrooms with the onion. Blanch 225g/8oz/2 cups broccoli florets for 3 minutes until tender, and add towards the end of cooking time.

1 Heat the oil and butter in a large, heavy pan, then cook the onion for 7 minutes until soft, stirring occasionally. Add the rice and stir to coat the grains in the hot oil and butter.

2 Add a quarter of the stock and cook over a low-medium heat, stirring frequently, until the liquid is absorbed. Add more stock, a little at a time, stirring, until all the liquid is added and absorbed.

3 After about 20 minutes, the grains will be creamy but still retain a bite. Turn off the heat, stir in the Parmesan and check the seasoning. Add salt and pepper to taste and serve immediately.

Japanese Rice Products

The Japanese are extremely resourceful when it comes to exploiting the vast potential of rice.

Sake This spirit is Japan's national drink; it can also be used in cooking.

Mirin Sweet rice wine that is delicious in marinades and savoury dishes, and is a key ingredient in teriyaki.

Rice vinegar Popular throughout Asia, this ranges in colour from white to brown. Japanese rice vinegar has a mild, mellow flavour. The Chinese version is much harsher.

Amasake A healthy rice drink made by adding enzymes from fermented rice to wholegrain pudding rice. It has a similar consistency to soya 'milk' and can be flavoured. Amasake may be used for baking or to make creamy desserts. It is also an excellent and easily digestible weaning food.

Right, clockwise from top left: amasake, mirin, rice vinegar and sake.

PUDDING RICE

This rounded, short grain rice is suitable for milk puddings and rice desserts. The grains swell and absorb a great deal of milk during cooking, which gives the dessert a soft, creamy consistency. Brown pudding rice is also available.

GLUTINOUS RICE

This rice is almost round in shape and has a slightly sweet flavour. Despite its name, the rice is gluten-free. The grains stick together when cooked due to their high starch content, making the rice easier to eat with chopsticks.

Pudding rice

Glutinous rice, which can be either white, black or purple, is used in many South-east Asian countries to make sticky, creamy desserts. In China, white glutinous rice is often wrapped in lotus leaves and steamed to make a popular dim sum dish.

White and black glutinous rice

JAPANESE SUSHI RICE

Similar to glutinous rice, this is mixed with rice vinegar to make sushi. Most sushi rice eaten in the West is grown in California.

Buying and Storing: To ensure freshness, always buy rice from stores that have a regular turnover of stock. Store in an airtight container in a cool, dry, dark place to keep out moisture and insects. Wash before use to remove any impurities. Cooked rice should be cooled quickly, then chilled and reheated thoroughly before serving.

Health Benefits: Rice is a valuable source of complex carbohydrates and fibre. In its whole form it is a good source of B vitamins. White rice is deprived of much of its nutrients because the bran and germ have been removed. The starch in rice is absorbed slowly, keeping blood sugar levels on an even keel and making it an important food for diabetics. Research shows that rice may benefit sufferers of psoriasis. It can also be used to

Sushi rice

Quick Ideas for Rice

Rice can be served plain, but it is also good in one-dish meals, marrying well with a host of exotic flavourings and simple store-cupboard ingredients.
• To make a Middle-Eastern inspired rice dish, cook long grain brown rice in vegetable stock, then stir in some toasted flaked (sliced) almonds, pieces of dried date and fig, cooked chickpeas, and chopped fresh mint.
• For a simple pullao, gently fry a finely chopped onion in sunflower oil with cardamom pods, a cinnamon stick and cloves, then stir in basmati rice. Add water, infused with a pinch of saffron, and cook until tender. Towards the end of the cooking time, add sultanas and cashew nuts, then garnish with chopped coriander (cilantro).

treat digestive disorders, calm the nervous system, prevent kidney stones and reduce the risk of bowel cancer. However, the phytates found in brown rice can inhibit the absorption of iron and calcium.

Rice Products

Rice flakes These are made by steaming and rolling whole or white grains. They are light and quick-cooking, and can be added raw to muesli (granola) or used to make porridge, creamy desserts, bread, cookies and cakes.

Rice bran Like wheat and oat bran, rice bran comes from the husk of the grain kernel. It is high in soluble dietary fibre and useful for adding texture and substance to bread, cakes and cookies, and stews.

Rice flour Often used to make sticky Asian cakes and sweets (candies), rice flour can also be used to thicken sauces. Because rice flour does not contain gluten, cakes made with it are rather flat. It can be combined with wheat flour to make cakes and bread, but produces a crumbly loaf. Rice powder is a very fine rice flour, found in Asian stores.

Right, clockwise from top left: rice bran, rice flour, rice powder and rice flakes.

Other Grains

Wheat and rice are undoubtedly the most widely used grains, yet there are others such as oats, rye, corn, barley, quinoa and spelt, that should not be ignored, because they provide variety in our diet and are packed with nutrients. Grains come in many forms, from whole grains to flour and are used for baking, breakfast cereals and cooked dishes.

OATS

Available rolled, flaked, as oatmeal or oatbran, oats are warming and sustaining when cooked. Like rye, oats are a popular grain in northern Europe, particularly Scotland, where they are commonly turned into porridge, oatcakes and pancakes.

Whole oats are unprocessed with the nutritious bran and germ remaining intact. Oat groats are the hulled, whole kernel, while rolled oats are made from groats that have been heated and pressed flat. Quick-cooking rolled oats have been pre-cooked in water and then dried, which diminishes their nutritional value. Medium oatmeal is best in cakes and breads, while fine is ideal in pancakes, and fruit and milk drinks. Oatmeal and oat flour contain very little gluten so should be mixed with wheat flour to make leavened bread. Oat bran can be sprinkled over breakfast cereals and mixed into natural (plain) yogurt.

Below, clockwise from top left: rolled oats, oatmeal, whole oats and oat bran

Health Benefits: Oats are perhaps the most nutritious of all the grains. Recent research has focused on the ability of oat bran to reduce blood cholesterol (sometimes with dramatic results), while beneficial HDL cholesterol levels increase. For best results, oat bran should be eaten daily at regular intervals.

High in fibre, oats are an effective laxative and also feature protease inhibitors, a combination that has been found to inhibit certain cancers. Oats also contain vitamin E and some B vitamins, as well as iron, calcium, magnesium, phosphorus and potassium.

RYE

The most popular grain for bread-making in Eastern Europe, Scandinavia and Russia, rye flour produces a dark, dense and dry loaf that keeps well. It is a hardy grain, which grows where most others fail – hence its popularity in colder climates. Rye is low in gluten and so rye flour is often mixed with high-gluten wheat flours to create lighter textured breads; the colour of which is sometimes intensified using molasses. The whole grain can be soaked overnight, then cooked in boiling water until tender, but the flour, with its robust, full flavour and greyish colour, is the most commonly used form. The flour ranges from dark to light, depending on whether the bran and germ have been removed.

Rye: grain and flour

Health Benefits: Rye is a good source of vitamin E and some B vitamins, as well as protein, calcium, iron, phosphorus and potassium. It is also high in fibre, and is used in natural medicine to help to strengthen the digestive system.

CORN

Although we are most familiar with yellow corn or maize, blue, red, black and even multi-coloured varieties can also be found. Corn is a key store cupboard (pantry) ingredient in the USA, the Caribbean and Italy, and comes in many forms.

Masa harina

Maize meal, or masa harina, is made from the cooked whole grain, which is ground into flour and commonly used to make the Mexican flat bread, tortilla.

Cornmeal

The main culinary uses for cornmeal are cornbread, a classic, southern American bread, and polenta, which confusingly is both the Italian name for cornmeal as well as a dish made with the grain. Polenta (the cooked dish) is a thick, golden porridge, which is often flavoured with butter and cheese or chopped herbs.

Making Polenta

Polenta makes an excellent alternative to mashed potato. It needs plenty of seasoning and is even better with a pat of butter and cheese, such as Parmesan, Gorgonzola or Taleggio. Serve with stews or casseroles.

1 Pour 1 litre/1¾ pints/4 cups water into a heavy pan and bring to the boil. Remove from the heat.

2 In a steady stream, gradually add 185g/6½oz/1½ cups instant polenta and mix with a balloon whisk to avoid any lumps forming.

3 Return the pan to the heat and cook, stirring continuously with a wooden spoon, until the polenta is thick and creamy and starts to come away from the sides of the pan – this will only take a few minutes if you are using instant polenta.

4 Season to taste with salt and plenty of ground black pepper, then add a generous pat of butter and mix well. Remove from the heat and stir in the cheese, if using.

Clockwise from top left:
Blue and yellow cornmeal,
cornflour (cornstarch), popcorn
masa harina and polenta

Once cooked, polenta can also be left to cool, then cut into slabs and fried, barbecued or griddled until golden brown. It is delicious with roasted vegetables. Ready-to-slice polenta is available from some supermarkets.

Polenta grain comes in various grades, ranging from fine to coarse. You can buy polenta that takes 40–45 minutes to cook or an 'instant' part-cooked version that can be cooked in less than 5 minutes.

In the Caribbean, cornmeal is used to make desserts and dumplings.

Cornflour (cornstarch)

This fine white powder is a useful thickening agent for sauces, soups and casseroles. It can also be added to cakes.

Hominy

These are the husked whole grains of corn. They should be cooked in boiling water until softened, then used in stews and soups, or added to cakes and muffins.

Grits

Coarsely ground, dried yellow or white corn is known as grits. Use for porridge and pancakes or add to baked goods.

Popcorn

This is a separate strain of corn that is grown specifically to make the popular snack food. The kernel's hard outer casing explodes when heated.

Quinoa

Popcorn can easily be made at home and flavoured sweet or savoury according to taste. The store-bought types are often high in salt or sugar.

Health Benefits: In American folk medicine, corn is considered a diuretic and a mild stimulant. Corn is said to prevent cancer of the colon, breast and prostate and to lower the risk of heart disease. It is believed to be the only grain that contains vitamin A as well as some of the B vitamins and iron.

BARLEY

Believed to be the oldest cultivated grain, barley is still a fundamental part of the everyday diet in Eastern Europe, the Middle East and Asia.

Pearl barley, the most usual form, is husked, steamed and then polished to give it its characteristic ivory-coloured appearance. It has a mild, sweet flavour and chewy texture, and can be added to soups, stews and bakes. It is also used to make old-fashioned barley water.

Pot barley is the whole grain with just the inedible outer husk removed. It takes much longer to cook than pearl barley. Barley flakes, which make a satisfying porridge, and barley flour are also available in stores.

Health Benefits: Pot barley is more nutritious than pearl barley, because it contains extra fibre, calcium, phosphorus, iron, magnesium and B vitamins. Barley was once used to increase potency and boost physical strength. More recently, studies have shown that its fibre content may help to prevent constipation and other digestive problems, as well as heart disease and certain cancers. In addition, the protease inhibitors in barley have been found to suppress cancer of the intestines, and eating barley regularly may also reduce the amount of harmful cholesterol produced by the liver.

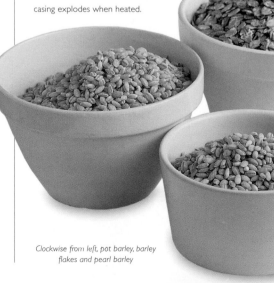

Clockwise from left, pot barley, barley flakes and pearl barley

Lemon Barley Water

INGREDIENTS

225g/8oz/1 cup pearl barley
1.75 litres/3 pints/7½ cups water
grated rind of 1 lemon
50g/2oz/¼ cup caster (superfine) sugar
juice of 2 lemons

1 Rinse the barley, then place in a large pan and cover with the water. Bring to the boil, then reduce the heat and simmer gently for 20 minutes, skimming off any scum from time to time. Remove the pan from the heat.

2 Add the lemon rind and sugar to the pan, stir well and leave to cool. Strain, and add the lemon juice.

3 Taste the lemon barley water and add more sugar, if necessary. Serve chilled with ice and slices of lemon.

QUINOA

Hailed as the supergrain of the future, quinoa (pronounced 'keen-wa') is a grain of the past. It was called 'the mother grain' by the Incas, who cultivated it for hundreds of years, high in the Andes, solely for their own use.

Nowadays, quinoa is widely available. The tiny, bead-shaped grains have a mild, slightly bitter taste and firm texture. It is cooked in the same way as rice, but the grains quadruple in size, becoming translucent with an unusual white outer ring. Quinoa is useful for making stuffings, pilaffs, bakes and breakfast cereals.

Health Benefits: Quinoa's supergrain status hails from its rich nutritional value. Unlike other grains, quinoa is a complete protein because it contains all eight essential amino acids. It is an excellent source of calcium, potassium and zinc as well as iron, magnesium and B vitamins. It is particularly valuable for people with coeliac disease as it is gluten-free.

MILLET

Although millet is usually associated with bird food, it is a highly nutritious grain. It once rivalled barley as the main food of Europe and remains a staple ingredient in many parts of the world, including Africa, China and India. Its mild flavour makes it an ideal accompaniment to spicy stews and curries, and it can be used as a base for pilaffs or milk desserts. The tiny, firm grains can also be flaked or ground into flour. Millet is gluten-free, so it is a useful food for people with coeliac disease. The flour can be used for baking, but needs to be combined with high-gluten flours to make leavened bread.

Health Benefits: Millet is an easily digestible grain. It contains more iron than other grains and is a good source of zinc, calcium, manganese and B vitamins. It is also believed to be beneficial to those suffering from candidiasis, a fungal infection caused by the yeast *Candida albicans.*

Millet

Amaranth

LESSER-KNOWN GRAINS

There are several other grains that deserve a mention, as they are not only becoming more popular, but also are often far richer in nutrients than their better-known counterparts.

Amaranth

This plant, which is native to Mexico, is unusual in that it can be eaten as both a vegetable and a grain. Like quinoa, amaranth is considered a supergrain due to its excellent nutritional content. The tiny pale seed or 'grain' has a strong and distinctive, peppery flavour. It is best used in stews and soups, or it can be ground into flour to make bread, pastries and cookies. The flour is gluten-free and has to be mixed with wheat or another flour that contains gluten in order to make leavened bread. Amaranth leaves are similar to spinach and can be cooked or eaten raw in salads.

Health Benefits: Although its taste may take some getting used to, amaranth contains more protein than pulses and is rich in amino acids, particularly lysine. Amaranth is also high in iron and calcium.

Kamut

An ancient relative of wheat, this grain has long, slender, brown kernels with a creamy, nutty flavour. It is as versatile as wheat and, when ground into flour, can be used to make pasta, breads, cakes and pastry. Puffed kamut cereals and kamut crackers are available in health food stores.

BUCKWHEAT

In spite of its name, buckwheat is not a type of wheat, but is actually related to the rhubarb family. Available plain or toasted, it has a nutty, earthy flavour. It is a staple food in Eastern Europe as well as Russia, where the triangular grain is milled into a speckled-grey flour and used to make blini, the small, tasty pancakes. The flour is also used in Japan for making soba noodles and in Italy for pasta. Buckwheat pancakes are popular in parts of the USA and France. The whole grain, which is also known as kasha, makes a fine porridge or a creamy dessert.

Health Benefits: Like quinoa, buckwheat is a complete protein. It contains all eight essential amino acids as well as rutin, which aids circulation and helps treat high blood pressure. It is an excellent, sustaining cereal, rich in both iron and some of the B complex vitamins. It is also reputed to be good for the lungs, the kidneys and the bladder. Buckwheat is gluten-free, and so is useful for people who suffer from coeliac disease.

Buckwheat, buckwheat flour and toasted buckwheat

Health Benefits: Kamut has a higher nutritional value than wheat and is easier to digest. Although it contains gluten, people suffering from coeliac disease have found that they can tolerate the grain if eaten in moderation.

Sorghum

This grain is best known for its thick sweet syrup, which is used in cakes and desserts. The grain is similar to millet and is an important, nutritious staple food in Africa and India. It can be used like rice, or ground into flour to make unleavened bread.

Health Benefits: Sorghum is a useful source of calcium, iron and B vitamins.

Spelt

This is one of the most ancient cultivated wheats and, because of its high nutritional value, is becoming more widely available in stores. The grain looks similar to wheat and the flour can be substituted for wheat flour in bread.

Health Benefits: Spelt is richer in vitamins and minerals than wheat, and they are in a more readily digestible form. Although spelt contains gluten, it usually can be tolerated in moderate amounts by people suffering from coeliac disease.

Triticale

A hybrid of wheat and rye, triticale was created by Swedish researchers in 1875. It has a sweet, nutty taste and can be used in the same way as rice, and is ground into flour. It contains more protein than

Spelt grain and flour

wheat but has less gluten and may need to be mixed with other flours when baking. Triticale flakes can be used in cereals and crumbles.

Health Benefits: Triticale contains significant amounts of calcium, iron and B vitamins. It is particularly rich in lysine.

Buying and Storing: To ensure freshness, buy grains in small quantities from a store with a high turnover of stock. Grains can be affected by heat and moisture, and easily become rancid. Store in a dry, cool, dark place.

HOW TO COOK GRAINS

Grains can be simply boiled in water but, to enhance their flavour, first cook them in a little oil for a few minutes. When they are well coated in oil, add two or three times their volume of water or stock. Bring to the boil, then simmer, covered, until the water is absorbed and the grains are tender. Do not disturb the grains while they are cooking. Other flavourings, such as chopped herbs and whole or ground spices, can be added to the cooking liquid.

Fabulous Fibre

Whole grains are one of the few food groups to contain both soluble and insoluble fibre. The former is prevalent in oats and rye, while wheat, rice and corn contain insoluble fibre. Both are fundamental to good health and may prevent constipation, ulcers, colitis, colon and rectal cancer, heart disease, diverticulitis and irritable bowel syndrome. Soluble fibre slows down the absorption of energy from the gut, which means there are no sudden demands on insulin, making it especially important for diabetics.

Kamut

Legumes

Lentils, peas and beans provide the cook with a diverse range of flavours and textures. They have long been a staple food in the Middle East, South America, India and the Mediterranean, but there is hardly a country that does not have its own favourite legume-based dish, from Boston baked beans in the USA to lentil dahl in India. In Mexico, they are spiced and used to make refried beans, while in China they are fermented for black bean and yellow bean sauces. Low in fat and high in complex carbohydrates, vitamins and minerals, legumes are also an important source of protein for vegetarians and, when eaten with cereals, easily match animal-based sources.

Lentils and Peas

The humble lentil is one of our oldest foods. It originated in Asia and north Africa and continues to be cultivated in those regions, as well as in France and Italy. Lentils are hard even when fresh, so they are always sold dried. Unlike most beans and peas, they do not need soaking.

Red lentils

Puy lentils

GREEN AND BROWN LENTILS

Sometimes referred to as continental lentils, these disc-shaped pulses retain their shape when cooked. They take longer to cook than split lentils – about 40–45 minutes – and are ideal for adding to warm salads, casseroles and stuffings.

RED LENTILS

Orange-coloured red split lentils, sometimes known as Egyptian lentils, are the most familiar variety. They cook in just 20 minutes, eventually disintegrating into a thick purée. They are ideal for thickening soups and casseroles and, when cooked with spices, make a delicious dahl. In the Middle East, red or yellow lentils are cooked and mixed with spices and vegetables to form balls known as *kofte*.

YELLOW LENTILS

Less well-known yellow lentils taste very similar to the red variety and are used in much the same way.

Green and brown lentils

Alternatively green and brown lentils can be cooked and blended with herbs or spices to make a nutritious pâté.

PUY LENTILS

These tiny, dark, blue-green, marbled lentils grow in the Auvergne region in central France. They are considered to be far superior in taste and texture than other varieties, and they retain their bead-like shape during cooking, which takes around 25–30 minutes. Puy lentils are a delicious addition to simple dishes such as warm salads, and are also good braised in wine and flavoured with fresh herbs.

PEAS

Dried peas come from the field pea not the garden pea, which is eaten fresh. Unlike lentils, peas are soft when young and require drying. They are available whole or split; the latter have a sweeter flavour and cook more quickly. Like split lentils, split peas do not hold their shape when cooked, making them perfect for dahls, purées, casseroles and soups. They take about 45 minutes to cook. Marrow fat peas are larger in size

Cooking Lentils

Lentils are easy to cook and don't need to be soaked. Split red and green lentils cook down to a soft consistency, while whole lentils hold their shape when cooked.

Green, Brown and Puy Lentils

1 Place 250g/9oz/generous 1 cup whole lentils in a sieve (strainer) and rinse under cold running water. Tip into a pan.

2 Cover with water and bring to the boil. Simmer for 25–30 minutes until tender, replenishing the water if necessary. Drain and season with salt and freshly ground black pepper.

Split Red and Yellow Lentils

1 Place 250g/9oz/generous 1 cup split lentils in a sieve (strainer) and rinse under cold running water. Tip into a pan.

2 Cover with 600ml/1 pint/2½ cups water and bring to the boil. Simmer for 20–25 minutes, stirring occasionally, until the water is absorbed and the lentils are tender. Season to taste.

and are used to make the traditional British dish 'mushy' peas. Like other whole peas, they require soaking overnight before use.

Buying and Storing: Although lentils and peas can be kept for up to a year, they toughen with time. Buy from stores with a fast turnover of stock and store in airtight containers in a cool, dark place. Look for bright, unwrinkled pulses that are not dusty. Rinse well before use.

Health Benefits: Lentils and peas share an impressive range of nutrients including iron, selenium, folate, manganese, zinc, phosphorus and some B vitamins. Extremely low in fat and richer in protein than most beans, lentils and peas are reputed to be important in fighting heart disease by reducing harmful LDL cholesterol in the body. They are high in fibre, which aids the functioning of the bowels and colon. Fibre also slows down the rate at which sugar enters the bloodstream, providing a steady supply of energy, which can help control and regulate diabetes.

Marrow fat peas (far right) and yellow and green split peas

COOK'S TIP

Avoid adding salt to the water when cooking lentils and peas as this prevents them softening. Season when cooked.

Beans

The edible seeds from plants belonging to the legume family, a vast range of beans, including chickpeas, are packed with protein, vitamins, minerals and fibre, and are extremely low in fat. For the cook, their ability to absorb the flavours of other foods means that beans can be used as the base for an infinite number of dishes. Most beans require soaking overnight in cold water before use, so it is wise to plan ahead if using the dried type.

BLACK BEANS

These shiny, black, kidney-shaped beans are often used in Caribbean cooking. They have a sweetish flavour, and their distinctive colour adds a dramatic touch to soups, mixed bean salads or casseroles.

Aduki beans

ADUKI BEANS

Also known as adzuki beans, these tiny, deep-red beans have a sweet, nutty flavour and are popular in Oriental dishes. In Chinese cooking, they form the base of red bean paste. Known as the 'king of beans' in Japan, the aduki bean is reputed to be good for the liver and kidneys. They cook quickly and can be used in casseroles and bakes. They are also ground into flour for use in cakes, breads and pastries.

BLACK-EYED BEANS (PEAS)

Known as black-eye peas or cow peas in the USA, black-eyed beans are an essential ingredient in Creole cooking and some spicy Indian curries. The small, creamy-coloured bean is characterized by the black spot on its side where it was once attached to the pod. Good in soups and salads, they can also be added to savoury bakes and casseroles, and can be used in place of haricot or cannellini beans in a wide variety of dishes.

Black beans (above), black-eyed beans (centre) and borlotti beans

Cannellini Bean Purée

Cooked cannellini beans make a delicious herb- and garlic-flavoured purée. Serve spread on toasted pitta bread or to use as a dip with chunky raw vegetable crudités.

INGREDIENTS

400g/14oz/2½ cups canned or 200g/
   7oz/1¼ cups dried cannellini beans
30ml/2 tbsp olive oil
1 large garlic clove, finely chopped
2 shallots, finely chopped
75ml/5 tbsp vegetable stock
30ml/2 tbsp chopped fresh flat
   leaf parsley
15ml/1 tbsp snipped fresh chives
salt and freshly ground black pepper

SERVES 4

1 If using dried beans, soak them overnight in cold water, then drain and rinse. Place in a pan and cover with cold water, then bring to the boil and boil rapidly for 10 minutes. Reduce the heat and simmer, uncovered, for about 1 hour, or until tender. If using canned beans, rinse and drain well.

2 Heat the oil in a pan and sauté the garlic and shallots for about 5 minutes, stirring occasionally, until soft. Add the beans, stock, parsley and seasoning, then cook for a few minutes until heated through.

3 To make a course purée, mash the beans with a potato masher. Alternatively, place in a food processor and blend until thick and smooth. Serve sprinkled with snipped chives.

Butter (lima) beans

Cannellini beans

BORLOTTI BEANS

These oval beans have red-streaked, pinkish-brown skin and a bitter-sweet flavour. When cooked, they have a tender, moist texture, which is good in Italian bean and pasta soups, as well as hearty vegetable stews. In most recipes, they are interchangeable with red kidney beans.

BROAD (FAVA) BEANS

These large beans were first cultivated by the ancient Egyptians. Usually eaten in their fresh form, broad beans change in colour from green to brown when dried, making them difficult to recognize in their dried state. The outer skin can be very tough and chewy, and some people prefer to remove it after cooking. They can also be bought ready-skinned.

Broad (fava) beans

BUTTER BEANS AND LIMA BEANS

Similar in flavour and appearance, both butter beans and lima beans are characterized by their flattish, kidney shape and soft, floury texture. Cream-coloured butter beans are familiar in Britain and Greece, while lima beans are popular in the USA.

In Greek cooking, butter beans are oven-baked with tomato, garlic and olive oil until tender and creamy. The pale-green lima bean is the main ingredient in succotash, an American dish that also includes corn kernels. Butter and lima beans are also good with creamy herb sauces. Care should be taken not to overcook both butter and lima beans as they become pulpy and mushy in texture.

CANNELLINI BEANS

These small, white, kidney-shaped beans have a soft, creamy texture when cooked and are popular in Italian cooking. They can be used in place of haricot (navy) beans and, when dressed with olive oil, lemon juice, crushed garlic and chopped parsley, make an excellent warm salad.

CHICKPEAS

Also known as garbanzo beans,
robust and hearty chickpeas
resemble shelled
hazelnuts and have a
delicious nutty flavour and
creamy texture. They need
lengthy cooking and
are much used in
Mediterranean and
Middle Eastern cooking. In
India, they are known as gram
and are ground into flour to make fritters
and flat breads. Gram flour, also called
besan, can be found in health food stores
and Asian grocery stores.

FLAGEOLET (SMALL CANNELLINI)
BEANS

These young haricot (navy) beans are
removed from the pod before they are
fully ripe, hence their delicate flavour. They
are the most expensive bean to buy and
are best treated simply. Cook them until
they are tender, then season and drizzle
with a little olive oil and lemon juice.

HARICOT (NAVY) BEANS

Most commonly used for canned
baked beans, these versatile, ivory-
coloured beans are small and oval in
shape. Called navy or Boston beans in
the USA, they suit slow-cooked dishes,
such as casseroles and bakes.

Chickpeas

PINTO BEANS

A smaller, paler version of the borlotti
bean, the savoury-tasting pinto has an
attractive speckled skin – it is aptly called
the painted bean. One of the many
relatives of the kidney bean, pinto beans
feature extensively in Mexican cooking,

most familiarly in refried beans, when they
are cooked until tender and fried with
garlic, chilli and tomatoes. The
beans are then mashed,
resulting in a wonderful,
spicy, rough purée that is
usually served with
warm tortillas. Sour
cream and garlic-
flavoured guacamole are
good accompaniments.

RED KIDNEY BEANS

Glossy, mahogany-red kidney
beans retain their colour and shape
when cooked. They have a soft, 'mealy'
texture and are much used in South
American cooking. An essential ingredient
in spicy chillies, they can also be used to
make refried beans (although this dish is
traditionally made from pinto beans).
Cooked kidney beans can be used to
make a variety of salads, but they are
especially good combined with red onion
and chopped flat leaf parsley and mint,
then tossed in an olive oil dressing.

It is essential to follow the cooking
instructions when preparing kidney beans
as they contain a substance that causes
severe food poisoning if they are not
boiled vigorously for 10–15 minutes.

*Above, clockwise from left: haricot (navy)
beans, red kidney beans, flageolet (small
cannellini) beans and pinto beans*

Cooking Kidney Beans

Most types of beans, with the exception of aduki beans and mung beans, require soaking for 5–6 hours or overnight and then boiling rapidly for 10–15 minutes to remove any harmful toxins. This is particularly important for kidney beans, which can cause serious food poisoning if not treated in this way.

1 Wash the beans well, then place in a bowl that allows plenty of room for expansion. Cover with cold water and leave to soak overnight or for 8–12 hours, then drain and rinse.

2 Place the beans in a large pan and cover with fresh cold water. Bring to the boil and boil rapidly, uncovered, for 10–15 minutes, then reduce the heat and simmer for 1–1½ hours until tender. Drain and serve.

The Flatulence-free Bean

The American space programme NASA is involved in research into flatulence-free foods. One such food is the manteca bean, discovered by Dr Colin Leakey in Chile. This small, yellow bean is flatulence-free and easy to digest. It is now being grown both in Cambridgeshire, England and the Channel Islands, and should become more widely available, called either manteca beans or Jersey yellow beans.

FUL MEDAMES

A member of the broad (fava) bean family, these small Egyptian beans form the base of the national dish of the same name, in which they are flavoured with ground cumin and then baked with olive oil, garlic and lemon, and served topped with hard-boiled egg. They have a strong, nutty flavour and tough, light brown outer skin. Ful medames need to be soaked overnight in cold water, then cooked slowly for about 1 hour until soft.

Ful medames

SOYA BEANS

These small, oval beans vary in colour from creamy-yellow through brown to black. In China, they are known as 'meat of the earth' and were once considered sacred. Soya beans contain all the nutritional properties of animal products but without the disadvantages. They are extremely dense and need to be soaked for 12 hours before cooking. They combine well with robust ingredients such as garlic, herbs and spices, and they make a healthy addition to soups, casseroles, bakes and salads.

Soya beans are also used to make tofu, tempeh, textured vegetable protein (TVP), flour and soy sauce.

White and black soya beans

How to Prepare and Cook Beans

There is much debate as to whether soaking beans before cooking is necessary, but it certainly reduces cooking times, and can enhance flavour by starting the germination process. First, wash beans under cold running water, then place in a bowl of fresh cold water and leave to soak overnight. Discard any beans that float to the surface, drain and rinse again. Put in a large pan and cover with fresh cold water. Boil rapidly for 10–15 minutes, then reduce the heat, cover and simmer until tender.

Cooking Times for Beans

As cooking times can vary depending on the age of the beans, this table should be used as a general guide.

Aduki beans	30–45 minutes
Black beans	1 hour
Black-eyed beans (peas)	1–1¼ hours
Borlotti beans	1–1½ hours
Broad (fava) beans	1½ hours
Butter/lima beans	1–1¼ hours
Cannellini or flageolet beans	1½ hours
Chickpeas	1½–2½ hours
Ful medames	1 hour
Haricot (navy) beans	1–1½ hours
Kidney beans	1–1½ hours
Mung beans	25–40 minutes
Pinto beans	1–1¼ hours
Soya beans	2 hours

MUNG BEANS

Instantly recognizable in their sprouted form as beansprouts, mung or moong beans are small, olive-coloured beans native to India. They are soft and sweet when cooked, and are used in the spicy curry, moong dahl. Soaking is not essential, but if they are soaked overnight this will reduce the usual 40 minutes cooking time by about half.

Mung beans

Using Canned Beans

Canned beans are convenient store-cupboard (pantry) stand-bys, because they require no soaking or lengthy cooking. Choose canned beans that do not have added sugar or salt, and rinse well and drain before use. The canning process reduces the levels of vitamins and minerals, but canned beans still contain reputable amounts.

Canned beans tend to be softer than cooked, dried beans so they are easy to mash, which makes them good for pâtés, stuffings, croquettes and rissoles, but they can also be used to make quick salads. They can, in fact, be used for any dish that calls for cooked, dried beans: a drained 425g/15oz can is roughly the equivalent of 150g/5oz/¾ cup dried beans. Firmer canned beans such as kidney beans can be added to stews and re-cooked, but softer beans such as cannellini should be just heated through.

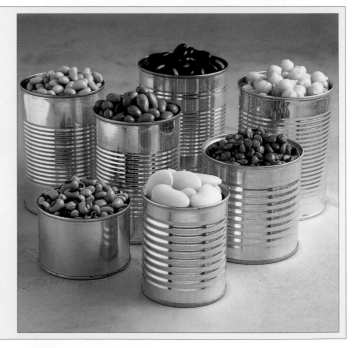

Buying and Storing: Look for plump, shiny beans with unbroken skin. Beans toughen with age so, although they will keep for up to a year in a cool, dry place, it is best to buy them in small quantities from stores with a regular turnover of stock. Avoid beans that look dusty or dirty and store them in an airtight container in a cool, dark, dry place.

Health Benefits: The health attributes of beans are plentiful. They are packed with protein, soluble and insoluble fibre, iron, potassium, phosphorous, manganese, magnesium, folate and most B vitamins.

Soya beans are the most nutritious of all beans. Rich in high-quality protein, this wonder-bean contains all eight essential amino acids that cannot be synthesized by the body but are vital for the renewal of cells and tissues.

Insoluble fibre ensures regular bowel movements, while soluble fibre has been found to lower blood cholesterol, thereby reducing the risk of heart disease and stroke. Studies show that eating dried beans on a regular basis can lower cholesterol levels by almost 20 per cent. Beans contain a concentration of lignins, also known as phytoestrogens, which protect against cancer of the breast, prostate and colon. Lignins may also help to balance hormone levels in the body.

COOK'S TIPS

• If you are short of time, the long soaking process can be speeded up: first, cook the beans in boiling water for 2 minutes, then remove the pan from the heat. Cover and leave for about 2 hours. Drain, rinse and cover with plenty of fresh cold water before cooking.
• Cooking beans in a pressure cooker will reduce the cooking time by around three-quarters.
• Do not add salt to beans while they are cooking as this will cause them to toughen. Cook the beans first, then season with salt and pepper. Acid foods such as tomatoes or lemons, or vinegar will also toughen beans, so only add these ingredients once the beans are soft.

Quick Cooking and Serving Ideas for Beans, Peas and Lentils

• To flavour beans, add an onion, garlic, herbs or spices before cooking. Remove whole flavourings before serving.

• Spoon spicy, red lentil dahl and some crisp, fried onions on top of a warm tortilla, then roll up and eat.

• Dress cooked beans with extra virgin olive oil, lemon juice, crushed garlic, diced tomato and fresh basil.

• Mix cooked chickpeas with spring onions (scallions), olives, chopped parsley, olive oil and lemon juice.

• Mash cooked beans with olive oil, garlic and coriander (cilantro) and pile on to toasted bread. Top with a poached egg.

• Fry cooked red kidney beans in olive oil with chopped onion, chilli, garlic and fresh coriander (cilantro) leaves.

• Sauté a little chopped garlic in olive oil, add cooked or canned flageolet or cannellini beans, canned tomatoes and chopped fresh chilli, then cook for a few minutes until the sauce has thickened and the beans are heated through.

• Roast cooked chickpeas, which have been drizzled with olive oil and garlic, for 20 minutes at 200°C/400°F/Gas 6, then toss in a little ground cumin and sprinkle with chilli flakes. Serve with chunks of feta cheese and naan bread.

Soya Bean Products

Soya beans are incredibly versatile and are used to make an extensive array of by-products that can be used in cooking – tofu, tempeh, textured vegetable protein, flour, miso, and a variety of sauces. The soya bean is the most nutritious of all beans. Rich in high-quality protein, it is one of the few vegetarian foods that contains all eight essential amino acids that cannot be synthesized in the body and are vital for the renewal of cells and tissues.

TOFU

Also known as beancurd, tofu is made in a similar way to soft cheese. The beans are boiled, mashed and sieved to make soya 'milk', and the 'milk' is then curdled using a coagulant. The resulting curds are drained and pressed to make tofu, and there are several different types to choose from.

Firm tofu

This type of tofu is sold in blocks and can be cubed or sliced and used in vegetable stir-fries, kebabs, salads, soups and casseroles. Alternatively, firm tofu can be mashed and used in baked dishes and burgers. The bland flavour of firm tofu is improved by marinating, because its porous texture readily absorbs flavours and seasonings, such as garlic, chilli or soy sauce.

Silken tofu

Soft with a silky, smooth texture, this type of tofu is ideal for use in sauces, dressings, dips and soups. It is a useful dairy-free alternative to cream, soft cheese or natural (plain) yogurt, and can be used to make creamy desserts.

Other forms of tofu

Smoked, marinated and deep-fried tofu are all readily available in health food stores and Oriental stores as well as some supermarkets.

Deep-fried tofu is fairly tasteless, but it has an interesting texture. It puffs up during cooking and, underneath the golden, crisp coating the tofu is white and soft, and easily absorbs the flavour of other ingredients. It can be used in much the same way as firm tofu and, as it has been fried in vegetable oil, it is suitable for vegetarian cooking.

Buying and Storing: All types of fresh tofu can be kept in the refrigerator for up to 1 week. Firm tofu should be kept covered in water, which must be changed regularly. Freezing tofu is not recommended, because it alters the texture. Silken tofu is often available in long-life vacuum packs, which do not have to be kept in the refrigerator and have a much longer shelf life.

TEMPEH

This Indonesian speciality is made by fermenting cooked soya beans with a cultured starter. Tempeh is similar to tofu but has a nuttier, more savoury flavour. It can be used in the same way as firm tofu and also benefits from marinating. While some types of tofu are regarded as a dairy replacement, the firmer texture of tempeh means that it can be used instead of meat in pies and casseroles.

Buying and Storing: Tempeh is available chilled or frozen in health food and Oriental stores. Chilled tempeh can be stored in the refrigerator for up to a week. Frozen tempeh can be left in the freezer for 1 month; defrost before use.

BEANCURD SKINS AND STICKS

Made from soya 'milk', dried beancurd skins and sticks, like fresh beancurd, have neither aroma nor flavour until they are cooked, when they will rapidly absorb the flavour of seasonings and other ingredients. Beancurd skins and sticks are used in Chinese cooking and need to be

Above, clockwise from left: Silken tofu, beancurd skins, firm tofu and deep-fried tofu

TVP

Textured vegetable protein, or TVP, is a meat replacement and is bought in dry chunks or in minced (ground) form.

Made from processed soya beans, TVP is very versatile and readily absorbs the strong flavours of ingredients such as herbs, spices and vegetable stock. It is inexpensive and is a convenient store-cupboard (pantry) item. TVP needs to be rehydrated in boiling water or vegetable stock, and can be used in stews and curries, or as a filling for pies.

Tempeh

soaked until pliable before use. Beancurd skins should be soaked in cold water for an hour or two and can be used to wrap a variety of fillings.

Beancurd sticks need to be soaked for several hours or overnight. They can be chopped and added to soups, stir-fries and casseroles.

Marinated Tofu Kebabs

Tofu is relatively tasteless but readily takes on other flavours. It is at its best when marinated in aromatic oils, soy sauce, spices and herbs.

1 Cut a block of tofu into 1cm/½in cubes and marinate in a mixture of groundnut (peanut) oil, sesame oil, soy sauce, crushed garlic, grated fresh root ginger and honey for at least 1 hour.

2 Thread the cubes of tofu on to skewers with chunks of courgettes (zucchini), onions and mushrooms. Brush with the marinade and grill (broil) or barbecue until golden, turning occasionally.

Tofu Fruit Fool

1 Place a packet of silken tofu in the bowl of a food processor. Add some soft fruit or berries – for example, strawberries, raspberries or blackberries.

2 Process the mixture to form a smooth purée, then sweeten to taste with a little honey, maple syrup or maize malt syrup.

SOYA FLOUR

This is a finely ground, high-protein flour, which is also gluten-free. It is often mixed with other flours in bread and pastries, adding a pleasant nuttiness, or it can be used as a thickener in sauces.

Buying and Storing: Store TVP and soya flour in an airtight container in a cool, dry, dark place.

SOY SAUCE

This soya by-product originated over 2,000 years ago and the recipe has changed little since then. It is made by combining crushed soya beans with wheat, salt, water and a yeast-based culture called koji, and the mixture is left to ferment for between 6 months and 3 years.

There are two basic types of soy sauce: light and dark. Light soy sauce is slightly thinner in consistency and saltier. It is used in dressings and soups. Dark soy sauce is heavier and sweeter, with a more rounded flavour, and is used in marinades, stir-fries and sauces. Try to buy naturally brewed soy sauce as many other kinds are now chemically prepared to hasten the fermentation process, and may contain flavourings and colourings.

SHOYU

Made in Japan, shoyu is aged for 1–2 years to produce a full-flavoured sauce that can be used in the same way as dark soy sauce. You can buy it in health food and Oriental stores.

TAMARI

This form of soy sauce is a natural by-product of making miso, although it is often produced in the same way as soy sauce. Most tamari is made without wheat, which means that it is gluten-free. It has a rich, dark, robust flavour and is used in cooking or as a condiment.

Buying and Storing: Keep soy sauce, shoyu and tamari in a cool, dark place.

MISO

This thick paste is made from a mixture of cooked soya beans, rice, wheat or barley, salt and water. Miso is left to ferment for up to 3 years. It can be used to add a savoury flavour to soups, stocks, stir-fries and noodle dishes, and is a staple food in Asia. There are three main types: kome, or white miso, is the lightest and sweetest; medium-strength mugi miso, which has a mellow flavour and is referred for everyday use; and hacho miso, which is a dark chocolate colour, and has a thick texture and a strong flavour.

Soya Bean Sauces

Black bean sauce Made from fermented black soya beans, this has a rich, thick consistency and a salty, full flavour. It should always be heated before use to bring out the flavour. Fermented black beans, which many Chinese cooks use to make home-made black bean sauce, can be bought in vacuum-packs or cans from Oriental stores.

Yellow bean sauce Produced from fermented yellow soya beans, this sauce has an intense flavour.

Hoisin sauce A thick red-brown sauce made from soya beans, flour, garlic, chilli, sesame oil and vinegar. Mainly intended as a marinade, it can be used as a dipping sauce.

Kecap manis An Indonesian-style dark, sweet soy sauce, which can be found in Oriental stores.

Minced (ground) and cubed textured vegetable protein (TVP)

Buying and Storing: Miso keeps well and can be stored for several months, but should be kept in the refrigerator once it has been opened.

Health Benefits: Soya is one of today's healthiest foods. Rich in minerals, particularly iron and calcium, it is also low in saturated fat and is cholesterol-free. It has the ability to help reduce osteoporosis, blood pressure and blood cholesterol, and there is evidence to suggest that it can help reduce the risk of cancer.

Japanese women (whose diets are rich in soya) have a lower incidence of breast cancer than women who consume a typical Western diet. Likewise, Japanese men have a lower incidence of prostate cancer than Western men. This is thought to be because soya contains hormone-like substances called phytoestrogens.

Studies have also shown that eating miso on a regular basis can increase the body's natural resistance to radiation. Additionally, miso is said to prevent cancer of the liver, and it can also help to expel toxins from the body.

Light soy sauce (below) and dark soy sauce

Mugi miso (left) and hacho miso

Tamari (left) and shoyu

Watch Point

Although soya beans and products are nutritionally beneficial, they are also common allergens and can provoke reactions such as headaches and digestive problems. Avoid eating excessive amounts of soya, and always cook sprouted soya beans before use.

Dairy Foods and Alternatives

Some people may question the inclusion of dairy products in a whole food cookbook, and while it would be foolish to advocate the consumption of vast quantities of high-fat milk, cream and cheese, a diet that includes moderate amounts of dairy products does provide valuable vitamins and minerals. There is little reason to reject dairy products as they can enrich vegetarian cooking. However, for those who choose to avoid dairy foods, there are plenty of alternatives.

Milk, Cream and Yogurt

This wide group of ingredients includes milk, cream and yogurt made from cow's, goat's and sheep's milk, as well as non-dairy products such as soya 'milk' and 'cream' and other non-dairy 'milks', which are made from nuts and grains. They are used in a huge range of sweet and savoury dishes, from sauces and soups to drinks and desserts.

MILK

Often referred to as a complete food, milk is one of our most widely used ingredients. Cow's milk remains the most popular type although, with the growing concern about saturated fat and cholesterol, semi-skimmed (low-fat) and skimmed milks now outsell the full-fat (whole) version. Skimmed milk contains half the calories of full-fat milk and only a fraction of the fat, but nutritionally it is on a par, retaining its vitamins, calcium and other minerals.

Buy organic milk if you can, because it comes from cows that have been fed on a pesticide-free diet, and are not routinely treated with hormones, antibiotics, or BST (bovine somatotrophin), which is used in some countries to boost the milk yield from cows.

Sour cream and crème fraîche

Goat's and sheep's milk

These milks make useful alternatives for people who are intolerant to cow's milk. The lactose in cow's milk can cause severe indigestion, and an intolerance to dairy products often manifests itself in eczema or sinus congestion. Goat's and sheep's milk are nutritionally similar to cow's milk, but are easier to digest. Goat's milk has a distinctive, musky flavour, while sheep's milk is a little creamier and has a less assuming flavour.

CREAM

The high fat content of cream means that it is not an ingredient to be eaten lavishly on a daily basis. Used with discretion, however, cream lends a richness to soups, sauces, baked goods and desserts.

The fat content of cream ranges enormously: half-cream contains about 12 per cent, single (light) cream 18 per cent, double (heavy) cream 48 per cent, and clotted cream, which is the highest contains about 55 per cent.

From left, goat's, cow's and sheep's milk, and soya 'milk'

Smetana

SOUR CREAM

This thick-textured cream is treated with lactic acid, which gives it its characteristic tang. Full-fat sour cream contains about 20 per cent fat, although low- and non-fat versions are available. It can be used in the same way as cream. Care should be taken when cooking, as it can curdle if heated to too high a temperature.

CRÈME FRAÎCHE

This rich, cultured cream is similar to sour cream, but its high fat content, at around 35 per cent, means that it does not curdle

when cooked. Crème fraîche is delicious served with fresh fruit such as ripe summer berries, puréed mangoes or sliced bananas.

BUTTERMILK

Traditionally made from the milky liquid left over after butter making, buttermilk is now more likely to be made from skimmed milk, mixed with milk solids and then cultured with lactic acid. It has a creamy, mild, sour taste and makes a tangy and distinctive addition to desserts. Used in baking, buttermilk gives cakes and soda bread a moist texture. It is low in fat, containing only 0.1 per cent.

SMETANA

Originally made in Russia, this rich version of buttermilk is made from skimmed milk and single cream with an added culture. It has a similar fat content to strained yogurt (about 10 per cent), and should be treated in the same way. Smetana can curdle if it is overheated.

Buying and Storing: When buying milk, cream and cream-related products, don't forget to check the label. Manufacturers and retailers are obliged to give a 'best before' or 'sell-by' date on the packet. The fat content, nutritional information and list

Buttermilk

of ingredients will also be detailed. Try to avoid products that contain unnecessary additives or flavourings. For instance, low-fat crème fraîche, yogurts and cream may contain animal-based gelatine, which acts as a thickener. Store dairy products in the refrigerator and consume within a few days of opening. Long-life cartons will keep indefinitely but once opened must be treated as fresh and kept in the refrigerator.

Health Benefits: Milk is an important source of calcium and phosphorus, both of which are essential for healthy teeth and bones, and are said to prevent osteoporosis. Milk also contains significant amounts of zinc and the B vitamins, including B_{12}, along with a small amount of vitamin D. Numerous studies have revealed that, due to its high calcium content, milk fortified with vitamin D may have a role in preventing colon cancer. The antibodies found in milk may boost the immune system and help gastrointestinal problems, and skimmed milk may reduce the amount of cholesterol produced by the liver.

Above, clockwise from bottom left: whipping cream, single (light) cream and whipped double (heavy) cream

Other Non-dairy 'Milks'

Apart from soya 'milk', non-dairy 'milks' or drinks are usually either nut- or grain-based. They can be used as a substitute for regular milk in a wide variety of sweet and savoury dishes such as milk desserts, custards, hot and cold milk drinks, sauces, but shouldn't be overheated or cooked for too long or they may curdle.

Oat 'milk' Made from oat kernels and either vegetable or sunflower oil, this nutritious drink is high in fibre.

Rice 'milk' With a similar consistency to soya 'milk', rice 'milk' is also non-mucous forming. Rice 'milk' is easily digested and almost non-allergenic.

Nut 'milk' Crushed and ground almonds or cashew nuts are mixed with water to form this mild-tasting non-dairy 'milk'.

Clockwise from left, 'milks' made from rice, almonds and oats

Making Yogurt

It is easy to make yogurt at home – simply make sure that you use live yogurt as a starter and that it is as fresh as possible. Once you have made the first batch, you can reserve some of the yogurt as a starter for the next. Don't use too much starter or the yogurt may become sour and grainy. Yogurt can be flavoured with fresh or dried fruit, or honey, or to make a more substantial dish, stir in soaked oats, chopped nuts and toasted seeds.

1 Pour 600ml/1 pint/2½ cups full-fat (whole), semi-skimmed (low-fat) or skimmed milk into a pan and bring to the boil. Remove the pan from the heat and leave the milk to cool to 45°C/113°F.

2 If you don't have a thermometer, you can use your finger – the milk should feel slightly hotter than is comfortable. Pour the warm milk into a medium sterilized bowl.

3 Whisk in 15–30ml/1–2 tbsp live yogurt – this acts as a starter. Leave in the bowl or transfer it to a large jar.

4 Cover with clear film (plastic wrap), then insulate the bowl or jar with several layers of dish towels and leave in a warm place. Alternatively, the yogurt can be transferred to a vacuum flask to keep it warm. Leave for 10–12 hours until set. Transfer to the refrigerator.

SOYA SUBSTITUTES

Soya 'milk'

This is the most widely used alternative to milk. Made from pulverized soya beans, it is suitable for both cooking and drinking and is used to make yogurt, cream and cheese. Soya 'milk' is interchangeable with cow's milk, although it has a slightly thicker consistency and a nutty flavour. Fruit- and chocolate-flavoured soya 'milk', and versions fortified with extra vitamins are widely available in health food stores and larger supermarkets.

Soya 'cream'

This is made from a higher proportion of beans than that in soya 'milk', which gives it a richer flavour and thicker texture. It has a similar consistency to single (light) cream and can be used in the same ways.

Buying and Storing: Most soya 'milks' and 'creams' are sold in long-life cartons, which extends their shelf-life and means that they do not require refrigeration until opened. Buy soya 'milk' that is fortified with extra vitamins and calcium and, depending on how you intend to use it, choose the sweetened or non-sweetened variety. Some retailers stock fresh soya 'milk' and this should be treated in the same way as cow's milk.

Health Benefits: Soya 'milk' and 'cream' are a valuable source of protein, calcium, iron, magnesium, phosphorus and vitamin E. The 'milk' is low in calories and contains no cholesterol. Numerous studies have shown that soya can reduce the risk of certain cancers, heart disease, kidney disease and osteoporosis.

YOGURT

Praised for its health-giving qualities, yogurt has earned a reputation as one of the most valuable health foods. The fat content ranges from 0.5g per 100g for very low-fat or virtually fat-free yogurts to 4g per 100g for wholemilk yogurt. The consistency may be thin or thick. Greek (US strained plain) and Greek-style yogurt, which is made from cow's or sheep's milk, contains about 10 per cent fat – just enough to prevent it from curdling during cooking. However, although it is higher in fat than other types of yogurt, it contains less fat than cream. Lower fat yogurts can also be used instead of cream, but are best used in uncooked dishes. Strained yogurt has its watery whey removed to make it thicker

and richer, and has a similar fat content to Greek and Greek-style yogurts. When buying yogurt, look for 'live' on the label. This signifies that it has been fermented with a starter culture bacteria (usually *lactobacillus bulgaricus* or *streptococcus thermophilous*), which is beneficial to health. Bio yogurts, which contain extra bacteria (often *lactobacillus acidophilus* or *bifidobacterium bifidum*), have a milder, creamier flavour than other yogurts, and may have far wider healing benefits.

Buying and Storing: Yogurt has a limited shelf-life, so it is important to check the 'best before' or 'sell-by' date on the label. Although yogurt making is essentially a natural process, many manufacturers add unnecessary amounts of sugar, colourings, flavourings and other additives, such as thickeners and stabilizers. Some yogurts, especially low-fat varieties may contain gelatine, an animal by-product. Low-calorie yogurts usually contain artificial sweeteners. Fruit yogurts may contain a high amount of sugar as well as colourings and flavourings; check the label before buying, and choose varieties that have a high fruit content – those with the highest amount will mention fruit first in the list of ingredients. More expensive, specialist yogurts may be the least adulterated.

Health Benefits: Yogurt is rich in calcium, phosphorus and B vitamins. The bacteria present in live yogurt ensures that it is easily digestible: it may stimulate the friendly bacteria in the gut and suppress harmful bacteria, so aiding digestion and relieving gastrointestinal problems. Evidence suggests that yogurt can help protect against vaginal thrush and may be applied externally.

Live and bio yogurts have extra health benefits, although their levels of good bacteria can vary. The bacteria in bio yogurt may help boost natural resistance to food poisoning and tummy bugs and, if eaten after a course of antibiotics, may restore the internal flora of the intestines. There is also evidence to suggest that bio yogurt that contains the *acidophilus* culture could prevent cancer of the colon.

> ### Cooking with Yogurt
> Yogurt is a useful culinary ingredient, but does not respond well to heating. It is best added at the end of cooking, just before serving, to prevent it from curdling and to retain its vital bacteria. High-fat yogurts are more stable, but it is possible to stabilize and thicken low-fat yogurt by stirring in a little blended cornflour (cornstarch) before cooking. Natural (plain) yogurt can be used in a wide range of sweet and savoury dishes, and it makes a calming addition to hot stews and curries.

Clockwise from top left: Thick cow's milk yogurt, thin cow's milk yogurt, Greek (US strained plain) yogurt, soya yogurt, goat's milk yogurt and sheep's milk yogurt

Soft and Hard Cheeses

The selection of cheeses in this section is a mere fraction of the extensive range that is available in good cheese stores and supermarkets. Some, such as mozzarella and feta, are more often cooked in pies or on pizzas, or used in salads, while others, like the soft, white, Camembert-type goat's cheeses, make a good addition to a cheese board.

MOZZARELLA

This delicate, silky-white cheese is usually made from cow's milk, although authentically it should be made from buffalo's milk. The sweet milky balls of cheese have excellent melting qualities, hence its use on pizzas and in bakes, but it is equally delicious served in salads. When combined with avocado and tomato it makes the classic Italian three-colour salad.

FETA

Believed to be one of the first cheeses, feta is curdled naturally without the addition of rennet. Although it was once made with goat's or sheep's milk, it is now more often made with milk from cows. It is preserved in brine, hence its saltiness, and has a firm, crumbly texture. It is used in the classic Greek salad with cucumber, tomatoes and olives. To reduce the salty taste of feta, rinse it in water, then leave to soak in cold water for 10 minutes.

Feta, which is packed in brine, can be bought as small rounds or larger blocks

GOAT'S CHEESE

Indispensable for those intolerant or allergic to cow's milk, goat's cheese varieties range from soft, mild and creamy through a Camembert-type, which has a soft centre and downy rind, to the firm Cheddar alternative. Similarly, the flavour of goat's cheese spans from fresh, creamy and mild to sharp and pungent.

HALLOUMI

This ancient cheese was first made by nomadic Bedouin tribes. It is commonly sold in small blocks, and is often sprinkled with mint. Halloumi has a firm, rubbery texture and retains its shape when grilled (broiled) or fried. Some people consider it to be the vegetarian alternative to bacon.

CHEDDAR

Unfortunately, much of the Cheddar sold today is made in factories. Avoid these fairly tasteless, rubbery blocks and look for traditional farmhouse Cheddar, which is matured for between nine and 24 months, and has a rich, strong, savoury flavour.

Mozzarella

Goat's cheese comes in a multitude of different forms

Halloumi

Health Benefits: Semi-soft cheeses, such as mozzarella, and hard cheeses, such as Parmesan and Cheddar, contain valuable amounts of calcium, protein, vitamins and minerals. Hard cheeses are also high in saturated fat. When buying hard cheeses, choose a mature (sharp), good-quality type, as the strong flavour means that relatively small quantities are needed to add flavour to a dish. Saturated fat is known to increase blood cholesterol, which can lead to heart disease and stroke, so always eat cheese in moderation. On the plus side, research shows that cheese – particularly a waxy, hard cheese like Cheddar – eaten after a meal, may reduce the likelihood of tooth decay by as much as 50 per cent.

Non-dairy Cheeses

Soya cheese is the most common non-dairy variety. It can lack the depth of flavour of cheese made from cow's, goat's or sheep's milk, but it is nevertheless a valuable alternative for people who prefer not to buy dairy products or who are lactose intolerant. Soya cheese is made from a blend of processed soya beans and vegetable fats and may be flavoured with herbs and spices. Other non-dairy cheeses include a Parmesan-type cheese made from rice and a spice-flavoured cheese produced from nuts.

PARMESAN

Allowed to mature for at least 18 months and up to four years, this richly flavoured cheese may be high in fat – though not as high as Cheddar – but a little goes a long way. Avoid ready-grated Parmesan and opt for a chunk freshly cut off the block. Parmesan keeps for a long time in the refrigerator and is excellent grated and added to pasta, risottos and bakes, or shaved over salads.

Buying and Storing: Hard cheeses are best stored in a cool pantry but, if kept in the refrigerator, the cheese should be left at room temperature for at least an hour before eating. It starts to dry out as soon as it is cut, so keep it in foil or greaseproof (waxed) paper.

Parmesan

Fresh Unripened Cheeses

As their name suggests, fresh unripened cheeses are young and immature. They have a light, mild taste that readily accepts stronger flavoured ingredients, such as herbs and spices. They are lower in fat and are less likely to induce migraines than mature hard cheeses. Fresh cheeses can be used in both savoury dishes and desserts.

FROMAGE FRAIS

This smooth, fresh cheese has the same consistency as thick yogurt, but is less acidic. It can be used in the same way as yogurt; mixed with fruit purée to make fools, combined with dried fruit, nuts and grains, or in sweet and savoury flans. The fat content varies from almost nothing to about 8 per cent. Full-fat fromage frais is the best choice for cooking as it is less likely to separate.

RICOTTA

A soft, low-fat unsalted cheese, which can be made from sheep's, goat's or cow's milk, ricotta has a slightly granular texture and is widely used in Italian cooking. Its mild, clean flavour means that it is incredibly versatile. It makes a neutral base for pancake fillings, and can be used as a stuffing for pasta, when it is often combined with spinach. Ricotta is also good in tarts, cakes and cheesecakes, or it can be served simply on its own with fruit. Mixed with herbs and garlic, it makes a tasty sandwich filling.

Below, clockwise from left: Ricotta, fromage frais, quark, cream cheese and cottage cheese

QUARK

This low-fat curd (farmer's) cheese is usually made with semi-skimmed (low-fat) or skimmed milk. Its mild, slightly tangy flavour and light, creamy texture makes it perfect in cheesecakes, or it can be diluted with milk to make an alternative to cream. In northern Europe countries, it is used as a spread instead of butter.

COTTAGE CHEESE

Lower in fat than most other cheeses (between 2 and 5 per cent), cottage cheese is not usually used for cooking but is good in salads and dips. It makes a fine accompaniment to soft fruits and is best eaten as fresh as possible.

CREAM CHEESE

Commonly used in cheesecakes, dips and spreads, this cheese has a rich, velvety consistency, mild flavour and a high fat content – about 35 per cent – although it is possible to buy lower-fat alternatives made from skimmed milk.

NON-DAIRY SOFT CHEESES

A wide range of soft, soya-based cheeses is available from health food stores. They are a valuable alternative for people who prefer not to buy dairy products.

Buying and Storing: Fresh unripened cheeses do not keep for very long and are best bought in small quantities and eaten soon after purchase. Store in an airtight container in the refrigerator.

Health Benefits: Fresh unripened cheeses generally have a lower fat content than hard cheeses and are less likely to trigger migraines. They also provide plenty of protein, calcium and vitamin B_{12}.

Always Read the Label

Check the labels on low-fat yogurts and soft cheeses as these products sometimes contain animal-derived gelatine, which is used as a setting agent. Until relatively recently, the rennet use for cheese-making was obtained from animals. Nowadays, however, vegetarian rennet is more widely used, although this may not be mentioned on the pack. If in doubt, check with the manufacturer.

Making Fresh Soft Cheese

Fresh soft cheese can be made using soured milk (made from milk mixed with yogurt) or sour cream. Use plain or sweeten with honey, orange flower water or soft fruit. Alternatively, mix with fresh chopped herbs and garlic.

1 Place 1 litre/1¾ pints/4 cups semi-skimmed (low-fat) milk and 120ml/4fl oz/½ cup live yogurt or sour cream in a pan and mix well. Bring to the boil, then simmer for 5 minutes or until the milk curdles, stirring continuously.

2 Line a metal sieve (strainer) or colander with muslin (cheesecloth) and place over a large bowl. Pour in the milk mixture and leave to drain for 1 hour or until it stops dripping. Alternatively, gather together the edges of the muslin, tie with string, and suspend over the bowl for about 1 hour until it stops dripping.

3 The residue left behind in the muslin is the soft cheese. Eat immediately or store in a covered bowl in the refrigerator for 3–4 days.

Butter Versus Margarine

Whether butter is better than margarine has been the focus of much debate. The taste, especially of good-quality, farmhouse butter, is certainly superior to margarine. However, butter, which contains 80 per cent saturated fat, has the ability to raise cholesterol levels in the body.

Vegetable margarine contains the same amount of fat as butter, but the fat is polyunsaturated, which was once considered to give margarine greater health benefits. Unfortunately, margarine manufacturing processes change the fats into trans fats, or hydrogenated fats. Studies have shown that trans fats may be more likely than the saturated fat in butter to damage the heart and blood vessels. In addition, cooking removes many of the health benefits of polyunsaturated fats.

SPREADS

Lower-fat margarines are known as spreads. They contain less than 80 per cent fat and those that are under 65 per cent fat can be classified as reduced-fat. When the fat content falls below 41 per cent, a spread can be called low-fat or half-fat. Very low-fat spreads may contain gelatine, and their high water content means they are not suitable for cooking. Olive-oil based spreads are rich in monounsaturated fats and are said to reduce cholesterol levels. They can be used for cooking.

Buying and Storing: When buying margarine and spreads always choose good-quality brands that contain no hydrogenated fats. Butter, margarines and spreads absorb other flavours, so they need to be kept well-wrapped. Always store these products in the refrigerator; unsalted butters will keep for up to 2 weeks, other butters for up to a month, and margarines and spreads will keep for about 2 months.

Below: There is a wide variety of different butters, margarines and spreads available. Whichever you choose to use, don't consume too much of these high-fat foods.

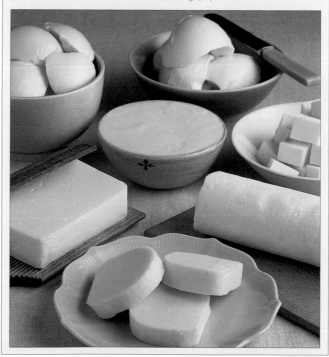

Eggs

An inexpensive, self-contained source of nourishment, hen's eggs offer the cook tremendous scope, whether served simply solo or as part of a dish. There are several different types, but the best are organic, free-range eggs from a small producer.

ORGANIC FREE-RANGE (FARM-FRESH) EGGS

These eggs are from hens that are fed on a natural pesticide-free diet, which has not had hormones or artificial colorants added. The hens are able to roam on land that has not been treated with chemical fertilizers and is certified organic. Free-range hens have the same indoor conditions as barn hens but also have access to the open air – although the term 'access' has sometimes been open to abuse.

Organic, free-range hens are said to have better conditions than normal free-range hens, and are not routinely debeaked.

Organic free-range (farm fresh) eggs

BATTERY EGGS

Laid by hens that are kept in cages with a minimum amount of space in which to move. The hens are debeaked to prevent them pecking each other. These eggs are the cheapest to buy.

BARN OR PERCH EGGS

These eggs are produced by hens that are kept indoors. Each hen can roam around in the barn, but they have no access to the outside. Barn or perch eggs are more expensive than battery eggs, but cheaper than eggs from free-range hens.

FOURGRAIN EGGS

These eggs are produced by hens that are fed a diet based on barley, oats, wheat and rye. The hens have the same living conditions as barn or perch hens, in that they are kept indoors without access to the outside.

Cooking with Eggs: Eggs can be cooked in myriad ways. Simply boiled, fried or poached, they make a wonderful breakfast dish. Lightly cooked poached eggs are also delicious served as a lunch dish with high-fibre lentils or beans. Eggs are delicious baked, either on their own, with a drizzle of cream, or broken into a nest of lightly cooked peppers or leeks. They make delicious omelettes, whether cooked undisturbed until just softly set, combined with tomatoes and peppers to make an Italian frittata, or cooked with diced potato and onions to make the classic Spanish omelette. They are also often used as a filling for pies, savoury tarts and quiches.

Eggs are not, however, used only in savoury dishes. They are an essential ingredient in many sweet dishes, too. They are added to cake mixtures and batters for pancakes and popovers, are crucial to meringues, whisked sponges, mousses and hot and cold soufflés, and are used in all manner of desserts, from ice creams and custards to rice pudding.

When separated, egg yolks are used to thicken sauces and soups, giving them a rich, smooth consistency, while egg whites can be whisked into peaks to make meringues and soufflés. It is important to use eggs at room temperature, so remove them from the refrigerator about 30 minutes before cooking.

> ### Misleading Labels
>
> The labels on egg boxes often have phrases such as 'farm fresh', 'natural' or 'country-fresh', which conjure up images of hens roaming around in the open, but they may well refer to eggs that are laid by birds reared in battery cages. It is advisable to avoid eggs that are labelled with such claims.

Battery eggs

Buying and Storing: Freshness is paramount when buying eggs. Buy from a store that has a high turnover of stock. You should reject any eggs that have a broken, dirty or damaged shell. Most eggs are date stamped, but you can easily check if an egg is fresh, by placing it in a bowl of cold water: if the egg sinks and lays flat it is fresh. The older the egg, the more it will stand on its end. A really old egg will actually float and shouldn't be eaten. Store eggs in their box in the main part of the refrigerator and not in a rack in the door as this can expose them to odours and damage. The shells are extremely porous, so eggs can be tainted by strong smells. Eggs should be stored large-end up for no longer than 3 weeks.

Health Benefits: Eggs have received much adverse publicity due to their high cholesterol levels. However, attention has moved away from dietary cholesterol to cholesterol that is produced in the body from saturated fats. Saturated fats are now claimed to play a bigger role in raising cholesterol levels, and as eggs are low in saturated fat, they have been somewhat reprieved. They should, however, be eaten in moderation, and people with raised cholesterol levels should take particular care. Nutritionists recommend that we eat no more than four eggs a week. Eggs provide B vitamins, especially B_{12}, vitamins A and D, iron, choline and phosphorus, and cooking does not significantly alter their nutritional content.

Quick Ideas for Eggs

• Brush beaten egg on to pastries and bread before baking to give them a golden glaze.
• For a protein boost, top Thai- or Chinese-flavoured rice or noodle dishes with strips of thin omelette.
• Turn a mixed leaf salad into a light supper dish by adding a soft-boiled egg and some half-fat mayonnaise.
• For a simple dessert, make a soufflé omelette. Separate 2 eggs and whisk the whites and yolks separately. Fold together gently and add a little sugar. Cook in the same way as a savoury omelette and serve plain or fill with fruit conserve or lemon curd.

Herb Omelette

A simple, herb-flavoured omelette is quick to cook and, served with a salad and a chunk of crusty bread, makes a nutritious, light meal. Even if you are going to serve more than one, it is better to cook individual omelettes and eat them as soon as they are ready.

INGREDIENTS

2 eggs
15ml/1 tbsp chopped fresh herbs,
    such as tarragon, parsley or chives
5ml/1 tsp butter
salt and freshly ground black pepper

SERVES 1

1 Lightly beat the eggs in a bowl, add the fresh herbs and season to taste.

2 Melt the butter in a heavy non-stick frying pan and swirl it around to coat the base evenly.

3 Pour in the egg mixture and, as the egg sets, push the edges towards the centre using a spoon, allowing the raw egg to run on to the hot pan.

4 Cook for about 2 minutes, without stirring, until the egg is just lightly set. Quickly fold over the omelette and serve immediately.

The Store Cupboard

The following section features a diverse range of foods that can enrich and add variety to a vegetarian diet. Some ingredients may be familiar, others less so, but all are useful to keep in the store cupboard (pantry). Each of the foods comes with notes on choosing, storage and preparation, when necessary, as well as nutritional or medicinal properties.

Nuts

With the exception of peanuts, nuts are the fruits of trees. The quality and availability of fresh nuts varies with the seasons, although most types are sold dried, either whole or prepared ready for use. Shelled nuts come in many forms: they may be whole, blanched, halved, sliced, shredded, chopped, ground or toasted.

Chestnuts

ALMONDS

There are two types of almond: sweet and bitter. The best sweet varieties are the flat and slender Jordan almonds from Spain. Heart-shaped Valencia almonds from Portugal and Spain, and the flatter Californian almonds are also widely available. For the best flavour, buy shelled almonds in their skins and blanch them yourself: cover with boiling water, leave for a few minutes, then drain and the skins will peel off easily. Almonds are available ready-blanched, flaked (sliced) and ground. The latter adds a richness to cakes, tarts, pastry and sauces. Bitter almonds are much smaller and are used in almond oil and extract. They should not be eaten raw as they contain traces of the lethal prussic acid.

BRAZIL NUTS

These are, in fact, seeds, and are grown mainly in the Amazon regions of Brazil and other neighbouring countries. Between 12 and 20 Brazil nuts grow, packed snugly together, in a large brown husk, hence their three-cornered wedge shape. Brazil nuts have a sweet, milky taste and are used mainly as dessert nuts. They have a high fat content, so go rancid very quickly.

CASHEW NUTS

These are the seeds of the 'cashew apple' – an evergreen tree with bright-orange fruit. Cashew nuts have a sweet flavour and crumbly texture. They make delicious nut butters, or can be sprinkled into stir-fries or over salads. They are never sold in the shell and undergo an extensive heating process that removes the seed from its outer casing.

CHESTNUTS

Raw chestnuts are not recommended as they are not only unpleasant to eat but also contain tannic acid, which inhibits the absorption of iron. Most chestnuts are imported from France and Spain and they are excellent after roasting, which complements their soft, floury texture. Unlike other nuts, they contain very little fat. Out of season, chestnuts can be bought dried, canned or puréed.

Blanched, whole and shelled almonds; shelled cashew nuts (in bowl); and shelled and whole Brazil nuts

Add whole chestnuts to winter stews, soups, stuffings or pies. The sweetened purée is delicious in desserts.

COCONUTS

This versatile nut grows all over the tropics. The white dense meat, or flesh, is made into desiccated (dry unsweetened shredded) coconut, blocks of creamed coconut, coconut cream and coconut milk. A popular ingredient in Asian, African and South American cuisines, coconut lends a sweet, creamy flavour to desserts, curries, soups and casseroles. Use in moderation, as it is high in fat.

HAZELNUTS

Grown in the USA, Britain, Turkey, Italy and Spain, hazelnuts are usually sold dried, and can be bought whole, shelled and ground. They can be eaten raw, and are especially good toasted. Hazelnuts can be chopped for use in cakes and desserts, but they are also tasty in savoury dishes and can be added to salads, stir-fries and pasta.

Hazelnuts

Macadamia nuts

Peeling Chestnuts

Peeling chestnuts can be fiddly and time-consuming but this is one of the simplest and quickest methods.

Place the chestnuts in a pan of boiling water, turn off the heat and leave to stand for 5 minutes.

2 Remove the nuts with a slotted spoon, then leave until cool enough to handle. Peel with a sharp knife.

MACADAMIA NUTS

This round nut, about the size of a large hazelnut, is native to Australia, but is now grown in California and South America. Macadamia nuts are commonly sold shelled (the shell is hard to crack). They have a crisp texture, a buttery flavour and a high fat content.

Coconut cream, coconut milk and desiccated (dry unsweetened) shredded coconut

Coconut Milk

Coconut milk or cream can be bought in stores, but it is easy to make at home: tip 225g/8oz/2⅔ cups desiccated (dry unsweetened shredded) coconut into a food processor, add 450ml/¾ pint/scant 2 cups boiling water and process for 30 seconds. Leave to cool slightly, then tip into a sieve (strainer) lined with muslin (cheesecloth) placed over a bowl. Twist the cloth to extract the liquid, then discard the spent coconut. Store any unused coconut milk in the refrigerator for 1–2 days, or freeze.

PEANUTS

Not strictly a nut but a member of the legume family, peanuts bury themselves just below the earth after flowering – hence their alternative name, groundnuts. They are a staple food in many countries, and are widely used in South-east Asia, notably for satay sauce, and in African cuisines, where they are used as an ingredient in stews. In the West, peanuts are a popular snack food; the shelled nuts are frequently sold roasted and salted, and they are used to make peanut butter. Peanuts are particularly high in fat and should be eaten in moderation.

PECAN NUTS

A glossy, reddish-brown, oval-shaped shell encloses the pecan kernel, which looks like an elongated walnut but has a sweeter, milder flavour. This native American nut is a favourite in sweet pies, especially the classic pecan pie, but is also good eaten on its own, or added to salads. However,

Pecan nuts

pecan nuts should be eaten only as an occasional treat, because they have the highest fat content of any nut, with a calorie content to match.

PINE NUTS

These tiny, cream-coloured nuts are the fruit of the Mediterranean stone pine tree. They have a rich, aromatic flavour, which lends itself to toasting. Buy in small quantities as their high oil content quickly turns them rancid. Pine nuts are a key

ingredient in Italian pesto sauce, where they are pounded or processsed with garlic, olive oil and basil, and in the Middle Eastern sauce, tarator, in which toasted pine nuts are combined with white bread, garlic, milk and olive oil to make a creamy paste that has a similar consistency to hummus.

PISTACHIO NUTS

Incredibly 'moreish' when served as a snack, pistachio nuts have pale-green flesh and thin, reddish-purple skin. Sold shelled or in a split shell, these mild nuts are often used chopped as a colourful garnish, sprinkled over both sweet and savoury foods. Pistachio nuts have a wonderful flavour, they are good in all manner of

Making Nut Butter

Store-bought nut butters often contain unwanted hydrogenated oil and can be loaded with sugar. To avoid additives, make your own butter using a combination of peanuts, hazelnuts and cashew nuts.

1 Place 75g/3oz/½ cup shelled nuts in a food processor or blender and process until finely and evenly ground.

2 Pour 15–30ml/1–2 tbsp sunflower oil into the processor or blender and process to a coarse paste. Store in an airtight jar.

Peanuts

Pine nuts

Walnuts

desccerts and can
be made into a
delicious ice cream. They are widely used
in Turkish and Arabic sweets, notably
nougat and Turkish Delight. Check before
buying pistachio nuts for cooking, as they
are often sold salted.

WALNUTS

Most walnuts are imported from France,
Italy and California, but they are also
grown in the Middle East, Britain and
China. This versatile nut has been around
for hundreds of years. When picked
young, walnuts are referred to as 'wet' and
have fresh, milky-white kernels, which can
be eaten raw, but are often pickled.

Dried walnuts have a bitter-sweet flavour
and can be bought shelled, chopped or
ground. They can be used to make cakes
and cookies as well as pie fillings, but are
also good added to savoury dishes such as
stir-fries and salads – the classic Waldorf
salad combines whole kernels with sliced
celery and apples in a mayonnaise dressing.

Buying and Storing: Always
buy nuts in small quantities from
a store with a high turnover of stock,
because if kept for too long, they can turn
rancid. Nuts in their shells should feel
heavy for their size. Store nuts in airtight
containers in a cool, dark place or in the
refrigerator and they should keep fresh
for at least 3 months. When buying a
coconut, make sure that there is no sign of
mould or a rancid smell. Give it a shake –
it should be full of liquid. Keep coconut
milk in the refrigerator or freezer once
opened. Desiccated (dry unsweetened
shredded) coconut can be stored in an
airtight container, but don't keep it too
long as its high fat content means that it is
prone to rancidity.

Health Benefits: Rich in B complex
vitamins, vitamin E, potassium, magnesium,
calcium, phosphorus and iron, nuts offer
the vegetarian an abundance of nutrients,
although they are high in calories. Most
nuts are rich in monounsaturated and
polyunsaturated fats, with the exception
of Brazil nuts and coconuts, which are high
in saturated fat, but do not contain
cholesterol. Numerous
studies highlight the

health benefits of walnuts. According to
one study, the essential fatty acids found in
walnuts can decrease cholesterol levels and
may reduce the risk of heart disease by
50 per cent. Almonds and hazelnuts have
similar properties.

Of all foods, Brazil nuts are the richest
in selenium, which is a known mood
enhancer. Apparently, a single Brazil nut
each day will ensure that you are never
deficient in this vital mineral.

Nuts are one of the richest vegetable
sources of the antioxidant vitamin E, which
has been associated with a lower risk of
heart disease, stroke and certain cancers.

Nut Allergy

Any food has the potential to cause
an allergic reaction, but peanuts, as
well as walnuts, Brazil nuts, hazelnuts
and almonds are known to be
common allergens. In cases of
extreme allergy, nuts can trigger a
life-threatening reaction known as
anaphylaxis. Symptoms include
facial swelling, shortness of breath,
dizziness and loss of consciousness, so
it is essential that sufferers take every
precaution to avoid nuts.

Roasting and Skinning Nuts

The flavour of most nuts, particularly
hazelnuts and peanuts, is improved by
roasting. It also enables the thin outer skin
to be removed more easily.

1 Place the nuts in a single layer on a
baking sheet. Bake at 180°C/350°F/
Gas 4 for 10–20 minutes or until the skins
begin to split and the nuts are golden.

2 Tip the nuts on to a dish towel and
rub to loosen and remove the skins.

Pistachio nuts

Seeds

They may look very small and unassuming, but seeds are nutritional powerhouses, packed with vitamins and minerals, as well as beneficial oils and protein. They can be used in a huge array of sweet and savoury dishes, and will add an instant, healthy boost, pleasant crunch and nutty flavour when added to rice and pasta dishes, salads, stir-fries, soups and yogurt.

Tahini (left) and black and white sesame seeds

SESAME SEEDS

These tiny, white or black seeds are a feature of Middle Eastern and Oriental cooking. In the Middle East they are ground into tahini, a thick paste that is a key component of hummus. Sesame seeds are also ground to make halvah, a sweet confection from Greece, Israel and Turkey. Gomassio, or gomashio, is the name of a crushed sesame seed condiment used in Japan. It can easily be made at home: toast the seeds, then crush with a little sea salt in a mortar using a pestle. Try a ratio of one part salt to five parts sesame seeds.

The flavour of sesame seeds is improved by roasting them in a dry frying pan; it gives them a distinctive nuttiness. The toasted seeds make a good addition to salads and noodle dishes. Unroasted seeds can be used as a topping for breads, buns, cakes and cookies, and they can be added to pastry dough.

When buying sesame seeds, try to find seeds that have been mechanically rolled – the tell-tale sign is a matt appearance. Seeds that have been subjected to other methods of processing, such as salt-brining or a chemical bath, are usually glossy. Salt brining can affect the flavour of the seeds, as can chemical processing, which also damages their nutritional value.

SUNFLOWER SEEDS

These are the seeds of the sunflower, a symbol of summer and an important crop throughout the world. The impressive, golden-yellow flowers are grown for their seeds and oil; the leaves are used to treat malaria and the stalks are made into fertilizer. Rich in vitamin E, the pale-green, tear-drop-shaped seeds have a semi-crunchy texture and an oily taste that is improved by dry-roasting. Sprinkle sunflower seeds over salads, rice pilaffs and couscous, or use in bread dough, muffins, casseroles and baked dishes.

Sunflower seeds

POPPY SEEDS

These are the seeds of the opium poppy but without any of the habit-forming alkaloids. Poppy seeds can be blue (usually described as black) or white. The black variety looks good sprinkled over cakes and breads, adding a pleasant crunch.

Black and white poppy seeds

Black poppy seeds can be used to make delicious seed cakes and teabreads, and they are used in German and Eastern European pastries, strudels and tarts. In India, the ground white seeds are used to thicken sauces, adding a nutty flavour.

PUMPKIN SEEDS

Richer in iron than any other seed and an excellent source of zinc, pumpkin seeds make a nutritious snack eaten on their own. They are also delicious lightly toasted, tossed in a little toasted sesame seed oil or soy sauce, and stirred into a mixed leaf or rice salad. Pumpkin seeds are widely used in South American cooking where they are generally roasted and ground to make into sauces.

Pumpkin seeds

HEMP SEEDS

The cultivation of hemp has a long history but for various reasons it fell out of fashion. Today, hemp is making a comeback as a food. Hemp seeds are best roasted as this enhances their nutty flavour, and they can be used in a variety of sweet and savoury dishes.

LINSEEDS

Linseed oil has long been used to embellish wooden furniture. However, the golden seed, also known as flaxseed, is a rich source of polyunsaturated fat, including the essential fatty acid, linoleic acid. Linseeds can be added to muesli (granola) and other breakfast cereals, mixed into bread dough or sprinkled over salads.

Buying and Storing: Seeds are best bought in small quantities from stores with a high turnover of stock. Purchase whole seeds, rather than ground, and store them in a cool, dark place as they are prone to turning rancid. After opening the packet, decant the seeds into an airtight container.

Health Benefits: Seeds contain valuable amounts of the antioxidant vitamin E, which enhances the immune system and protects cells from oxidation. Vitamin E also improves blood circulation, and promotes healing and normal blood clotting as well as reducing infections associated with ageing. Numerous studies show that the vitamin works in tandem with beta carotene and vitamin C to fight off certain cancers and heart disease as well as slow the progression of Alzheimer's disease.

Seeds, particularly sunflower seeds, may help to reduce blood cholesterol levels in the body because they contain plentiful amounts of linoleic acid, which is also known as omega-6 fatty acid.

For their size, seeds contain a huge amount of iron. Sesame seeds are particularly rich – just 25g/1oz provides nearly half the daily requirement of iron, and 50g/2oz pumpkin seeds provide almost three-quarters of the iron we need each day. Sunflower seeds are often prescribed by natural medicine practitioners for their restorative qualities.

Roasting Seeds

The flavour of seeds is much improved by 'roasting' them in a dry frying pan. Black poppy seeds won't turn golden brown, so watch them carefully to make sure that they don't scorch.

1 Spread out a spoonful or two of seeds in a thin layer in a large, non-stick frying pan and heat gently.

2 Cook over a medium heat for 2–3 minutes, tossing the seeds frequently, until they are golden brown.

Quick Ideas for Seeds

• Sprinkle over breads, cakes and cookies just before baking.
• Combine with dried or fresh fruit, chopped nuts and natural (plain) yogurt to make a nutritious breakfast.
• Add to flapjacks, scones and pastry to give them a nutty flavour.
• Add a spoonful of seeds to rissoles, vegetable burgers or casseroles.
• Mix with rolled oats, flour, butter or margarine, and sugar to make a sweet crumble topping. Omit the sugar to make a savoury topping and combine with chopped fresh or dried herbs.
• Use sunflower or pumpkin seeds in place of pine nuts to make pesto.
• Scatter over a mixed green salad.
• Add an instant nutritional boost to vegetable stir-fries or noodle dishes, by scattering a handful of seeds over the top before serving.

Linseeds (left) and hemp seeds

Spices

Highly revered for thousands of years, spices – the seeds, fruit, pods, bark and buds of plants – have been the reason for wars and were sometimes traded as a currency. In addition to their ability to add flavour and interest to the most unassuming of ingredients, the evocative aroma of spices stimulates the appetite. Today, spices are still prized for their medicinal properties and culinary uses, and they play a vital role in healthy and appetizing vegetarian cooking.

Caraway seeds

Ground allspice

ALLSPICE

These small, dried berries of a tropical, South American tree have a sweet, warming flavour reminiscent of a blend of cloves, cinnamon and nutmeg. Although allspice is available ready-ground, it is best to buy the spice whole to retain its flavour, and grind just before use in cakes and cookies. The whole berries can be added to marinades or mulled wine. Allspice is used to relieve digestive problems, including flatulence.

CARAWAY

An important flavouring in Eastern European, Austrian and German cooking, caraway seeds are sprinkled over rye bread, cakes and cookies. They have a distinctive, sweet, aniseed flavour, which is also a welcome addition to potato- and cheese-based dishes, steamed carrots or cabbage. Caraway is recommended for colicky babies and has a similar effect in adults, relieving wind and aiding digestion. It can also be used to relieve menstrual pain.

CARDAMOM

Often used in Middle Eastern and Indian cooking, cardamom is best bought whole in its pod as it soon loses its aromatic flavour when ground. The pod can be used whole, slightly crushed, or for a more intense flavour, the seeds can be ground.

Cardamom pods

Cardamom is superb in both sweet and savoury dishes. It can be infused in milk used to flavour rice pudding or ice cream, and is often added to curries and other Indian dishes. The seeds can be chewed whole to freshen the breath and calm indigestion. Colds and coughs are also said to be relieved by eating cardamom.

CAYENNE

This fiery, reddish-brown powder adds colour and heat, rather than flavour, to curries, soups and stews. It comes from the ground pod and seeds of a very pungent variety of chilli, *Capsicum frutescens*, and is sometimes referred to as red pepper. Cayenne possesses stimulant, antiseptic and digestive properties. It can improve blood circulation, but if eaten in large quantities may aggravate the stomach. A more unusual use of cayenne is to sprinkle it in your shoes to warm up cold feet!

Cayenne, celery seeds, chilli powder and chilli flakes.

Above, clockwise from left: cinnamon sticks, coriander seeds, cloves and ground cinnamon

CELERY SEEDS

These tiny brown seeds have a similar flavour to celery, but are more highly aromatic. It is important to grind or crush them before use to avoid any bitterness. Celery seeds can be used in almost any dish that calls for celery, and they add a pungent flavour to vegetarian bakes, stews, soups, sauces and egg dishes. Celery salt is a mixture of ground celery seeds, salt and other herbs. Celery seeds are carminative, relieving both flatulence and indigestion.

CHILLIES

Fresh chillies are covered in the vegetable section, but this versatile spice is also sold in dried, powdered and flaked form. Dried chillies tend to be hotter than fresh, and this is certainly true of chilli flakes, which contain both the seeds and the flesh. The best pure chilli powders do not contain added ingredients, such as onion and garlic. A powerful stimulant and expectorant, chilli also has a reputation as an aphrodisiac.

CINNAMON

This warm, comforting spice is available in sticks (quills) and ground. As the bark is difficult to grind, it is useful to keep both forms in the store cupboard (pantry). Cinnamon can enhance both sweet and savoury dishes. Use the sticks to flavour pilaffs, curries, couscous and dried fruit compotes, but remove before serving.

Ground cinnamon adds a pleasing fragrance to cakes, cookies and fruit. Cinnamon is an effective detoxifier and cleanser, containing substances that kill bacteria and other micro-organisms.

CLOVES

The unopened bud of an evergreen tree from South-east Asia, this spice is often used in combination with cinnamon to flavour desserts, cakes and cookies. Cloves are often used to flavour the syrup when poaching oranges, but they are also delicious with cooked apples.

Clove oil has long been used as a cure for toothache, and both its antiseptic and anaesthetic qualities can relieve pain and discomfort throughout the body.

CORIANDER

Alongside cumin, ground coriander is a key ingredient in Indian curry powders and garam masala, and in northern Europe the ivory-coloured seeds are used as a pickling spice. Coriander seeds have a sweet, earthy, burnt-orange flavour that is more pronounced than the fresh leaves. The ready-ground powder rapidly loses its flavour and aroma, so it is best to buy whole seeds, which are easily ground in a mortar using a pestle, or in a coffee grinder. Before grinding, lightly dry-roast the seeds in a frying pan to enhance their flavour. Coriander has been prescribed as a digestive for thousands of years, relieving indigestion, diarrhoea and nausea. It also has antibacterial properties.

Cumin seeds, ground cumin and (front) fenugreek

CUMIN

Extensively used in Indian curries, cumin is also a familiar component of Mexican, North African and Middle Eastern cooking. The seeds have a robust aroma and slightly bitter taste, which is tempered by dry-roasting. Black cumin seeds, which are also known as nigella, are milder and sweeter. Ground cumin can be harsh, so it is best to buy the whole seeds and grind them just before use to ensure a fresh flavour. Cumin is good in tomato- or grain-based dishes, and its digestive properties mean that it is also ideal with beans.

FENUGREEK

This spice is commonly used in commercial curry powders, along with cumin and coriander. On its own though, fenugreek should be used in moderation because its bitter-sweet flavour, which is mellowed by dry-frying, can be quite overpowering if used to excess. The seeds have a hard shell and are difficult to grind, but they can be sprouted and make a good addition to mixed leaf and bean salads, as well as sandwich fillings. Fenugreek has long been prescribed to treat stomach and intestinal disorders, and its ability to cleanse the body may help in the release of toxins.

Fresh root ginger

GINGER

This spice is probably one of the oldest and most popular herbal medicines. The fresh root, which is spicy, peppery and fragrant, is good in both sweet and savoury dishes, adding a hot, yet refreshing, flavour to marinades, stir-fries, soups, curries, grains and fresh vegetables. It also adds warmth to poached fruit, pastries and cakes.

Ground ginger is the usual choice for flavouring cakes, cookies and other baked goods, but finely grated fresh ginger can also be used and is equally good.

Ground ginger

Ginger tea, made by steeping a few slices of fresh root ginger in hot water for a few minutes, can calm and soothe the stomach after a bout of food poisoning as well as ward off colds and flu.

Pink pickled ginger

This pretty, finely sliced ginger pickle is served as an accompaniment to Japanese food and is used to flavour sushi rice.

Stem ginger

Preserved in a thick sugar syrup and sold in jars, this sweet ginger can be chopped and used in desserts, or added to cake mixtures, steamed desserts, scones, shortbread and muffins.

Buying and Storing: Fresh root ginger should look firm, thin-skinned and unblemished. Avoid withered, woody looking roots as these are likely to be dry and fibrous. Store in the refrigerator. Ground ginger should smell aromatic; keep in a cool, dark place.

Preparing Fresh Ginger

1 Fresh root ginger is most easily peeled using a vegetable peeler or a small, sharp paring knife.

3 Grate ginger finely – special graters can be found in Asian stores, but a box grater will do the job equally well.

2 Chop ginger using a sharp knife to the size specified in the recipe.

4 Freshly grated ginger can be squeezed to release the juice.

Pink pickled ginger

Health Benefits: The health benefits of ginger have been well documented for centuries. Recent studies confirm that ginger can successfully prevent nausea and may be more effective than prescribed drugs. Research also shows ginger to be effective in the treatment of pain and gastrointestinal disorders, and it may even halt certain cancers.

LEMON GRASS

This long fibrous stalk has a fragrant citrus aroma and flavour when cut and is a familiar part of South-east Asian and particularly Thai cooking, where it is used in coconut-flavoured curries. If you have difficulty finding lemon grass, lemon rind is a suitable alternative but it lacks the distinctive flavour of the fresh stalks.

To use, remove the tough, woody outer layers, trim the root, then cut off the lower 5cm/2in and slice into thin rounds or pound in a mortar using a pestle. Bottled, chopped lemon grass and lemon grass purée are also available. Lemon grass is reputed to benefit rheumatism.

GALANGAL

Closely related to ginger, fresh galangal looks similar but has a reddish-brown or cream-coloured skin. It was popular in England during the Middle Ages, but fell out of favour. With the increased interest in South-east Asian cooking, this knobbly root is again widely available and can be found in Oriental stores. Its fragrant, slightly peppery taste can be overpowering if used in excess. Avoid the powdered version as it is nothing like the fresh. Prepare the root in the same way as ginger: peel, then slice, grate or pound in a mortar using a pestle. Galangal has similar medicinal properties to ginger, relieving nausea and stomach problems.

MUSTARD

There are three different types of mustard seed, white, brown, and black, which is the most pungent. The flavour and aroma is only apparent when the seeds are crushed or mixed with liquid. If fried in a little oil before use, the flavour of the seeds is improved. As the intensity of mustard diminishes with both time and cooking; it is best added to dishes towards the end of cooking, or just before the dish is served.

Like many hot spices, mustard is traditionally used as a stimulant, cleansing the body of toxins and helping to ward off colds and flu.

Galangal

Above: American mustard, Dijon mustard, wholegrain mustard, mustard powder and black and white mustard seeds

Lemon grass

NUTMEG AND MACE

When it is picked, the nutmeg seed is surrounded by a lacy membrane called mace. Both are dried and used as spices. Nutmeg and mace taste similar, and their warm, sweet flavour enlivens white sauces, cheese-based dishes and vegetables, as well as custards, cakes and cookies. Freshly grated nutmeg is far superior to the ready-ground variety, which loses its flavour and aroma with time. Although it is a hallucinogen if eaten in excess, when consumed in the small quantities that are needed in recipes, nutmeg improves both appetite and digestion.

Ground saffron and saffron threads

White, black and pink peppercorns

ground in a peppermill when you need them because they quickly lose their aroma.

White pepper

This has a less aromatic flavour than black pepper and is generally used in white sauces and other dishes to avoid dark specks of black pepper.

PEPPER

Undoubtedly the oldest, most widely used spice in the world, pepper was as precious as gold and silver in Medieval Europe. It is a very useful seasoning, because it not only adds flavour of its own to a dish, but also brings out the flavour of the other ingredients. Pepper is a digestive stimulant, as well as a decongestant and antioxidant.

Black peppercorns

These are the dried green berries of the vine pepper and they are relatively mild. Black peppercorns are best when freshly

Right, clockwise from top left: mixed (apple pie) spice, ground and whole nutmegs, and paprika

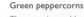

Green peppercorns

These unripened berries have a milder flavour than black or white peppercorns and may be dried or preserved in brine. They are sometimes used to make a spicy peppercorn sauce.

Pink peppercorns

These pretty, pink berries are not a true pepper. They are the processed berry of a type of poison ivy and should be used in small amounts as they are mildly toxic.

PAPRIKA

Paprika is a milder relative of cayenne and can be used more liberally, adding flavour as well as heat. Like cayenne, it is a digestive stimulant and has antiseptic properties. Paprika can also improve blood circulation but if eaten in large quantities may aggravate the stomach.

SAFFRON

The world's most expensive spice is made from the dried stigmas of *Crocus salivus*. Only a tiny amount of this bright-orange spice is needed to add a wonderful colour and delicate bitter-sweet flavour to rice, stews, soups and milky desserts. Saffron has the ability to calm and balance the body and is believed to be an aphrodisiac.

Ground and fresh turmeric

Grinding Spices

Whole spices ground by hand provide the best flavour and aroma. Grind as you need them and do not be tempted to grind too much as they tend to lose their potency and flavour. Some spices such as mace, fenugreek, cloves, turmeric and cinnamon are difficult to grind at home and are better bought ready-ground.

Grind whole spices in a mortar using a pestle – or use an electric coffee grinder if you prefer.

Toasting Spices

This process enhances the flavour and aroma of spices and is thought to make them more digestible.

Put the spices in a dry frying pan and cook over a low heat, shaking the pan frequently, for 1 minute or until the spices release their aroma.

TURMERIC

Sometimes used as an alternative to saffron, turmeric delivers a similar yellow colour but has an earthy, peppery flavour. Turmeric is valued for its anti-bacterial and antifungal qualities. It can aid digestion and in Asia it is believed to be a remedy for liver problems.

VANILLA

These slender, chocolate-brown pods have a fragrant, exotic aroma and luscious, almost creamy flavour. They can be used more than once; rinse and dry before storing in

an airtight jar. Buy natural vanilla extract, which is made by infusing the pods in alcohol: artificial vanilla flavouring is not as good. Vanilla is considered to be an aphrodisiac and a tonic for the brain.

Buying and Storing: Buy spices in small quantities from a store with a regular turnover of stock. Aroma is the best indication of freshness, as this diminishes when the spice is stale. Store in airtight jars in a cool place away from direct light. Stored correctly, whole spices will keep up to a year and ground spices for up to six months.

Natural vanilla extract and vanilla pods

Salt

Moderate amounts of salt are needed by the body, but it is easy to consume too much, as salt is added to many processed foods. Too much salt can lead to high blood pressure, hypertension, water retention and may increase the risk of heart disease. Used in small amounts, salt can enhance the flavour of food. Use rock or sea salt rather than refined table salt.

Table salt (top), rock salt (right) and sea salt

Pasta

Once considered a fattening food, pasta is now recognized as an important part of a healthy diet. The variety of shapes is almost endless, from the myriad tiny soup pastas to huge shells used for stuffing. Pasta can be plain, made with egg or flavoured with ingredients such as tomato or spinach. Low in fat and high in complex carbohydrates, it provides plenty of long-term energy. Corn and buckwheat varieties are also available, as is whole-wheat pasta, which is high in fibre.

Pasta is one of our most simple, yet most versatile foods. A combination of wheat flour and water produces the basic dough, which can then be formed into an infinite number of shape variations. Alter the type of flour, add fresh eggs or a vegetable purée, and the options are even greater. Although pasta is itself a low-fat food, it is important to take care when choosing the accompanying sauce, as overloading on cheese or cream can soon transform pasta into a high-fat food.

Spaghetti, linguine and tagliatelle

DURUM WHEAT PASTA

This is the most readily available type of pasta and can be made with or without egg. Plain wheat pasta is used for straight long shapes such as spaghetti, while long shapes made with egg pasta, because it is more delicate, are traditionally packed in nests or compressed into waves. Lasagne can be made with either plain or egg pasta. At one time, almost all short pasta shapes were made from plain pasta, but shapes made with egg pasta are becoming increasingly available. Pasta made with egg has several advantages over plain pasta: it is more nutritious, many people consider it to have a superior flavour, and it is more difficult to overcook.

COLOURED AND FLAVOURED PASTA

A variety of ingredients can be added to the pasta dough to give it both flavour and colour. The most common additions are tomato and spinach, but beetroot (beet), saffron, fresh herbs such as basil, and even chocolate are used. Mixed bags of pasta are also available – the traditional combination of plain and spinach-

Buckwheat pasta spirals and short-cut pizzoccheri

Right: Corn or maize pasta can be bought in a wide variety of shapes, from simple elbow macaroni to fusilli and three-coloured radiatori

flavoured pasta is called paglia e fieno, which means straw and hay. But there are many other mixtures, some having as many as seven different flavours and colours of pasta.

WHOLE-WHEAT PASTA

This substantial pasta is made using wholemeal (whole-wheat) flour and it contains more fibre than plain durum wheat pasta. It has a nutty flavour and takes longer to cook. Whole-wheat spaghetti (bigoli), a traditional Italian variety that comes from the area around Venice known as the Veneto, can be found in good Italian delicatessens, and in health food stores and supermarkets. There is an increasing range of whole-wheat shapes, from tiny soup pastas to rotelle (wheels) and lasagne.

BUCKWHEAT PASTA

Pasta made from buckwheat flour has a nutty taste and is darker in colour than whole-wheat pasta. Pizzoccheri from Lombardy is the classic shape. These thin, flat noodles are traditionally sold in nests like tagliatelle, but they are also available cut into short strips. Other buckwheat pasta shapes are available in health food stores and larger supermarkets. Buckwheat pasta is gluten-free and suitable for people who are intolerant to gluten or wheat. It is also very nutritious, containing all eight amino acids, calcium, zinc and B vitamins, so makes a healthy alternative to wheat pasta.

Above: Pasta can be coloured and flavoured in a variety of ways, but plain, spinach and tomato varieties are the most popular

CORN PASTA

This pasta is made with corn or maize flour, is gluten-free and is a good alternative pasta for people who cannot tolerate gluten or wheat. It is made in a wide range of shapes, including spaghetti, fusilli (spirals) and conchiglie (shells), as well as more unusual varieties. Plain corn pasta is a sunshine-yellow colour, and may be flavoured with spinach or tomato. It is cooked and used in the same way as wheat pasta and is available from many health food stores and supermarkets.

PASTA SHAPES

Long pasta

Dried long pasta in the form of spaghetti is probably the best known, but there are many other varieties, from fine vermicelli to pappardelle – broad ribbon noodles. Tagliatelle, the most common form of ribbon noodles, is usually sold coiled into nests. Long pasta is best served with a thin sauce, made with olive oil, butter, cream, eggs, grated cheese or chopped fresh herbs. When vegetables are added to the sauce, they should be finely chopped.

Fresh spaghetti, tagliatelle and fettuccine are widely available.

Short pasta

There are hundreds of different short dried pasta shapes, which may be made with plain pasta dough or the more nutritious yellow, egg pasta. Short pasta isn't often sold fresh because most shapes are difficult to produce, but you may find one or two in some Italian delicatessens, and a few fresh shapes are also available from larger supermarkets.

Conchiglie (shells) are one of the most useful shapes because they are concave and trap virtually any sauce. Fusilli (spirals) are good with thick tomato-based sauces and farfalle (butterflies) can be served with creamy sauces, but are very versatile and work equally well with tomato- or olive oil-based sauces. Macaroni used to be the most common short shape, and being hollow, it is good for most sauces and baked dishes. However, penne (quills) have become more popular, perhaps because the hollow tubes with diagonally cut ends

Right: Farfalle, penne and fusili

go well with virtually any sauce. They are particularly good with chunky vegetable sauces or baked with cheese sauce.

Flat pasta

Lasagne is designed to be baked between layers of sauce, or cooked in boiling water, then layered, or rolled around a filling to make cannelloni. Lasagne is made from plain or egg pasta and both fresh and dried versions are available. The pasta sheets may be flavoured with tomato or spinach, or made with whole-wheat flour.

Stuffed pasta

The most common stuffed pasta shapes are ravioli, tortellini (little pies) and cappelletti (little hats), although there are other less well-known shapes available from Italian delicatessens. Plain, spinach and tomato doughs are the most usual, and there is a wide range of vegetarian fillings.

Pasta for soup

These tiny shapes are mostly made from plain durum wheat pasta, though you may find them with egg. There are hundreds of different ones, from tiny risi, which look like grains of rice, to alfabeti (alphabet shapes), which are popular with children. Slightly larger shapes such as farfalline (little bows) and tubetti (little tubes) are used in thicker soups such as minestrone.

Buying and Storing: The quality of pasta varies tremendously – choose good-quality Italian brands of pasta made from 100 per cent durum wheat, and visit your local Italian delicatessen to buy fresh pasta, rather than buying pre-packed pasta from the supermarket. Dried pasta will keep almost indefinitely, but if you decant the pasta into a storage jar, it is a good idea to use up the remaining pasta before adding any from a new packet. Fresh pasta from a delicatessen is usually sold loose

---

Quick Ideas for Pasta

• To make a simple, but richly flavoured tomato sauce: place some plum or cherry tomatoes in a baking dish and drizzle with a little olive oil. Roast in a hot oven for 15 minutes, then add one or two peeled garlic cloves and continue roasting for about 15 minutes more. Transfer to a food processor and blend with basil leaves. Season and stir into cooked pasta.

• Toss cooked pasta in a little chilli oil, scatter over rocket (arugula) leaves and pine nuts and serve with finely grated Parmesan cheese.

• Stir a spoonful of black olive tapenade into cooked pasta, then scatter a few lightly toasted walnuts on top before serving.

• Roast a head of garlic, then squeeze out the puréed cloves and mix with olive oil. Toss with cooked pasta and sprinkle over plenty of fresh, chopped flat leaf parsley.

• Olives, mushrooms, aubergines (eggplants) and artichokes bottled in olive oil make good additions to pasta.

• Combine cooked pasta with small chunks of mozzarella cheese, sliced sun-dried tomatoes, chopped fresh mint and a splash of olive oil.

Large and small conchiglie (shells)

Choosing the Right Shape

While it is unnecessary to stick rigidly to hard and fast rules, some pasta shapes definitely work better than others with particular sauces.

• Long pasta shapes such as spaghetti, linguine, tagliatelle and fettuccine suit smooth cream- or olive oil-based sauces, or vegetable sauces where the ingredients are very finely chopped.

• Hollow shapes such as penne (quills), fusilli (spirals) and macaroni all work well with more robust sauces, such as cheese, tomato and vegetable.

• Stuffed pasta shapes such as ravioli and cappelletti are good with simple sauces made with butter, extra virgin olive oil or tomatoes.

• In soups, the delicate small shapes, risi (rice), orzi (barley) and quadrucci (squares) suit lighter broths, while the more substantial conchigliette (little shells) and farfalline (little butterflies) go well in heartier vegetable soups.

Fresh tortellini

Health Benefits: Pasta provides the body with fuel for all kinds of physical activity, from running a marathon to walking to the bus stop. High in complex carbohydrates, pasta is broken down slowly, providing energy over a long period of time. Whole-wheat pasta is the most nutritious, containing a richer concentration of vitamins, minerals and fibre. Nevertheless, all pasta is a useful source of protein, as well as being low in fat. Buckwheat pasta is very nutritious; it contains all eight essential amino acids, making it a complete protein. It is also particularly high in fibre.

Cooking Pasta

Pasta should be cooked in a large pan of boiling salted water to allow the strands or shapes to expand, and stirred occasionally to prevent them from sticking together. Do not add oil to the cooking water as it makes the pasta slippery and prevents it from absorbing the sauce. Cooking instructions are given on the packaging but always taste just before the end of the given time to prevent overcooking. Dried pasta should be al dente, or firm to the bite, while fresh pasta should be just tender.

Bring a large pan of salted water to the boil. For shapes, tip in the pasta and cover the pan. Bring quickly back to the boil and remove the lid. Reduce the heat slightly, then stir the pasta and cook according to the packet instructions. For long straight pasta such as spaghetti, coil the pasta into the water as it softens.

and is best cooked the same day, but can be kept in the refrigerator for a day or two. Fresh pasta from a supermarket is likely to come in plastic packs, and these will keep for 3–4 days in the refrigerator. Fresh pasta freezes well and should be cooked from frozen. Packs of supermarket pasta have the advantage of being easy to store in the freezer.

Above: Tiny soup pasta is available in hundreds of different shapes

Noodles

The fast food of the East, noodles can be made from wheat flour, rice, buckwheat flour or mung bean flour. Both fresh and dried noodles are readily available in health food stores and Asian stores as well as supermarkets. Like pasta, noodles are low in fat and high in complex carbohydrates, so provide long-term energy.

Rice noodles

WHEAT NOODLES

There are two main types of noodle: plain and egg. Plain noodles are made from strong flour and water, they can be flat or round and come in various thicknesses.

Udon noodles

These thick Japanese noodles can be round or flat and are available fresh, pre-cooked or dried. Whole-wheat udon noodles have a more robust flavour.

Somen noodles

Usually sold in bundles, held together by a paper band, these thin, white noodles are available from Oriental stores.

Egg noodles

Far more common than the plain wheat variety, egg noodles are sold both fresh and dried. The Chinese type come in various thicknesses. Very fine egg noodles, which resemble vermicelli, are usually sold in coils. Whole-wheat egg noodles are widely available from larger supermarkets.

Ramen noodles

These Japanese egg noodles are also sold in coils and are often cooked and served with an accompanying broth.

RICE NOODLES

These fine, delicate noodles are made from rice and are opaque-white in colour. Like wheat noodles, they come in various widths, from the very thin strands known as rice vermicelli, which are popular in Thailand and southern China, to the thicker rice sticks, which are used more in Vietnam and Malaysia. A huge range of rice noodles is available dried in Oriental grocers and fresh ones are occasionally found in the chiller cabinets. Since all rice noodles are pre-cooked, they need only to be soaked in hot water for a few minutes to soften them before use in stir-fries and salads.

Udon noodles (above) and cellophane noodles

CELLOPHANE VERMICELLI AND NOODLES

Made from mung bean starch, these translucent noodles, also known as bean thread vermicelli and glass noodles, come in a variety of thicknesses and are only available dried. Although very fine, the strands are firm and fairly tough. Cellophane noodles don't need to be boiled, and are simply soaked in boiling water for 10–15 minutes. They have a fantastic texture, which they retain when cooked, never becoming soggy. Cellophane noodles are almost tasteless unless combined with other strongly flavoured foods and seasonings. They are never eaten on their own, but used as an ingredient. They are good in vegetarian dishes, and as an ingredient in spring rolls.

BUCKWHEAT NOODLES

Soba are the best-known type of buckwheat noodles. They are a much darker colour than wheat noodles – almost brownish grey. In Japan, soba noodles are traditionally served in soups or stir-fries with a variety of sauces.

Dried and fresh egg noodles

Quick Ideas for Noodles

• To make a broth, dissolve mugi miso in hot water, add cooked soba noodles; sprinkle with chilli flakes and sliced spring onions (scallions).

• Cook ramen noodles in vegetable stock, then add a splash of dark soy sauce, shredded spinach and grated ginger (above). Serve sprinkled with sesame seeds and coriander (cilantro).

• Stir-fry sliced shiitake and oyster mushrooms in garlic and ginger, then toss with rice or egg noodles (above). Scatter with fresh chives and a little roasted sesame oil.
• In a food processor, blend together some lemon grass, chilli, garlic, ginger, kaffir lime leaves and fresh coriander. Fry the paste in a little sunflower oil and combine with cooked ribbon noodles. Sprinkle fresh basil and chopped spring onions on top before serving.

Buying and Storing: Packets of fresh noodles are found in the chiller cabinets of Asian stores. They usually carry a use-by date and must be stored in the refrigerator. Dried noodles will keep for many months if stored in an airtight container in a cool, dry place.

Health Benefits: Noodles are high in complex carbohydrates, which are broken down slowly, providing energy over a long period of time. Whole-wheat noodles are the most nutritious, containing a richer concentration of vitamins, minerals and fibre. Nevertheless, all noodles are a useful source of protein, as well as being low in fat. Buckwheat noodles are made from buckwheat flour, which contains all eight essential amino acids, making it a complete protein. It is also high in fibre. Cellophane noodles are made from mung bean starch, which is reputed to be one of the most powerful detoxifiers.

Cooking Wheat Noodles

Wheat noodles are very easy to cook. Both dried and fresh noodles are cooked in a large pan of boiling water; how long depends on the type of noodle and the thickness of the strips. Dried noodles need about 3 minutes cooking time, while fresh ones will often be ready in less than a minute. Fresh noodles may need to be rinsed quickly in cold water to prevent them from overcooking.

Whole-wheat egg noodles

Oils

There is a wide variety of cooking oils and they are produced from a number of different sources: from cereals such as corn; from fruits such as olives; from nuts such as walnuts, almonds and hazelnuts; and from seeds such as rapeseed, safflower and sunflower. They can be extracted by simple mechanical means such as pressing or crushing, or by further processing, usually heating. Virgin oils, which are obtained from the first cold pressing of the olives, nuts or seeds, are sold unrefined, and have the most characteristic flavour. They are also the most expensive.

OLIVE OIL

Indisputably the king of oils, olive oil varies in flavour and colour, depending on how it is made and where it comes from. Climate, soil, harvesting and pressing all influence the end result – generally, the hotter the climate the more robust the oil. Thus oils from southern Italy, Greece and Spain have a stronger flavour and a darker colour than those from the rest of Italy and France. Olive oil is rich in monounsaturated fat, which has been found to reduce cholesterol, thereby reducing the risk of heart disease. There are different grades to choose from.

Extra virgin olive oil

This premium olive oil has a superior flavour. It comes from the first cold pressing of the olives and has a low acidity – less than 1 per cent. Extra virgin olive oil is not recommended for frying, as heat impairs its flavour, but it is good in salad dressings, especially when combined with lighter oils. It is delicious as a sauce on its own, stirred into pasta with chopped garlic and black pepper, or drizzled over steamed vegetables.

Virgin olive oil

Also a pure first-pressed oil, this has a slightly higher level of acidity than extra virgin olive oil, and can be used in much the same way.

Essential Fats

We all need some fat in our diet. It keeps us warm, adds flavour to our food, carries essential vitamins A, D, E and K around the body, and provides essential fatty acids, which cannot be produced in the body, but are vital for growth and development, and may reduce the risk of heart attacks.

What is more important is the type and amount of fat that we eat. Some fats are better for us than others, and we should adjust our intake accordingly. It is recommended that fat should make up no more than 35 per cent of our diet.

Extra virgin olive oil (left), sunflower oil (right) and safflower oil (far right)

Groundnut (peanut) oil (left) and almond oil

Pure olive oil

Refined and blended to remove impurities, this type of olive oil has a much lighter flavour than virgin or extra virgin olive oil and is suitable for all types of cooking. It can be used for shallow frying.

OTHER OILS

There is a wide range of light, processed oils on the market, which are all relatively taste-free and have a variety of uses in the kitchen.

Corn oil

One of the most economical and widely used vegetable oils, corn oil has a deep golden colour and a fairly strong flavour. It is suitable for cooking and frying, but should not be used for salad dressings. Corn is rich in omega-6 (linoleic) fatty acids, which are believed to reduce harmful cholesterol in the body.

Safflower oil

This is a light, all-purpose oil, which comes from the seeds of the safflower. It can be used in place of sunflower and groundnut (peanut) oils, but is a little thicker and has a slightly stronger flavour. It is suitable for deep-frying, but is best used with other more strongly flavoured ingredients, and is ideal for cooking spicy foods. Safflower oil contains more polyunsaturated fat than any other type of oil and it is low in saturated fat.

Sunflower oil

Perhaps the best all-purpose oil, sunflower oil is very light and almost tasteless. It is very versatile, and can be used for frying and in cooking, or to make salad dressings, when it can be combined with a stronger flavoured oil

such as olive oil or walnut oil. Sunflower oil is extracted from the seeds of the sunflower. It is very high in polyunsaturated fat and low in saturated fat.

Soya oil

This neutral flavoured, all-purpose oil, which is extracted from soya beans, is probably the most widely used oil in the world. It is useful for frying because it has a high smoking point, and remains stable at high temperatures. It is also widely used in margarines. It is rich in polyunsaturated and monounsaturated fats and low in saturates. Find a brand that is not made from genetically modified soya beans.

Groundnut (peanut) oil

Also known as peanut oil, this relatively tasteless oil is useful for frying, cooking and dressing salads. Chinese peanut oil is darker in colour than groundnut oil and has a more distinctive nutty flavour. It is good in Oriental salads and stir-fries.

Soya oil

Quick Ideas for Marinades

• Mix olive oil with chopped fresh herbs such as parsley, chives, oregano, chervil and basil. Add a splash or two of lemon juice and season with salt and pepper.

• Combine groundnut (peanut) oil, toasted sesame oil, dark soy sauce, sweet sherry, rice vinegar and garlic. Use as a marinade for tofu or tempeh.

• Mix together olive oil, lemon juice, sherry, honey and crushed garlic and and use as a simple marinade for vegetable and halloumi kebabs.

Groundnut oil has a higher percentage of monounsaturated fat than soya oil but also contains polyunsaturated fat.

Rapeseed (canola) oil

This bland-tasting, all-purpose oil, also known as canola, can be used for frying, cooking and in salad dressings. It contains a higher percentage of monounsaturated fat than any other oil, with the exception of olive oil.

Grapeseed oil

A delicate, mild flavoured oil, which does not impose on other ingredients, grapeseed oil is pressed from grape seeds left over from wine-making. It is good in cooking and for frying, and can be used to make salad dressings, especially when combined with a stronger flavoured nut or olive oil. Grapeseed oil is high in polyunsaturated fat.

Rapeseed (canola) oil

SPECIALITY OILS

As well as the light, all-purpose oils that are used for everyday cooking, there are several richly flavoured oils that are used in small quantities, often as a flavouring ingredient in salad dressings and marinades, rather than for cooking.

Sesame oil

There are two types of sesame oil – the pale and light version that is pressed from untoasted seeds, and the rich, dark, toasted oil that is used in Oriental cuisines. The lighter oil, popular in India and the Middle East, has a mild flavour and a high smoking point and is useful for cooking. Dark sesame oil, which has a wonderfully nutty aroma and taste, is useful for flavouring marinades and stir-fries. It has a much stronger taste than either walnut oil or olive oil and is too overpowering to use in large quantities. However, it can be mixed with milder oils, such as groundnut (peanut) or soya. Heating helps to intensify the aroma of toasted sesame oil, but it should never be heated for too long. Both types of sesame oil are high in polyunsaturated fat.

Walnut oil

This is an intensely flavoured oil that is delicious in salad dressings and marinades, but shouldn't be used for frying as heat diminishes its rich taste (it is also far too expensive to use in any great quantity). Instead, drizzle a little of the oil over roasted or steamed vegetables, use it to make a simple sauce for pasta, or stir into freshly cooked noodles just before serving. It can be used in small quantities, in place of some of the fat or oil in a recipe, to add flavour to cakes and cookies, especially those that contain walnuts. Walnut oil does not keep for long and, after opening, should be kept in a cool, dark place to prevent it from becoming rancid. It can be stored in the refrigerator, though this may cause the oil to solidify. It is rich in poly-unsaturated fats and contains vitamin E.

Hazelnut oil

This fine, fragrant oil is rich brown in colour and has a delicious, roasted hazelnut flavour. It is quite expensive to buy but, because it has such a strong flavour, only a little is needed. It is good, combined with less strongly flavoured oils, for salad dressings and sauces, and can be used to add a nutty flavour to teabreads, cakes, cookies and pastry. Hazelnut oil is rich in monounsaturated fat.

Almond oil

This pale, delicate oil is mainly used in confectionery and desserts. It has a subtle, sweet flavour of almonds, though not enough to give an almond flavour to baked goods such as cakes and cookies. Almond oil is rich in monounsaturated fat

Walnut, sesame and hazelnut oils

as well as vitamins A and E. It is reputed to be very good for the skin and is often used as a massage oil.

Buying and Storing: Cooking oils such as sunflower, soya and safflower are more stable than nut or seed oils, and have longer keeping properties. To keep them at their peak, store in a cool, dark place away from direct sunlight. Nut and seed oils are more volatile and turn rancid quickly and should be kept in the refrigerator after opening.

Health Benefits: Oils are undeniably high in calories and should always be used in moderation, but they also have a number of health benefits. Monounsaturated fats, found particularly in olive oil and rapeseed oil, stabilize or raise the level of the beneficial high density lipoproteins (HDLs), while lowering harmful low density lipoproteins (LDLs), thus keeping down cholesterol levels in the body. A high level of LDLs in the blood is usually an indication of increased cholesterol

levels, as the LDLs carry the fatty substance (cholesterol) around the body; HDLs carry much less fat.

Olive oil also contains vitamin E, a natural antioxidant that can help fight off free radicals, which damage cells in the body and have the potential to cause cancer. Polyunsaturated fats provide essential fatty acids known as omega-3 (alpha-linolenic) and omega-6 (linolenic acid), which must be included in the diet. Omega-3, which is found in walnut, rapeseed (canola) and soya oil, has been found to reduce the likelihood of heart disease and blood clots; while omega 6, provided by safflower, sunflower and walnut oil, reduces harmful cholesterol levels. Polyunsaturated fats are more unstable than monounsaturated fats and are prone to oxidation, which can lead to the build-up of free radicals. Although polyunsaturates do contain vitamin E, it appears in varying amounts and so it is advisable to eat other foods that are rich in vitamin E to protect the fatty acids and the body from damage due to oxidation.

Vinegars

One of our oldest condiments, vinegar is made by acetic fermentation, a process that occurs when a liquid containing less than 18 per cent alcohol is exposed to the air. Most countries produce their own type of vinegar, usually based on their most popular alcoholic drink – wine in France and Italy; sherry in Spain; rice wine in Asia; and beer and cider in Great Britain. Commonly used as a preservative in pickles and chutneys, it is also an ingredient in marinades and salad dressings. A spoonful or two of a good-quality vinegar can add flavour to cooked dishes and sauces.

WINE VINEGARS

These can be made from white, red or rosé wine, and the quality of the vinegar will depend on the quality of the original ingredient. The finest wine vinegars are made by the slow and costly Orleans method. Cheaper and faster methods of fermentation involve heating, which produces a harsher vinegar that lacks the complexities of the original wine. Use in dressings, mayonnaise, sauces or to add flavour to stews and soups.

BALSAMIC VINEGAR

This is a rich, dark, mellow vinegar, which has become hugely popular. Made in Modena in northern Italy, balsamic vinegar

Balsamic vinegar

Sherry vinegar

is made from grape juice (predominantly from Trebbiano grapes), which is fermented in vast wooden barrels for a minimum of four to five years and up to 40 or more years, resulting in an intensely rich vinegar with a concentrated flavour. Balsamic vinegar is delicious in dressings or sprinkled over roasted vegetables. It is even good with strawberries.

SHERRY VINEGAR

This vinegar can be just as costly as balsamic vinegar and, if left to mature in wooden barrels, can be equally good. Sweet and mellow in flavour, sherry vinegar is caramel in colour and can be used in the same way as balsamic vinegar – in dressings, sprinkled over roasted vegetables or added to sauces and stews.

RASPBERRY VINEGAR

Any soft fruit can be used to enhance the flavour of white wine vinegar but raspberries are the most popular. Raspberry vinegar can be made at home by macerating fresh raspberries in good-quality wine vinegar for 2–3 weeks. Once the mixture is strained, the vinegar is delicious as part of a salad dressing, or in sauces. It can be mixed with sparkling mineral water to make a refreshing drink.

MALT VINEGAR

Made from soured beer, malt vinegar is used in Britain and other northern European countries for pickling onions and other vegetables, or for sprinkling over chips (French fries). It can be clear, but is often sold coloured with caramel. Malt vinegar has a robust, harsh flavour and it is not suitable for salad dressings.

Red and white wine vinegars

Raspberry vinegar

Above: Cider vinegar

RICE VINEGAR

There are two kinds of rice vinegar: the type from Japan is mellow and sweet and is most often used to flavour sushi rice, but it can also be added to dressings, stir-fries and sauces; Chinese rice vinegar is much sharper in taste. Rice vinegar is usually a clear, pale-brown colour, but it can also be inky-black, red or white.

CIDER VINEGAR

Made from cider and praised for its health-giving properties, cider vinegar is made in the same way as wine vinegar. It is a clear, pale-brown colour and has a slight apple flavour, but it is too strong and sharp to use in the same ways as wine vinegar. It can be used for salad dressings, but it is perhaps best kept for pickling fruits such as pears. Cider vinegar can be served as a soothing drink, mixed with honey, lemon juice and hot water, as a remedy for colds and flu.

Health Benefits: Hippocrates prescribed vinegar as a cure for respiratory problems, and it may also be beneficial in cases of food poisoning. Cider vinegar is said to have many therapeutic benefits, which were highlighted in a book written in the 1960s by Dr DeForest Clinton Jarvis, entitled *Folk Medicine*. He attributed cider as a cure for everything, from arthritis and headaches to obesity and hiccoughs.

Fragrant Spiced Vinegar

This aromatic vinegar is good in dressings and marinades. Any type of vinegar can be used as a base but, to achieve the best results, ensure that it is good quality. If the vinegar develops an unpleasant appearance or aroma, it should be discarded straight away.

Different flavourings including herb sprigs such as tarragon or rosemary, or whole spices such as cinnamon, star anise or black, white or green peppercorns can be used and will impart a distinctive flavour.

1 Place a few red chillies, 1–2 garlic cloves and some thick strips of lemon rind into a bottle of rice vinegar. Leave to infuse on a sunny windowsill or in a warm place for 3–4 weeks.

2 Strain the vinegar into a clean bottle and seal tightly with a cork. Store in a cool, dark place.

Rice vinegar (left) and brown malt vinegar

Teas & Tisanes

Tea has been a popular reviving drink for centuries and comes in many different forms, from traditional teas such as green tea, oolong tea and black tea to fragrant fruit infusions and healing herbal tisanes.

Black tea (left) and green tea

GREEN TEA

This tea is popular with the Chinese and Japanese who prefer its light, slightly bitter but nevertheless refreshing flavour. It is produced from leaves that are steamed and dried but not fermented, a process that retains their green colour.

OOLONG TEA

Partially fermented to produce a tea that falls between the green and black varieties in strength and colour. It is particularly fragrant.

BLACK TEA

This is the most widely available tea and is made by fermenting withered tea leaves, then drying them. It produces a dark brown brew that has a more assertive taste than green tea. Darjeeling and English breakfast tea are two examples.

Health Benefits: The latest research shows that drinking about five cups of tea a day may help to prevent heart disease, stroke and certain cancers. These benefits have been attributed to a group of antioxidants found in tea, which are called polyphenols or flavonoids. Flavonoids have antiviral,

antibacterial and anti-inflamatory properties. Green tea contains the highest amount of flavonoids and black tea the lowest. Antioxidants help to mop up harmful free radicals, which cause damage to the body's cells and may cause cancer. Tea also contains fluoride, which can protect the teeth against decay. On the down side, tea can reduce the absorption of iron if drunk after a meal and it contains caffeine (although less than coffee), which is a well-known stimulant.

FRUIT TEAS

These are made from a blend of fruit flavours, such as rosehip, strawberry, orange, raspberry and lemon, along with fruit pieces and sometimes herbs or real tea. It is a good idea to check the packaging to make sure the 'tea' is naturally, rather than artificially, flavoured. Fruit teas make refreshing caffeine-free drinks, which are almost calorie-free. They are an ideal drink for pregnant women and, because of their low-sugar content, are suitable for diabetics.

Coffee

Although coffee is generally viewed as unhealthy, largely due to its high level of caffeine, studies have shown that it can enhance concentration and elevate mood. However, drinking more than six cups a day can increase the risk of heart disease and high blood pressure.

Oolong tea

HERBAL TISANES

Although herbal tisanes are of little nutritional value, herbalists have prescribed them for centuries for a multitude of ailments and diseases. These teas (made from the leaves, seeds and flowers of herbs) are a convenient and simple way of taking medicinal herbs. They do, however, vary in strength and effectiveness. Store-bought teas are generally mild in their medicinal properties but are good, healthy, caffeine-free drinks. Even so, some varieties are not recommended for young children and pregnant women and so it is advisable to check the packaging. Teas that are prescribed by herbalists can be incredibly powerful and should be taken with care.

The most popular types of herbal teas are listed below.

Peppermint tea is recommended as a digestive to be drunk after a meal. It is also effective in settling other stomach problems and for treating colds. **Camomile tea** soothes and calms the nerves and can induce sleep. **Raspberry leaf tea** prepares the uterus

Below: Naturally flavoured fruit teas are caffeine-free and contain hardly any calories

Elderflower and dandelion herbal tisanes

for birth and is said to reduce labour pains, but it is not recommended in early pregnancy. It can also relieve period pains. **Rosehip tea** is high in Vitamin C and may help to ward off colds and flu. **Dandelion and lemon verbena** teas are effective diuretics. **Rosemary tea** can stimulate the brain and improve concentration. **Thyme tea** can boost the immune system and fight viral, bacterial and fungal infections. **Elderflower** tea can ease painful sinuses and bronchial conditions.

Flavoured Teas

These could not be easier to make: simply steep your chosen herb, spice or fruit in boiling water and leave to infuse before straining. Ginger tea is effective against nausea, colds and flu and stomach upsets.

1 To make ginger tea, roughly chop a 2.5cm/1in piece of fresh root ginger. Place in a cup and pour in boiling water.

2 Cover and leave for 7–10 minutes. Strain or drink as it is – the ginger will stay in the bottom of the cup.

Sweeteners

Nutritionists have wide-ranging – and often extreme – opinions on sugar and sugar alternatives. Some maintain that these products cause hyperactivity in children, while others believe that sugars can induce relaxation and sleep. Many recipes from breads and cakes to cookies and desserts contain different types of sugar and/or sugar substitutes such as molasses, honey, malt and grain syrups, as well as dried fruit, and wouldn't be palatable without them. So, provided that a diet is well balanced and varied, it is considered that moderate amounts of sugar are nutritionally acceptable.

Blackstrap molasses

MOLASSES

This rich, syrupy liquid is a by-product of sugar refining and ranges in quality and colour. The most nutritionally valuable type is thick and very dark blackstrap molasses, which contains less sugar than lighter alternatives and is richer in iron, calcium, copper, magnesium, phosphorus, potassium and zinc. However, it may be better to choose organically produced molasses, which doesn't contain the chemicals and additives that are used in the sugar-refining process.

Honey

HONEY

One of the oldest sweeteners used by man, honey was highly valued by the ancient Egyptians for its medicinal and healing properties. The colour, flavour, consistency and quality of honey depends on the source of nectar as well as the method of production. In general the darker the colour, the stronger the flavour. Many commercial brands of honey are pasteurized and blended to give a uniform taste and texture, but from the point of view of both flavour and health, it is best to buy raw unfiltered honey from a single flower source.

Nutritionally, honey offers negligible benefits, but as it is much sweeter than sugar,

Carob and carob powder

less is needed; it is also lower in calories. Today, honey still retains its reputation as an antiseptic, and recent studies show that it is effective in healing and disinfecting wounds if applied externally. Mixed with lemon and hot water, it can relieve sore throats and is also thought to be helpful in treating diarrhoea and asthma.

CAROB

This caffeine-free alternative to chocolate and unsweetened cocoa powder is made from the aromatic bean pod of a Mediterranean tree.

Malt extract

Dried fruit

Carob powder (flour) looks and tastes similar to unsweetened cocoa powder and can be used to replace it in hot drinks, confectionery and baked goods. It is naturally sweeter and lower in fat than cocoa powder, as well as being more nutritious, providing iron, calcium, vitamin B_6, riboflavin and potassium.

MAPLE SYRUP
This is made from the sap of the maple tree. Look for pure varieties rather than maple-flavoured syrup, which contains additives. Maple syrup has a rich, distinctive flavour and is sweeter than sugar, so less is required in cooking.

GRAIN SYRUPS
Corn, barley, wheat and rice can be transformed into syrups that are used in place of sugar. Grain syrups tend to be easier to digest and enter the bloodstream more slowly than other forms of refined sugar, which cause

swings in blood sugar levels. Grain syrups are not as sweet as sugar and have a mild, subtle flavour. Malt extract, a by-product of barley, has a more intense flavour and is good in breads and other baked goods.

FRUIT JUICE
Freshly squeezed fruit juice is a useful alternative to sugar in baked goods, sauces, pies and ice cream. Fruit juice concentrates such as apple, pear and grape, which have no added sugar or preservatives, are available from health food stores. They can be diluted or used in concentrated form in cakes, pies and desserts.

Clockwise from left: date syrup, barley malt syrup and brown rice syrup

DRIED FRUIT
Dates are made into a syrup that can be used to sweeten cakes. Puréed dried fruits such as prunes, figs and apricots can also replace sugar in pies and cakes. Dried fruit can be added to sweet and savoury foods.

Spiced Apricot Purée

This richly spiced purée is delicious stirred into thick natural (plain) yogurt or can be used to sweeten cakes, crumbles and pies.

1 Place 350g/12oz/1½ cups dried apricots in a pan with enough water to cover. Add 1 cinnamon stick, 2 cloves and 2.5ml/½ tsp freshly grated nutmeg. Bring to the boil, then simmer for 20 minutes until the apricots are plump.

2 Leave to cool, then purée in a food processor until smooth. Add more water if the mixture seems a little thick.

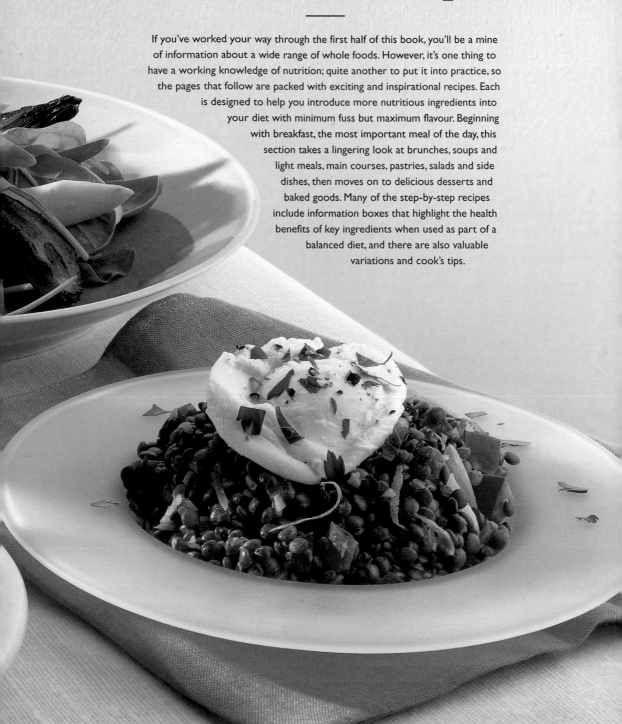

Whole Food Recipes

If you've worked your way through the first half of this book, you'll be a mine of information about a wide range of whole foods. However, it's one thing to have a working knowledge of nutrition; quite another to put it into practice, so the pages that follow are packed with exciting and inspirational recipes. Each is designed to help you introduce more nutritious ingredients into your diet with minimum fuss but maximum flavour. Beginning with breakfast, the most important meal of the day, this section takes a lingering look at brunches, soups and light meals, main courses, pastries, salads and side dishes, then moves on to delicious desserts and baked goods. Many of the step-by-step recipes include information boxes that highlight the health benefits of key ingredients when used as part of a balanced diet, and there are also valuable variations and cook's tips.

Breakfasts
and
Brunches

There's no better way to start the day than with a well-balanced breakfast. Base it on high-carbohydrate whole foods such as cereals, grains or beans, and you not only replenish nutrients and energy stocks depleted overnight, but also set yourself up sensibly for whatever lies ahead. High-carbohydrate foods provide sustained, slow-release energy and are much more effective at fighting hunger than fry-ups or sugary cereals. Choices such as Porridge with Date Purée and Pistachio Nuts, Griddled Tomatoes on Soda Bread or a fish-free Kedgeree are not only undeniably delicious, they also stave off snack attacks. Recent research suggests that those who eat a carbohydrate-based breakfast are likely to eat less during the day, perform better at school or work and find it easier to control their weight. Can't face solid food that early in the morning? Wake to a shake instead. Cleansing juices and fruit smoothies take only seconds to make, but give you energy for hours.

Breakfasts and Brunches

Banana and Strawberry Smoothie

FULL OF ENERGY-GIVING OATS and fruits, this tasty drink makes a brilliant breakfast.

INGREDIENTS

2 bananas, quartered
250g/9oz/2 cups strawberries
30ml/2 tbsp oatmeal
500g/1¼lb/2½ cups natural (plain) live yogurt

Serves 2

1 Process all the ingredients in a blender or food processor for a few minutes until creamy. Pour into tall glasses and serve.

Citrus Shake

PACKED WITH VITAMIN C, this refreshing juice is a great way to start the day.

INGREDIENTS

1 pineapple
6 oranges, peeled and chopped
juice of 1 lemon
1 pink grapefruit, peeled and chopped

Serves 4

1 To prepare the pineapple, cut the bottom and top off the fruit. Stand the pineapple upright and cut off the skin, removing all the spikes. Lay the pineapple on its side and cut into bitesize chunks.

2 Process the pineapple, oranges, lemon juice and grapefruit in a blender or food processor for a few minutes until combined.

3 Press the juice through a sieve (strainer) to remove any pith or. Serve.

Smoothie: Energy 326kcal/1777kJ; Protein16g; Carbohydrate 50g, of which sugars 48g; Fat 8g, of which saturates 4g; Cholesterol 28mg; Calcium 526mg; Fibre 6g; Sodium 209mg.
Shake: Energy 153kcal/655kJ; Protein 4g; Carbohydrate 36g, of which sugars 36g; Fat 1g, of which saturates 0g; Cholesterol 0mg; Calcium 147mg; Fibre 7g; Sodium 16mg.

Cranberry and Apple Juice

THIS GINGER-FLAVOURED, CLEANSING JUICE offers a fine balance of sweet and sour tastes.

INGREDIENTS

4 eating apples
600ml/1 pint/2½ cups cranberry juice
2.5cm/1in piece fresh root ginger, peeled and sliced

Serves 4

HEALTH BENEFITS

Brightly coloured fruits, such as cranberries, contain valuable amounts of antioxidant vitamins, which are believed to have cancer-fighting properties.

1 Peel the apples, if you wish, then core and chop.

2 Pour the cranberry juice into a food processor or blender. Add the chopped apples and sliced ginger and process for a few minutes until combined and fairly smooth. Serve chilled.

Zingy Vegetable Juice

GINGER PACKS A POWERFUL punch and certainly gets you going in the morning, even if you're feeling groggy.

INGREDIENTS

1 cooked beetroot (beet) in natural juice, sliced
1 large carrot, sliced
4cm/1½in piece fresh root ginger, peeled and finely grated
2 apples, peeled, if liked, chopped and cored
150g/5oz/1¼ cups seedless white grapes
300ml/½ pint/1¼ cups fresh orange juice

Serves 2

1 Place the beetroot, carrot, ginger, apples, grapes and orange juice in a blender or food processor and process for a few minutes until combined and fairly smooth. Serve immediately or chill until ready to serve.

Right: Clockwise from top right, Cranberry and Apple Juice, Citrus Shake, Banana and Strawberry Smoothie, Zingy Vegetable Juice.

Cranberry juice: Energy 141kcal/598kJ; Protein 0g; Carbohydrate 34g, of which sugars 12g; Fat 0g, of which saturates 0g; Cholesterol 0mg; Calcium 5mg; Fibre 2g; Sodium 4mg.
Vegetable juice: Energy 202kcal/860kJ; Protein 3g; Carbohydrate 49g, of which sugars 42g; Fat 1g, of which saturates 0g; Cholesterol 0mg; Calcium 63mg; Fibre 7g; Sodium 88mg.

Griddled Pineapple and Mango on Toasted Panettone with Vanilla Yogurt

GRIDDLING CONCENTRATES the sweetness of the pineapple and mango, giving a caramel flavour that is complemented by the vanilla yogurt.

INGREDIENTS

1 large pineapple
1 large mango
25g/1oz/2 tbsp unsalted butter, melted
4 thick slices panettone

For the vanilla yogurt

250g/9oz/generous 1 cup Greek
* (US strained plain) yogurt*
30ml/2 tbsp clear honey
2.5ml/1/2 tsp ground cinnamon
a few drops vanilla extract

Serves 4

1 To prepare the pineapple, cut the bottom and the spiky top off the fruit. Stand the pineapple upright and cut off the skin, removing all the spikes, but as little of the flesh as possible. Lay the pineapple on its side and cut into quarters; remove the core if it is hard. Cut the pineapple into thick wedges.

HEALTH BENEFITS

Pineapple contains the powerful enzyme bromelain, which improves the digestion. It contains compounds that have an anti-inflammatory effect, so is good for people who suffer from arthritis. Pineapple has also been shown to reduce the incidence of blood clots and to ease bronchitis.

2 To prepare the mango, cut away the two thick sides of the mango as close to the stone (pit) as possible. Peel the mango, then cut the remaining flesh from the stone. Slice the fruit and discard the stone.

3 Heat a griddle pan over a medium heat. Add the pineapple and mango (you may need to do this in batches). Brush with melted butter, and cook for 8 minutes, turning once, until soft and slightly golden. Alternatively, heat the grill (broiler) to high and line the rack with foil. Place the pineapple and mango on the foil and grill (broil) for 4 minutes on each side.

4 Meanwhile, make the vanilla yogurt. Place the yogurt in a bowl with the honey, cinnamon and vanilla and stir well.

5 Lightly toast the panettone, then serve, topped with the pineapple and mango and accompanied by the vanilla yogurt.

Energy 208kcal/875kJ; Protein 5g; Carbohydrate 24g, of which sugars 24g; Fat 12g, of which saturates 7g; Cholesterol 14mg; Calcium 124mg; Fibre 3g; Sodium 49mg.

Oaty Pancakes with Caramel Bananas and Pecan Nuts

THESE PANCAKES ARE MORE LIKE drop scones than the classic thin French crêpes. Bananas and pecan nuts, cooked in maple syrup, make a sweet and delicious topping.

INGREDIENTS

75g/3oz/²/₃ cup plain (all-purpose) flour
50g/2oz/¹/₂ cup wholemeal
  (whole-wheat) flour
50g/2oz/¹/₂ cup rolled oats
5ml/1 tsp baking powder
pinch of salt
25g/1oz/2 tbsp caster (superfine) sugar
1 egg
15ml/1 tbsp sunflower oil, plus extra
  for frying
250ml/8fl oz/1 cup semi-skimmed
  (low-fat) milk

For the caramel bananas and
  pecan nuts
50g/2oz/4 tbsp butter
15ml/1 tbsp maple syrup
3 bananas, halved and quartered lengthways
25g/1oz/¹/₄ cup pecan nuts
Makes 5

1 To make the pancakes, mix together the plain and wholemeal flours, oats, baking powder, salt and sugar in a bowl.

HEALTH BENEFITS

• *Pecan nuts are one of the richest sources of vitamin B₆, which can help relieve the symptoms of PMS (pre-menstrual syndrome), as well as giving our immune system a boost.*
• *Bananas are a good source of energy, making them an excellent food to start the day. They also contain potassium, which is essential for the functioning of all the cells in our bodies.*
• *Rolled oats contain useful amounts of soluble fibre, which has been found to lower cholesterol levels in the body.*

2 Make a well in the centre of the flour mixture and add the egg, oil and a quarter of the milk. Mix well, then gradually add the rest of the milk to make a thick batter. Leave to rest for 20 minutes in the refrigerator.

4 To make the caramel bananas and pecan nuts, wipe out the frying pan and add the butter. Heat gently until the butter melts, then add the maple syrup and stir well. Add the bananas and pecan nuts to the pan.

3 Heat a large, heavy, lightly oiled frying pan. Using 30ml/2 tbsp of batter for each pancake, cook two or three pancakes at a time. Cook for 3 minutes on each side or until golden. Keep warm while you cook the remaining 7–8 pancakes.

5 Cook for about 4 minutes, turning once, or until the bananas have softened and the sauce has caramelized. To serve, place two pancakes on each of five warm plates and top with the caramel bananas and pecan nuts. Serve immediately.

Energy 367kcal/1539kJ; Protein 7g; Carbohydrate 49g, of which sugars 23g; Fat 17g, of which saturates 7g; Cholesterol 24mg; Calcium 112mg; Fibre 4g; Sodium 182mg.

Luxury Muesli

COMMERCIALLY MADE MUESLI can't compete with this home-made version. This combination of seeds, grains, nuts and dried fruits works particularly well, but you can alter the balance of ingredients, or substitute others, if you like.

INGREDIENTS

50g/2oz/¹/2 cup sunflower seeds
25g/1oz/¹/4 cup pumpkin seeds
115g/4oz/1 cup rolled oats
115g/4oz/heaped 1 cup wheat flakes
115g/4oz/heaped 1 cup barley flakes
115g/4oz/1 cup raisins
115g/4oz/1 cup chopped hazelnuts, roasted
115g/4oz/¹/2 cup unsulphured dried apricots, chopped
50g/2oz/2 cups dried apple slices, halved
25g/1oz/¹/3 cup desiccated (dry unsweetened shredded) coconut
Serves 4

1 Put the sunflower and pumpkin seeds in a dry frying pan and cook over a medium heat for 3 minutes until golden, tossing the seeds regularly to prevent them burning.

VARIATION

Serve the muesli (granola) in a long glass layered with raspberries and yogurt. Soak the muesli first in a little water or fruit juice in order to soften it slightly.

2 Mix the toasted seeds with the remaining ingredients and leave to cool. Store in an airtight container.

HEALTH BENEFITS

• Sunflower seeds are rich in vitamin E, which is thought to reduce the risk of heart disease.
• Apricots are high on the list of fruits that are considered likely to help prevent certain cancers, notably that of the lung.

Granola

HONEY-COATED NUTS, SEEDS AND oats, combined with sweet dried fruits, make an excellent and nutritious start to the day – without the additives often found in pre-packed cereals. Serve the granola with semi-skimmed milk or natural live yogurt and fresh fruit.

INGREDIENTS

115g/4oz/1 cup rolled oats
115g/4oz/1 cup jumbo oats
50g/2oz/¹/2 cup sunflower seeds
25g/1oz/2 tbsp sesame seeds
50g/2oz/¹/2 cup hazelnuts, roasted
25g/1oz/¹/4 cup almonds, roughly chopped
50ml/2fl oz/¹/4 cup sunflower oil
50ml/2fl oz/¹/4 cup clear honey
50g/2oz/¹/2 cup raisins
50g/2oz/¹/2 cup dried sweetened cranberries
Serves 4

1 Preheat the oven to 140°C/275°F/ Gas 1. Mix together the oats, seeds and nuts in a bowl.

HEALTH BENEFITS

Oats have been the focus of much publicity in recent years; numerous studies have shown that their soluble fibre content can significantly lower blood cholesterol levels. They also supply vitamins B and E, and iron.

2 Heat the oil and honey in a large pan until melted, then remove the pan from the heat. Add the oat mixture and stir well. Spread out on one or two baking sheets.

3 Bake for about 50 minutes until crisp, stirring occasionally to prevent the mixture sticking. Remove from the oven and mix in the raisins and cranberries. Leave to cool, then store in an airtight container.

Muesli: Energy 777kcal/3260kJ; Protein 21g; Carbohydrate 95g, of which sugars 16g; Fat 37g, of which saturates 6g; Cholesterol 0mg; Calcium 106mg; Fibre 13g; Sodium 404mg.
Granola: Energy 569kcal/2388kJ; Protein 16g; Carbohydrate 67g, of which sugars 20g; Fat 28g, of which saturates 2g; Cholesterol 0mg; Calcium 101mg; Fibre 7g; Sodium 31mg.

Kedgeree

THIS SPICY LENTIL and rice dish is a delicious variation of the original Indian version of kedgeree, *kitchiri*. You can serve it as it is, or topped with quartered hard-boiled eggs if you'd like to add more protein. It is delicious served on grilled large field mushrooms.

INGREDIENTS

50g/2oz/¼ cup dried red lentils, rinsed
1 bay leaf
225g/8oz/1 cup basmati rice, rinsed
4 cloves
50g/2oz/4 tbsp butter
5ml/1 tsp curry powder
2.5ml/½ tsp mild chilli powder
30ml/2 tbsp chopped flat leaf parsley
salt and freshly ground black pepper
4 hard-boiled eggs, quartered,
  to serve (optional)
Serves 4

1 Put the lentils in a pan, add the bay leaf and cover with cold water. Bring to the boil, skim off any foam, then reduce the heat. Cover and simmer for 25–30 minutes, until tender. Drain, then discard the bay leaf.

2 Meanwhile, place the rice in a pan and cover with 475ml/16fl oz/ 2 cups boiling water. Add the cloves and a generous pinch of salt. Cook, covered, for 10–15 minutes, until all the water is absorbed and the rice is tender. Discard the cloves.

3 Melt the butter over a gentle heat in a large frying pan, then add the curry and chilli powders and cook for 1 minute.

4 Stir in the lentils and rice and mix well until they are coated in the spiced butter. Season and cook for 1–2 minutes until heated through. Stir in the parsley and serve with the hard-boiled eggs, if using.

HEALTH BENEFITS

• *Lentils are especially good for the heart, because of their ability to lower cholesterol levels in the body. They also contain compounds that inhibit cancer and can regulate blood sugar levels.*
• *Rice is a high-carbohydrate food that provides sustained amounts of energy, making it a perfect food to start the day. Rice can also help to ease diarrhoea and stomach upsets.*

Griddled Tomatoes on Soda Bread

NOTHING COULD BE SIMPLER than this breakfast or brunch dish, yet a drizzle of olive oil and balsamic vinegar and shavings of Parmesan transform it into something really special.

INGREDIENTS

olive oil, for brushing and drizzling
6 tomatoes, thickly sliced
4 thick slices soda bread
balsamic vinegar, for drizzling
salt and freshly ground black pepper
shavings of Parmesan cheese, to serve
Serves 4

COOK'S TIP

Using a griddle pan reduces the amount of oil required for cooking the tomatoes and gives them a barbecued flavour.

1 Brush a griddle pan with olive oil and heat. Add the tomatoe slices and cook for 4–6 minutes, turning once, until softened and slightly blackened. Alternatively, heat a grill (broiler) to high and line the rack with foil. Grill (broil) the tomatoe slices for 4–6 minutes, turning once, until softened.

2 Meanwhile, lightly toast the soda bread. Place the tomatoes on top of the toast and drizzle each portion with a little olive oil and vinegar. Season to taste with salt and ground black pepper and serve immediately with thin shavings of Parmesan.

HEALTH BENEFITS

Numerous studies have shown that tomatoes are effective in preventing many forms of cancer, including lung, stomach and prostate cancer. This is probably explained by their antioxidant content, notably beta carotene and vitamins C and E. Antioxidants are also believed to prevent appendicitis.

Kedgeree: Energy 427kcal/1794kJ; Protein 15g; Carbohydrate 56g, of which sugars 0g; Fat 18g, of which saturates 8g; Cholesterol 258mg; Calcium 61mg; Fibre 3g; Sodium 209mg.
Tomatoes: Energy 218kcal/923kJ; Protein 6g; Carbohydrate 40g, of which sugars 7g; Fat 5g, of which saturates 1g; Cholesterol 0mg; Calcium 102mg; Fibre 4g; Sodium 287mg.

Porridge with Date Purée and Pistachio Nuts

FULL OF VALUABLE FIBRE and nutrients, dates give a natural sweet flavour to this warming winter breakfast dish.

INGREDIENTS

250g/9oz/scant 2 cups fresh dates
225g/8oz/2 cups rolled oats
475ml/16fl oz/2 cups semi-skimmed (low-fat) milk
pinch of salt
50g/2oz/1/2 cup shelled, unsalted pistachio nuts, roughly chopped

Serves 4

HEALTH BENEFITS

Oats have a reputation for being warming foods due to their fat and protein content, which is greater than that of most other grains. They also provide energy and are one of the most nutritious cereals.

1 First make the date purée. Halve the dates and remove the stones (pits) and stems. Cover the dates with boiling water and leave to soak for about 30 minutes, until softened. Strain, reserving 90ml/6 tbsp of the soaking water.

2 Remove the skin from the dates and place them in a food processor with the reserved soaking water. Process to a smooth purée.

3 Place the oats in a pan with the milk, 300ml/1/2 pint/1 1/4 cups water and salt. Bring to the boil, then reduce the heat and simmer for 4–5 minutes until cooked and creamy, stirring frequently.

4 Serve the porridge in warm serving bowls, topped with a spoonful of the date purée and sprinkled with chopped pistachio nuts.

Apricot and Ginger Compote

FRESH GINGER ADDS WARMTH to this stimulating breakfast dish and complements the flavour of the plump, juicy apricots.

INGREDIENTS

350g/12oz/1 1/2 cups dried unsulphured apricots
4cm/1 1/2in piece fresh root ginger, finely chopped
200g/7oz/scant 1 cup natural (plain) live yogurt or low-fat fromage frais

Serves 4

COOK'S TIP

Fresh ginger freezes well. Peel the root and store it in a plastic bag in the freezer. You can grate it from frozen, then return the root to the freezer until the next time you need it for a recipe.

1 Cover the apricots with boiling water, then leave to soak overnight.

2 Place the apricots and their soaking water in a pan, add the ginger and bring to the boil. Reduce the heat and simmer for 10 minutes until the fruit is soft and plump and the water becomes syrupy. Strain the apricots, reserving the syrup, and discard the ginger.

3 Serve the apricots warm with the reserved syrup and a spoonful of yogurt or fromage frais.

HEALTH BENEFITS

• *In Chinese medicine, ginger is revered for its health-giving properties. It is anti-spasmodic, aids digestion and can help treat colds and flu.*
• *Of all the dried fruits, apricots are the richest source of iron. They also provide calcium, phosphorus and vitamins A and C.*
• *Live yogurt can relieve gastrointestinal disorders by replacing valuable bacteria in the gut. The lactic acids, which yogurt contains, can help to regulate bowel function and they have bacterial properties that can prevent infection. Yogurt also boosts our immune system.*

Porridge: Energy 495kcal/2085kJ; Protein 16g; Carbohydrate 68g, of which sugars 26g; Fat 20g, of which saturates 3g; Cholesterol 7mg; Calcium 214mg; Fibre 6g; Sodium 195mg.
Compote: Energy 181kcal/772kJ; Protein 6g; Carbohydrate 37g, of which sugars 36g; Fat 2g, of which saturates 1g; Cholesterol 6mg; Calcium 165mg; Fibre 16g; Sodium 53g.

Chive Scrambled Eggs in Brioches

AN INDULGENT, BUT DELICIOUS, breakfast that should be reserved for Sundays or special occasions.

INGREDIENTS

115g/4oz/¹/2 cup unsalted butter
75g/3oz/generous 1 cup brown cap
  (cremini) mushrooms, finely sliced
4 individual brioches
8 eggs
15ml/1 tbsp snipped fresh chives,
  plus extra to garnish
salt and freshly ground black pepper

Serves 4

I Preheat the oven to 180°C/350°F/
Gas 4. Place a quarter of the butter
in a frying pan and heat until melted.
Fry the mushrooms for 3 minutes
or until soft, then set aside and
keep warm.

COOK'S TIP

*Timing and temperature are crucial for
perfect scrambled eggs. When cooked
for too long over too high a heat, eggs
become dry and crumbly; vice versa,
and they are sloppy and unappealing.*

HEALTH BENEFITS

*Eggs are a good source of protein,
selenium (which is an efficient antioxidant), iron, zinc and the complete range
of B vitamins. However, although they are
low in saturated fat, they are high in
cholesterol, so should be eaten only
occasionally and in moderation.*

2 Slice the tops off the brioches,
then scoop out the centres and
discard. Put the brioches and lids on a
baking sheet and bake for 5 minutes
until hot and slightly crisp.

3 Meanwhile, beat the eggs lightly
and season to taste. Heat the
remaining butter in a heavypan over
a gentle heat. When the butter has
melted and is foaming slightly, add
the eggs. Using a wooden spoon, stir
constantly, to ensure the egg does
not stick.

4 Continue to stir gently until about
three-quarters of the egg is
semi-solid and creamy – this should
take 2–3 minutes. Remove the pan
from the heat – the egg will continue
to cook in the heat from the pan –
then stir in the snipped chives.

5 To serve, spoon a little of the
mushrooms into the bottom of
each brioche and top with the
scrambled eggs. Sprinkle with extra
chives, balance the brioche lids on top
and serve immediately.

Energy 533kcal/2218kJ; Protein 17.9g; Carbohydrate 31.9g, of which sugars 9.9g; Fat 38.2g, of which saturates 19.2g; Cholesterol 443mg; Calcium 137mg; Fibre 1.7g; Sodium 507mg.

Cannellini Bean and Rosemary Bruschetta

MORE BRUNCH THAN BREAKFAST, this dish is a sophisticated version of beans on toast.

INGREDIENTS

150g/5oz/²⁄₃ cup dried cannellini beans
5 tomatoes
45ml/3 tbsp olive oil, plus extra for drizzling
2 sun-dried tomatoes in oil, drained and
    finely chopped
1 garlic clove, crushed
30ml/2 tbsp chopped fresh rosemary
salt and freshly ground black pepper
a handful of fresh basil leaves, to garnish

To serve

12 slices Italian-style bread, such as ciabatta
1 large garlic clove, halved

Serves 4

1 Place the beans in a large bowl and cover with water. Leave to soak overnight. Drain and rinse the beans, then place in a pan and cover with fresh water. Bring to the boil and boil rapidly for 10 minutes. Reduce the heat and simmer for 50–60 minutes or until tender. Drain and set aside.

2 Meanwhile, place the tomatoes in a bowl, cover with boiling water, leave for 30 seconds, then peel, seed and chop the flesh. Heat the oil in a frying pan, add the fresh and sun-dried tomatoes, garlic and rosemary. Cook for 2 minutes until the tomatoes begin to break down and soften.

3 Add the tomato mixture to the cannellini beans, season to taste and mix well.

HEALTH BENEFITS

• *Cannellini beans are high in protein and low in fat. They are also a valuable source of B vitamins and minerals.*
• *Rosemary is reputed to have many healing qualities. It is said to alleviate headaches, to improve the circulation and to ease rheumatism. Use fresh rosemary if possible, as dried will have lost most of its beneficial oils.*

4 Rub the cut sides of the bread slices with the garlic clove, then toast lightly. Spoon the cannellini bean mixture on top of the toast. Sprinkle with basil leaves and drizzle with a little extra olive oil before serving.

COOK'S TIP

Canned beans can be used instead of dried; use 275g/10oz/2 cups drained, canned beans and add to the tomato mixture in step 3. If the beans are canned in brine, then rinse and drain them well before use.

Energy 499kcal/2111kJ; Protein 20.2g; Carbohydrate 84.3g, of which sugars 8.5g; Fat 11.3g, of which saturates 1.7g; Cholesterol 0mg; Calcium 195mg; Fibre 8.1g; Sodium 749mg.

Soups
and
Light Meals

Warming, nutritious and sustaining, home-made soup is the perfect health food. There's nothing simpler to make, as quantities are seldom crucial and timing is as flexible as you need it to be. For families on the fast track, having a big pot of soup simmering on the stove means that everyone can enjoy the same nourishing meal, even if they all come in at different times. Soup is a wonderful vehicle for vegetables, from potatoes to peppers, and many children who scorn salads will happily accept the soft option – a puréed vegetable soup. This chapter introduces soups for all seasons, including Roasted Root Vegetable Soup, Gazpacho with Avocado Salsa and Spiced Red Lentil and Coconut Soup. The selection of light meals is equally varied and ranges from a picnic loaf stuffed with courgettes (zucchini), garlic mushrooms, cheese and pesto to the unusual yet irresistible Thai Tempeh Cakes with Sweet Dipping Sauce.

Gazpacho with Avocado Salsa

TOMATOES, CUCUMBER AND peppers form the basis of this classic, chilled soup. Add a spoonful of chunky, fresh avocado salsa and a scattering of croutons, and serve for a light lunch on a warm summer's day.

INGREDIENTS

2 slices day-old bread
1kg/2¼lb tomatoes
1 cucumber
1 red (bell) pepper, seeded and chopped
1 green chilli, seeded and chopped
2 garlic cloves, chopped
30ml/2 tbsp extra virgin olive oil
juice of 1 lime and 1 lemon
a few drops Tabasco sauce
600ml/1 pint/2½ cups chilled water
salt and freshly ground black pepper
a handful of basil leaves, to garnish
8 ice cubes, to serve

For the croûtons

2 slices day-old bread, crusts removed
1 garlic clove, halved
15ml/1 tbsp olive oil

For the avocado salsa

1 ripe avocado
5ml/1 tsp lemon juice
2.5cm/1in piece cucumber, diced
½ red chilli, finely chopped
Serves 4

1 Soak the bread in 150ml/¼ pint/ ⅔ cup of water for 5 minutes.

2 Meanwhile, place the tomatoes in a bowl and cover with boiling water. Leave for 30 seconds, then peel, seed and chop the flesh.

HEALTH BENEFITS

The powerful combination of fresh raw vegetables, garlic, lemon and lime juice, olive oil and chilli boosts the immune system and the circulation, and helps to cleanse the body.

3 Peel the cucumber, cut it in half lengthways and scoop out the seeds with a teaspoon. Discard the seeds and chop the flesh.

4 Place the bread, tomatoes, cucumber, red pepper, chilli, garlic, olive oil, citrus juices and Tabasco in a food processor or blender with 450ml/¾ pint/scant 2 cups chilled water and blend until well combined but still chunky. Season to taste and chill for 2–3 hours.

5 To make the croûtons, rub the slices of bread with the garlic clove. Cut the bread into cubes and place in a plastic bag with the olive oil. Seal the bag and shake until the bread cubes are coated with the oil.

6 Heat a large non-stick frying pan and fry the croûtons over a medium heat until crisp and golden.

7 Just before serving, make the avocado salsa. Halve the avocado, remove the stone (pit), then peel and dice. Toss the avocado in the lemon juice to prevent it browning, then mix with the cucumber and chilli.

8 Ladle the soup into bowls, add the ice cubes, and top with a spoonful of avocado salsa. Garnish with the basil and hand round the croûtons separately.

Energy 164kcal/685kJ; Protein 3.5g; Carbohydrate 16.6g, of which sugars 7.9g; Fat 9.7g, of which saturates 1.7g; Cholesterol 0mg; Calcium 40mg; Fibre 3.1g; Sodium 112mg.

Japanese-style Noodle Soup

THIS DELICATE, FRAGRANT SOUP is flavoured with just a hint of chilli. It is best served as a light lunch or as a first course. According to Japanese etiquette, slurping while eating the soup is a sign of appreciation.

INGREDIENTS

45ml/3 tbsp mugi miso
200g/7oz/scant 2 cups udon noodles,
  soba noodles or Chinese noodles
30ml/2 tbsp sake or dry sherry
15ml/1 tbsp rice or wine vinegar
45ml/3 tbsp Japanese soy sauce
115g/4oz asparagus tips or mangetouts
  (snow peas), thinly sliced diagonally
50g/2oz/scant 1 cup shiitake mushrooms,
  stalks removed and thinly sliced
1 carrot, sliced into julienne strips
3 spring onions (scallions), sliced diagonally
salt and freshly ground black pepper
5ml/1 tsp dried chilli flakes, to serve
Serves 4

1 Bring 1 litre/1¾ pints/4 cups water to the boil in a pan. Pour 150ml/¼ pint/⅔ cup of the boiling water over the miso and stir until dissolved, then set aside.

2 Meanwhile, bring another large pan of lightly salted water to the boil, add the noodles and cook according to the packet instructions until just tender.

3 Drain the noodles in a colander. Rinse under cold running water, then drain again.

4 Add the sake or sherry, rice or wine vinegar and soy sauce to the pan of boiling water. Boil gently for 3 minutes or until the alcohol has evaporated, then reduce the heat and stir in the miso mixture.

5 Add the asparagus or mangetouts, mushrooms, carrot and spring onions, and simmer for about 2 minutes until the vegetables are just tender. Season to taste.

6 Divide the noodles among four warm bowls and pour the soup over the top. Serve immediately, sprinkled with the chilli flakes.

HEALTH BENEFITS

Miso shares many of the health qualities of soya. It has shown itself to be effective against stomach cancer, which no doubt stems from its antioxidant qualities.

Energy 232kcal/972kJ; Protein 6g; Carbohydrate 49g, of which sugars 4g; Fat 1g, of which saturates 0g; Cholesterol 0mg; Calcium 40mg; Fibre 1g; Sodium 1225mg.

Italian Pea and Basil Soup

PLENTY OF CRUSTY COUNTRY BREAD is a must with this fresh-tasting soup.

INGREDIENTS

75ml/5 tbsp olive oil
2 large onions, chopped
1 celery stick, chopped
1 carrot, chopped
1 garlic clove, finely chopped
400g/14oz/3½ cups petit pois (baby peas)
900ml/1½ pints/3¾ cups vegetable stock
25g/1oz/1 cup fresh basil leaves, roughly torn, plus extra to garnish
salt and freshly ground black pepper
freshly grated Parmesan cheese, to serve

Serves 4

VARIATION

Use mint or a mixture of parsley, mint and chives in place of the basil.

1 Heat the oil in a large pan and add the onions, celery, carrot and garlic. Cover the pan and cook over a low heat for 45 minutes or until the vegetables are soft, stirring occasionally to prevent the vegetables sticking.

2 Add the peas and stock to the pan and bring to the boil. Reduce the heat, add the basil and seasoning, then simmer for 10 minutes.

3 Spoon the soup into a food processor or blender and process until the soup is smooth. Ladle into warm bowls, sprinkle with grated Parmesan and garnish with basil.

HEALTH BENEFITS

As freezing usually takes place soon after picking, frozen peas may have a higher vitamin C content than fresh.

Spiced Red Lentil and Coconut Soup

HOT, SPICY AND RICHLY FLAVOURED, this substantial soup is almost a meal in itself. If you are really hungry, serve with chunks of warmed naan bread or thick slices of toast.

INGREDIENTS

30ml/2 tbsp sunflower oil
2 red onions, finely chopped
1 bird's eye chilli, seeded and finely sliced
2 garlic cloves, chopped
2.5cm/1in piece fresh lemon grass, outer layers removed and inside finely sliced
200g/7oz/scant 1 cup red lentils, rinsed
5ml/1 tsp ground coriander
5ml/1 tsp paprika
400ml/14fl oz/1²/3 cups coconut milk
juice of 1 lime
3 spring onions (scallions), chopped
20g/³/4oz/scant 1 cup fresh coriander (cilantro), finely chopped
salt and freshly ground black pepper

Serves 4

1 Heat the oil in a large pan and add the onions, chilli, garlic and lemon grass. Cook gently for 5 minutes or until the onions have softened, stirring occasionally.

HEALTH BENEFITS

Lentils provide a rich supply of minerals, including iron and calcium, as well as folic acid. The latter is recommended for pregnant women as it can lower the risk of spina bifida in the unborn child.

2 Add the lentils and spices. Pour in the coconut milk and 900ml/1½ pints/3¾ cups water, and stir. Bring to the boil, stir, then reduce the heat and simmer for 40–45 minutes or until the lentils are soft and mushy.

3 Pour in the lime juice and add the spring onions and fresh coriander, reserving a little of each for the garnish. Season, then ladle into bowls. Garnish with the reserved spring onions and chopped coriander.

Pea: Energy 261kcal/1078kJ; Protein 8.7g; Carbohydrate 22.9g, of which sugars 10.9g; Fat 15.7g, of which saturates 2.3g; Cholesterol 0mg; Calcium 73mg; Fibre 7.3g; Sodium 16mg.
Lentil: Energy 265Kcal/1119kJ; Protein 14g; Carbohydrate 40g, of which sugars 11g; Fat 7g, of which saturates 1g; Cholesterol 0mg; Calcium 84mg; Fibre 3.7g; Sodium 0.4g.

Hot-and-sour Soup

THIS LIGHT AND INVIGORATING soup originates from Thailand. It is best served at the beginning of a Thai meal to stimulate the appetite.

INGREDIENTS

2 carrots
900ml/1¹/2 pints/3³/4 cups vegetable stock
2 Thai chillies, seeded and finely sliced
2 lemon grass stalks, outer leaves removed
    and each stalk cut into 3 pieces
4 kaffir lime leaves
2 garlic cloves, finely chopped
4 spring onions (scallions), finely sliced
5ml/1 tsp sugar
juice of 1 lime
45ml/3 tbsp chopped fresh
    coriander (cilantro)
salt
130g/4¹/2oz/1 cup Japanese
    tofu, sliced

Serves 4

1 To make carrot flowers, cut each carrot in half crossways, then, using a sharp knife, cut four v-shaped channels lengthways. Slice the carrots into thin rounds and set aside.

COOK'S TIP

Kaffir lime leaves have a distinctive citrus flavour. The fresh leaves can be bought from Asian stores, and some supermarkets now sell them dried.

2 Pour the stock into a large pan. Reserve 2.5ml/¹/2 tsp of the chillies and add the rest to the pan with the lemon grass, lime leaves, garlic and half the spring onions. Bring to the boil, then reduce the heat and simmer for 20 minutes. Strain the stock and discard the flavourings.

3 Return the stock to the pan, add the reserved chillies and spring onions, the sugar, lime juice, coriander and salt to taste.

4 Simmer for 5 minutes, then add the carrot flowers and tofu, and cook for a further 2 minutes until the carrot is just tender. Serve hot.

HEALTH BENEFITS

Hot spices, including chillies, are good for the respiratory system. They help to relieve congestion and may, as a result, soothe the symptoms of colds, flu and hayfever. Chillies encourage the brain to release endorphins, which increase the sensation of pleasure, and so they have been described as aphrodisiacs.

Energy 56kcal/234kJ; Protein 4g; Carbohydrate 6g, of which sugars 5g; Fat 2g, of which saturates 0g; Cholesterol 0mg; Calcium 196mg; Fibre 1g; Sodium 434mg.

Roasted Root Vegetable Soup

ROASTING THE VEGETABLES GIVES this winter soup a wonderful depth of flavour. You can use other vegetables, if you wish, or adapt the quantities depending on what's in season.

INGREDIENTS

50ml/2fl oz/¹/4 cup olive oil
1 small butternut squash, peeled, seeded
    and cubed
2 carrots, cut into thick rounds
1 large parsnip, cubed
1 small swede (rutabaga), cubed
2 leeks, thickly sliced
1 onion, quartered
3 bay leaves
4 thyme sprigs, plus extra to garnish
3 rosemary sprigs
1.2 litres/2 pints/5 cups vegetable stock
salt and freshly ground black pepper
sour cream, to serve

Serves 6

1 Preheat the oven to 200°C/400°F/ Gas 6. Put the olive oil into a large bowl. Add the prepared vegetables and toss until coated in the oil.

2 Spread out the vegetables in a single layer on one large or two small baking sheets. Tuck the bay leaves and thyme and rosemary sprigs amongst the vegetables.

COOK'S TIP

Dried herbs can be used in place of fresh; sprinkle 2.5ml/¹/2 tsp of each type over the vegetables in step 2.

3 Roast for 50 minutes until tender, turning the vegetables occasionally to make sure they brown evenly all over. Remove from the oven, discard the herbs and transfer the vegetables to a large pan.

HEALTH BENEFITS

This nutritious soup is packed with health-giving vegetables. Butternut squash is particularly high in beta carotene and potassium, which is essential for the functioning of the cells, nerves and muscles. Carrots also contain a high level of beta carotene and are effective detoxifiers.

4 Pour the stock into the pan and bring to the boil. Reduce the heat, season to taste, then simmer for 10 minutes. Transfer the soup to a food processor or blender (or use a hand blender) and process for a few minutes until thick and smooth.

5 Return the soup to the pan to heat through. Season and serve with a swirl of sour cream. Garnish each serving with a sprig of thyme.

Energy 159kcal/662kJ; Protein 3g; Carbohydrate 16g, of which sugars 11g; Fat 10g, of which saturates 1g; Cholesterol 0mg; Calcium 87mg; Fibre 5g; Sodium 413mg.

Jerusalem Artichoke Soup with Gruyère Toasts

SMALL, KNOBBLY JERUSALEM artichokes have a delicious, mild, nutty flavour. They make a remarkably good, creamy soup, which is delicious served with crunchy, grilled Gruyère and French bread toasts.

INGREDIENTS

30ml/2 tbsp olive oil
1 large onion, chopped
1 garlic clove, chopped
1 celery stick, chopped
675g/1 1/2lb Jerusalem artichokes, peeled or scrubbed, and chopped
1.2 litres/2 pints/5 cups vegetable stock
300ml/1/2 pint/1 1/4 cups semi-skimmed (low-fat) milk
salt and freshly ground black pepper

To serve
8 slices French bread
115g/4oz/1 cup Gruyère cheese, grated
Serves 4–6

1 Heat the butter and oil in a large pan. Add the onion, garlic and celery, and cook over a medium heat for 5 minutes or until softened, stirring occasionally. Add the prepared Jerusalem artichokes and cook for a further 5 minutes.

2 Add the stock and seasoning, and bring the soup to the boil. Reduce the heat and simmer for 20–25 minutes, stirring occasionally, until the artichokes are tender.

3 Transfer the soup to a food processor or blender (or use a hand blender) and process for a few minutes until smooth. Return the soup to the pan, stir in the milk and heat through gently for 2 minutes.

4 To make the Gruyère toasts, heat the grill (broiler) to high. Lightly grill (broil) the bread on one side, then sprinkle the untoasted side with the Gruyère. Grill until the cheese melts and is golden.

5 Ladle the soup into bowls and top with the Gruyère toasts.

COOK'S TIP

To preserve soluble nutrients, scrub the Jerusalem artichokes rather than peel them.

HEALTH BENEFITS

High in fibre and low in fat, jerusalem artichokes also contain valuable amounts of vitamin C

Energy 284kcal/1227kJ; Protein 12g; Carbohydrate 33g, of which sugars 7g; Fat 13g, of which saturates 5g; Cholesterol 22mg; Calcium 321mg; Fibre 2g; Sodium 714mg.

Borlotti Bean and Pasta Soup

A COMPLETE MEAL IN A BOWL, this is a version of a classic Italian soup. Traditionally, the person who finds the bay leaf is honoured with a kiss from the cook.

INGREDIENTS

1 onion, chopped
1 celery stick, chopped
2 carrots, chopped
75ml/5 tbsp olive oil
1 bay leaf
1 glass white wine (optional)
1.2 litres/2 pints/5 cups vegetable stock
400g/14oz/3 cups canned
   chopped tomatoes
175g/6oz/1 1/2 cups pasta shapes,
   such as farfalle or conchiglie
400g/14oz/3 cups canned borlotti
   beans, drained
250g/9oz spinach, washed and thick
   stalks removed
salt and freshly ground black pepper
50g/2oz/2/3 cup freshly grated Parmesan
   cheese, to serve

Serves 4

1 Place the chopped onion, celery and carrots in a large pan with the olive oil. Cook gently over a medium heat for 5 minutes or until the vegetables soften but do not brown, stirring occasionally.

COOK'S TIP

Other pulses, such as cannellini beans, haricot (navy) beans or chickpeas, are equally good in this soup.

2 Add the bay leaf, wine, if using, stock and tomatoes and bring to the boil. Reduce the heat and simmer for 10 minutes until the vegetables are just tender.

3 Add the pasta and beans and bring the soup back to the boil, then simmer for 8 minutes until the pasta is *al dente*. Stir frequently to prevent the pasta sticking.

4 Season to taste, add the spinach and cook for a further 2 minutes. Serve, sprinkled with the Parmesan.

HEALTH BENEFITS

• *Spinach contains many valuable nutrients and is rich in folates, vitamin C, beta carotene, zinc, potassium and iron. Spinach, like rhubarb, contains oxalic acid, which limits the absorption of iron and calcium in the body. However, the vitamin C content found in spinach and other vegetables may temper the effects of the oxalic acid to some extent. In natural medicine, spinach is often prescribed to treat constipation, arthritis and high blood pressure.*
• *Onions are considered to have a powerful antibiotic effect and they are a strong diuretic.*

Energy 515kcal/2157kJ; Protein 19g; Carbohydrate 57g, of which sugars 11g; Fat 25g, of which saturates 5g; Cholesterol 12mg; Calcium 295mg; Fibre 10g; Sodium 836mg.

Aubergine, Smoked Mozzarella and Basil Rolls

SLICES OF GRILLED AUBERGINE are stuffed with smoked mozzarella, tomato and fresh basil to make an attractive hors-d'oeuvre, or a light lunch if served with a green salad. The rolls are also good barbecued.

INGREDIENTS

1 large aubergine (eggplant)
45ml/3 tbsp olive oil, plus extra for
    drizzling (optional)
165g/5¹/₂oz smoked mozzarella cheese,
    cut into 8 slices
2 plum tomatoes, each cut into 4 slices
8 large basil leaves
balsamic vinegar, for drizzling (optional)
salt and freshly ground black pepper
Serves 4

1 Cut the aubergine lengthways into 10 thin slices and discard the two outermost slices. Sprinkle the slices with salt and leave for 20 minutes. Rinse, then pat dry with kitchen paper.

2 Preheat the grill (broiler) and line the rack with foil. Place the dried aubergine slices on the grill rack. Brush with oil. Grill (broil) for 8–10 minutes until tender and golden, turning once.

3 Remove the aubergine slices from the grill, then place a slice of mozzarella, a slice of tomato and a basil leaf in the centre of each and season to taste. Fold the aubergine over the filling and cook seam-side down under the grill until heated through and the mozzarella begins to melt. Serve drizzled with olive oil and a little balsamic vinegar, if using.

HEALTH BENEFITS

Aubergines (eggplants) are low in calories but frying will dramatically increase their calorific value. Salting the aubergine first not only draws out any bitter juices, it also makes the flesh denser, so that less fat is absorbed during cooking. Aubergines contain bioflavonoids, which help to prevent strokes and haemorrhages.

Creamy Lemon Puy Lentils

TINY, GREEN PUY LENTILS HAVE a very good flavour and, combined with lemon juice and crème fraîche, make a delicious, slightly tangy base for poached eggs.

INGREDIENTS

250g/9oz/generous 1 cup Puy lentils
1 bay leaf
30ml/2 tbsp olive oil
4 spring onions (scallions), sliced
2 large garlic cloves, chopped
15ml/1 tbsp Dijon mustard
finely grated rind and juice of 1 large lemon
4 plum tomatoes, seeded and diced
4 eggs
60ml/4 tbsp crème fraîche
salt and freshly ground black pepper
30ml/2 tbsp chopped fresh flat leaf parsley,
    to garnish
Serves 4

1 Put the lentils and bay leaf in a pan, cover with cold water, and bring to the boil. Reduce the heat and simmer for 25 minutes or until tender. Drain. When the lentils are almost ready, poach the eggs in a pan of barely simmering, salted water.

2 Heat the oil and fry the spring onions and garlic for 1 minute or until softened.

3 Add the Dijon mustard, lemon rind and juice to the spring onion mixture, and mix well. Stir in the tomatoes and seasoning, then cook gently for 1–2 minutes until the tomatoes are heated through but still retain their shape. Add a little water if the mixture becomes too dry.

4 Stir in the lentils and crème fraîche, remove the bay leaf, and heat through for 1 minute. Top each portion with a poached egg, and sprinkle with parsley.

HEALTH BENEFITS

Studies have shown that lentils may help prevent heart disease and cancer, and lower cholesterol levels.

Aubergine: Energy 230kcal/953kJ; Protein 9g; Carbohydrate 4g, of which sugars 3g; Fat 20g, of which saturates 7g; Cholesterol 24mg; Calcium 165mg; Fibre 3g; Sodium 169mg.
Lentils: Energy 429kcal/1799kJ; Protein 24g; Carbohydrate 38g, of which sugars 4g; Fat 21g, of which saturates 7g; Cholesterol 249mg; Calcium 100mg; Fibre 7g; Sodium 320mg.

Courgette, Mushroom and Pesto Panino

GRILLED COURGETTES are layered with garlic mushrooms, creamy Italian Taleggio cheese and pesto in this very tasty picnic loaf. Use a round, crusty, country-style Italian or French loaf and chill overnight after filling, to allow the flavours to mingle together.

INGREDIENTS

1 medium country-style loaf
3 courgettes (zucchini), sliced lengthways
45ml/3 tbsp olive oil
250g/9oz/3²/3 cups brown cap (cremini)
    mushrooms, thickly sliced
1 garlic clove, chopped
5ml/1 tsp dried oregano
45ml/3 tbsp pesto
250g/9oz Taleggio cheese, rind removed
    and sliced
50g/2oz/2 cups green salad leaves
salt and freshly ground black pepper

Serves 6

1 Slice off the top third of the loaf and remove the inside of both the lid and base, leaving a thickness of about 1cm/¹/₂in around the edge. (Use the inside of the loaf to make breadcrumbs for another dish.)

2 Preheat the grill (broiler) to high and line the grill rack with foil. Brush the courgettes with 15ml/1 tbsp of the olive oil and grill (broil) for 8–10 minutes, turning them occasionally, until tender and browned.

3 Meanwhile, heat the remaining oil in a frying pan. Add the mushrooms, garlic and oregano and fry for 3 minutes.

4 Arrange half of the courgettes in the base of the loaf, then spread with 25ml/1¹/₂ tbsp of the pesto. Top with half the cheese and salad leaves and all the mushroom mixture.

5 Add one more layer each of the remaining cheese, salad leaves and courgettes. Spread the remaining pesto over the inside of the bread lid and place it on top.

6 Press the lid down gently, wrap in clear film (plastic wrap) and leave to cool. Chill overnight or at least for a few hours. Serve cut into wedges.

HEALTH BENEFITS

• Courgettes (zucchini) provide vitamin C, beta carotene and folates.
• Garlic is highly valued, particularly for its ability to detoxify the body and strengthen the immune system.

Energy 446kcal/1860kJ; Protein 24g; Carbohydrate 27g, of which sugars 3g; Fat 28g, of which saturates 11g; Cholesterol 44mg; Calcium 575mg; Fibre 3g; Sodium 645mg.

Coriander Omelette Parcels with Oriental Vegetables

STIR-FRIED VEGETABLES in black bean sauce make a remarkably good omelette filling, which is quick and easy to prepare.

INGREDIENTS

130g/4¹/₂oz broccoli, cut into small florets
30ml/2 tbsp groundnut (peanut) oil
1cm/¹/₂in piece fresh root ginger, grated
1 large garlic clove, crushed
2 red chillies, seeded and finely sliced
4 spring onions (scallions), sliced diagonally
175g/6oz/3 cups pak choi (bok choy), finely shredded
50g/2oz/2 cups fresh coriander (cilantro) leaves, plus extra to garnish
115g/4oz/¹/₂ cup beansprouts
45ml/3 tbsp black bean sauce
4 eggs
salt and freshly ground black pepper
Serves 4

1 Blanch the broccoli in boiling salted water for 2 minutes, drain, then refresh under cold running water.

2 Meanwhile, heat 15ml/1 tbsp of the oil in a frying pan or wok. Add the ginger, garlic and half of the chilli and stir-fry for 1 minute. Add the spring onions, broccoli and pak choi, and stir-fry for 2 minutes more, tossing the vegetables continuously to prevent sticking and to cook them evenly.

3 Chop three-quarters of the coriander and add to the frying pan or wok. Add the beansprouts and stir-fry for 1 minute, then add the black bean sauce and heat through for 1 minute more. Remove the pan from the heat and keep warm.

HEALTH BENEFITS

Pak choi (bok choy) is a member of the brassica family. People who regularly eat this type of green leafy vegetable have a lower risk of developing certain cancers. They also assist in the treatment of asthma, gout and constipation.

4 Mix the eggs lightly with a fork and season well. Heat a little of the remaining oil in a small frying pan and add a quarter of the beaten egg. Swirl the egg until it covers the base of the pan, then scatter over a quarter of the reserved coriander leaves. Cook until set, then turn out the omelette on to a plate and keep warm while you make three more omelettes, adding more oil, when necessary.

5 Spoon the vegetable stir-fry on to the omelettes and roll up. Cut in half crossways and serve garnished with coriander leaves and chilli.

Energy 202kcal/838kJ; Protein 12g; Carbohydrate 5g, of which sugars 4g; Fat 15g, of which saturates 3g; Cholesterol 232mg; Calcium 121mg; Fibre 2g; Sodium 381mg.

Thai Tempeh Cakes with Sweet Dipping Sauce

MADE FROM SOYA BEANS, TEMPEH is similar to tofu but has a nuttier taste. Here, it is combined with a fragrant blend of lemon grass, coriander and ginger and formed into small patties.

INGREDIENTS

1 lemon grass stalk, outer leaves removed
   and inside finely chopped
2 garlic cloves, chopped
2 spring onions (scallions), finely chopped
2 shallots, finely chopped
2 chillies, seeded and chopped
2.5cm/1in piece fresh root ginger, chopped
60ml/4 tbsp chopped fresh coriander
   (cilantro), plus extra to garnish
250g/9oz/2 1/4 cups tempeh, defrosted
   if frozen, sliced
15ml/1 tbsp lime juice
5ml/1 tsp caster (superfine) sugar
45ml/3 tbsp plain (all-purpose) flour
1 large egg, lightly beaten
vegetable oil, for frying
salt and freshly ground black pepper

For the dipping sauce
45ml/3 tbsp mirin
45ml/3 tbsp white wine vinegar
2 spring onions (scallions), finely sliced
15ml/1 tbsp sugar
2 chillies, finely chopped
30ml/2 tbsp chopped fresh
   coriander (cilantro)
large pinch of salt
Makes 8 Cakes

HEALTH BENEFITS

Although tempeh does not contain quite the same levels of calcium, iron and B vitamins as tofu, in many ways it is healthier. It is made from fermented whole soya beans and the mould used in the fermentation process is said to boost the immune system and free the body of harmful toxins.

1 To make the dipping sauce, mix together the mirin, vinegar, spring onions, sugar, chillies, coriander and salt in a small bowl and set aside.

2 Place the lemon grass, garlic, spring onions, shallots, chillies, ginger and coriander in a food processor or blender, then process to a coarse paste. Add the tempeh, lime juice and sugar, then blend until combined. Add the seasoning, flour and egg. Process again until the mixture forms a coarse, sticky paste.

3 Take 1 heaped serving-spoonful of the tempeh mixture at a time and form into rounds with your hands – the mixture will be quite sticky.

4 Heat enough oil to cover the base of a large frying pan. Fry the tempeh cakes for 5–6 minutes, turning once, until golden.

5 Drain the tempeh cakes on kitchen paper and serve warm with the dipping sauce, garnished with the reserved coriander.

Energy 156kcal/653kJ; Protein 8g; Carbohydrate 16g, of which sugars 8g; Fat 7g, of which saturates 1g; Cholesterol 0mg; Calcium 61mg; Fibre 2g; Sodium 5mg.

Sesame Seed-coated Falafel with Tahini Yogurt Dip

SESAME SEEDS are used to give a crunchy coating to these spicy bean patties. Serve with the tahini yogurt dip and warm pitta bread as a light lunch or supper dish.

INGREDIENTS

250g/9oz/1 1/3 cups dried chickpeas
2 garlic cloves, crushed
1 red chilli, seeded and finely sliced
5ml/1 tsp ground coriander
5ml/1 tsp ground cumin
15ml/1 tbsp chopped fresh mint
15ml/1 tbsp chopped fresh parsley
2 spring onions (scallions), finely chopped
1 large egg, beaten
sesame seeds, for coating
sunflower oil, for frying
salt and freshly ground black pepper

For the tahini yogurt dip
30ml/2 tbsp light tahini
200g/7oz/scant 1 cup live natural
    (plain) yogurt
5ml/1 tsp cayenne pepper, plus extra
    for sprinkling
15ml/1 tbsp chopped fresh mint
1 spring onion (scallion), finely sliced
Serves 4

2 Meanwhile, make the tahini yogurt dip. Mix together the tahini, yogurt, cayenne pepper and mint in a small bowl. Sprinkle the spring onion and extra cayenne pepper and chopped mint on top and chill.

1 Place the chickpeas in a bowl, cover with cold water and leave to soak overnight. Drain and rinse, then place in a pan and cover with cold water. Bring to the boil and boil rapidly for 10 minutes, then reduce the heat and simmer for 1 1/2–2 hours until tender.

3 Combine the chickpeas with the garlic, chilli, ground spices, herbs, spring onions and seasoning, then mix in the egg. Place in a food processor and blend until the mixture forms a coarse paste. If the paste seems too soft, chill it for 30 minutes.

4 Form the chilled chickpea paste into 12 patties with your hands, then roll each one in the sesame seeds to coat thoroughly.

5 Heat enough oil to cover the base of a large frying pan. Fry the falafel, in batches if necessary, for 6 minutes, turning once.

HEALTH BENEFITS

Chickpeas are a good source of iron, manganese, folate, zinc and vitamin E.

Energy 484kcal/2024kJ; Protein 23g; Carbohydrate 36g, of which sugars 6g; Fat 28g, of which saturates 5g; Cholesterol 69mg; Calcium 288mg; Fibre 5g; Sodium 93mg.

Tortilla Wrap with Tabbouleh and Guacamole

TO BE SUCCESSFUL THIS CLASSIC Middle Eastern salad needs onions, lemon juice, plenty of fresh herbs and lots of freshly ground black pepper. It is best served at room temperature and goes well with the Mexican-style dip.

INGREDIENTS

175g/6oz/1 cup bulgur wheat
30ml/2 tbsp chopped fresh mint
30ml/2 tbsp chopped fresh flat
    leaf parsley
6 spring onions (scallions), sliced
1/2 cucumber, diced
50ml/2fl oz/1/4 cup extra virgin olive oil
juice of 1 large lemon
salt and freshly ground black pepper
4 wheat tortillas, to serve
flat leaf parsley, to garnish (optional)

For the guacamole

1 ripe avocado, stoned (pitted),
    peeled and diced
juice of 1/2 lemon
1/2 red chilli, seeded and sliced
1 garlic clove, crushed
1/2 red (bell) pepper, seeded and diced

Serves 4–6

1 To make the tabbouleh, place the bulgur wheat in a large heatproof bowl and pour over enough boiling water to cover. Leave for 30 minutes until the grains are tender but still retain a little resistance to the bite. Drain thoroughly in a sieve (strainer), then tip back into the bowl.

2 Add the mint, parsley, spring onions and cucumber to the bulgur wheat and mix thoroughly. Blend together the olive oil and lemon juice and pour over the tabbouleh, season to taste and toss well to mix. Chill for 30 minutes to allow the flavours to mingle.

COOK'S TIP

The soaking time for bulgur wheat can vary. For the best results, follow the instructions on the packet and taste the grain every now and again to check whether it is tender enough.

3 To make the guacamole, place the avocado in a bowl and add the lemon juice, chilli and garlic. Season to taste and mash with a fork to form a smooth purée. Stir in the red pepper.

4 Warm the tortillas in a dry frying pan and serve either flat, folded or rolled up with the tabbouleh and guacamole. Garnish with parsley, if using.

HEALTH BENEFITS

• Bulgur wheat is a useful source of dietary fibre and B complex vitamins.
• Parsley and mint are good digestives.

Energy 336kcal/1405kJ; Protein 7g; Carbohydrate 48g, of which sugars 3g; Fat 14g, of which saturates 2g; Cholesterol 0mg; Calcium 90mg; Fibre 2g; Sodium 110mg.

Courgette Fritters with Chilli Jam

CHILLI JAM IS HOT, sweet and sticky — rather like a thick chutney. It adds a piquancy to these light fritters but is also delicious with pies or a chunk of cheese.

INGREDIENTS

450g/1lb/3 1/2 cups coarsely grated courgettes (zucchini)
50g/2oz/2/3 cup freshly grated Parmesan cheese
2 eggs, beaten
60ml/4 tbsp plain (all-purpose) flour
vegetable oil, for frying
salt and freshly ground black pepper

For the chilli jam
75ml/3fl oz/5 tbsp olive oil
4 large onions, diced
4 garlic cloves, chopped
1–2 Thai chillies, seeded and sliced
25g/1oz/2 tbsp soft dark brown sugar
Makes 12 Fritters

2 Leave the onion mixture to cool, then transfer to a food processor or blender. Add the chillies and sugar and blend until smooth, then return the mixture to the pan. Cook for 10 minutes, stirring frequently, until the liquid evaporates and the mixture has the consistency of jam. Cool slightly.

3 To make the fritters, squeeze the courgettes in a dish towel to remove any excess water, then combine with the Parmesan, eggs, flour and salt and pepper.

4 Heat enough oil to cover the base of a large frying pan. Add 30ml/ 2 tbsp of the mixture for each fritter and cook three fritters at a time. Cook for 2–3 minutes on each side until golden, then keep warm while you cook the remaining fritters. Drain on kitchen paper and serve warm with a spoonful of the chilli jam.

COOK'S TIP

Stored in an airtight jar in the refrigerator, the chilli jam will keep for up to 1 week.

1 First make the chilli jam. Heat the oil in a frying pan until hot, then add the onions and garlic. Reduce the heat to low, then cook for 20 minutes, stirring frequently, until the onions are very soft.

HEALTH BENEFITS

• *Parmesan provides valuable amounts of vitamin B12, protein and calcium but its high saturated fat content means it should be eaten in moderation.*
• *Vitamin C and beta carotene are both found in courgettes (zucchini).*

Energy 157kcal/652kJ; Protein 4.4g; Carbohydrate 11.1g, of which sugars 6.1g; Fat 10.8g, of which saturates 2.2g; Cholesterol 36mg; Calcium 85mg; Fibre 1.2g; Sodium 59mg.

Main Dishes

The majority of recipes in this chapter are carbohydrate-based, putting the focus firmly on peas, beans and lentils, and pasta and rice. Not only are these foods sustaining, they are also packed with fibre, vitamins and minerals, and supply valuable low-fat protein. If this sounds worthy, but not wildly exciting, read on. Included are some of the most innovative vegetarian main course dishes on anybody's menu, from Thai Vegetable Curry with Lemon Grass Rice to Potato, Red Onion and Feta Frittata. Spiced Couscous with Halloumi and Courgette Ribbons is another option, along with Jamaican Black Bean Pot. The emphasis is on interesting ingredients used in imaginative ways. Take a tour of the treats on offer – it's a great way to increase your repertoire of vegetarian dishes and bring new taste sensations to your table.

Potato, Red Onion and Feta Frittata

THIS ITALIAN OMELETTE is cooked with vegetables and cheese, and is served flat, like a Spanish tortilla. Cut it into wedges and serve with crusty bread and a tomato salad for a light supper.

INGREDIENTS

25ml/1½ tbsp olive oil
1 red onion, sliced
350g/12oz cooked new potatoes,
*   halved or quartered, if large*
6 eggs, lightly beaten
115g/4oz/1 cup feta cheese, diced
salt and freshly ground black pepper
Serves 2–4

1 Heat the oil in a large, heavy, flame-proof frying pan. Add the onion and sauté for 5 minutes until softened, stirring occasionally.

2 Add the potatoes and cook for a further 5 minutes until golden, stirring to prevent them sticking. Spread the mixture evenly over the base of the pan.

HEALTH BENEFITS

Eggs are an important source of vitamin B$_{12}$, which is vital for the nervous system and the development of red blood cells. They also supply other B vitamins, zinc and selenium and a useful amount of iron. It is beneficial to eat a food rich in vitamin C at the same time in order to help the absorption of iron. Do not eat too many eggs, though – no more than a maximum of three per week.

3 Preheat the grill (broiler) to high. Season the eggs, then pour the mixture over the onion and potatoes. Sprinkle the cheese on top and cook over a moderate heat for 5–6 minutes until the eggs are just set and the base of the frittata is lightly golden.

4 Place the pan under the grill and cook the top for 3 minutes until set and lightly golden. Serve the frittata warm or cold, cut into wedges.

Energy 289kcal/1207kJ; Protein 15.5g; Carbohydrate 15.7g, of which sugars 2.4g; Fat 18.9g, of which saturates 7g; Cholesterol 306mg; Calcium 155mg; Fibre 1.1g; Sodium 529mg.

Fresh Herb Risotto

DISTINCTIVE, NUTTY-FLAVOURED wild rice is combined with arborio rice to create this creamy, comforting risotto. An aromatic blend of fresh herbs adds a light summery flavour.

INGREDIENTS

90g/3^{1}/2oz/^{1}/2 cup wild rice
15ml/1 tbsp butter
15ml/1 tbsp olive oil
1 small onion, finely chopped
450g/1lb/2^{1}/2 cups arborio rice
300ml/^{1}/2 pint/1^{1}/4 cups dry white wine
1.2 litres/2 pints/5 cups vegetable stock
45ml/3 tbsp chopped fresh oregano
45ml/3 tbsp snipped fresh chives
60ml/4 tbsp chopped fresh flat leaf parsley
60ml/4 tbsp chopped fresh basil
75g/3oz/1 cup freshly grated
   Parmesan cheese
salt and freshly ground black pepper
Serves 4

1 Cook the wild rice in boiling salted water according to the instructions on the packet.

HEALTH BENEFITS

• Wild rice, which is not in fact a rice but a grass, contains twice as much protein and three times as much iron, weight for weight, as brown rice.
• Parsley is an unassuming herb but it contains considerable amounts of vitamin C as well as iron, folic acid, potassium and calcium. It is also known for its cleansing power – just nibble on a leaf to get rid of the lingering odour of garlic.

2 Heat the butter and oil in a large heavy pan. When the butter has melted, add the onion and cook for 3 minutes, Add the arborio rice and cook for 2 minutes, stirring to coat it in the oil mixture.

3 Pour in the wine and bring to the boil. Reduce the heat and cook for 10 minutes until the wine is absorbed. Add the stock, a little at a time, and simmer, stirring, for 20–25 minutes until the liquid is absorbed and the rice is creamy. Season well.

4 Add the herbs and wild rice; heat for 2 minutes, stirring frequently. Stir in two-thirds of the Parmesan and cook until melted. Serve sprinkled with the remaining Parmesan.

COOK'S TIP

Risotto rice is essential to achieve the right creamy texture in this dish. Other types of rice simply will not do. Fresh herbs are also a must, but you can use tarragon, chervil, marjoram or thyme instead of those listed here.

Energy 632kcal/2637kJ; Protein 18g; Carbohydrate 109.3g, of which sugars 1.2g; Fat 12.8g, of which saturates 6.2g; Cholesterol 27mg; Calcium 280mg; Fibre 0.8g; Sodium 232mg.

Thai Vegetable Curry with Lemon Grass Rice

FRAGRANT JASMINE RICE, subtly flavoured with lemon grass and cardamom, is the perfect accompaniment to this richly spiced vegetable curry. Don't be put off by the long list of ingredients, this curry is very simple to make.

INGREDIENTS

10ml/2 tsp vegetable oil
400ml/14fl oz/1²/3 cups coconut milk
300ml/¹/2 pint/1¹/4 cups vegetable stock
225g/8oz new potatoes, halved or
    quartered, if large
130g/4¹/2oz baby corn
5ml/1 tsp golden caster (superfine) sugar
185g/6¹/2oz broccoli florets
1 red (bell) pepper, seeded and
    sliced lengthways
115g/4oz spinach, tough stalks removed
    and shredded
30ml/2 tbsp chopped fresh
    coriander (cilantro)
salt and freshly ground black pepper

For the spice paste

1 red chilli, seeded and chopped
3 green chillies, seeded and chopped
1 lemon grass stalk, outer leaves removed
    and inside finely chopped
2 shallots, chopped
finely grated rind of 1 lime
2 garlic cloves, chopped
5ml/1 tsp ground coriander
2.5ml/¹/2 tsp ground cumin
1cm/¹/2in fresh galangal, finely chopped or
    2.5ml/¹/2 tsp dried (optional)
30ml/2 tbsp chopped fresh coriander
    (cilantro) leaves, plus 15ml/1 tbsp
    chopped roots and stems (optional)

For the rice

225g/8oz/generous 1 cup jasmine rice, rinsed
1 lemon grass stalk, outer leaves removed
    and cut into 3 pieces
6 cardamom pods, bruised

Serves 4

1 Make the spice paste. Place all the ingredients in a food processor or blender and blend to a coarse paste.

2 Heat the oil in a large, heavy pan and fry the spice paste for 1–2 minutes, stirring constantly. Add the coconut milk and stock, and bring to the boil.

3 Reduce the heat, add the potatoes and simmer for 15 minutes. Add the baby corn and seasoning, then cook for 2 minutes. Stir in the sugar, broccoli and red pepper, and cook for 2 minutes more until the vegetables are tender. Stir in the shredded spinach and half the fresh coriander. Cook for 2 minutes.

HEALTH BENEFITS

Broccoli provides valuable amounts of calcium, vitamin C, folic acid, zinc and iron. The vitamin and mineral content of this dish is given a further boost by the addition of all the other vegetables.

4 Meanwhile, prepare the rice. Tip the rinsed jasmine rice into a pan and add the lemon grass and cardamom pods. Pour over 475ml/16fl oz/2 cups water.

5 Bring to the boil, then reduce the heat, cover the pan, and cook for 10–15 minutes until the water is absorbed and the rice is tender and slightly sticky. Season with salt, leave to stand for 10 minutes, then fluff up the rice with a fork.

6 Remove the spices and serve the rice with the curry, sprinkled with the remaining fresh coriander.

Energy 346kcal/1465kJ; Protein 10g; Carbohydrate 70g, of which sugars 12g; Fat 5g, of which saturates 1g; Cholesterol 0mg; Calcium 132mg; Fibre 4g; Sodium 314mg.

Potato Rösti and Tofu with Fresh Tomato and Ginger Sauce

ALTHOUGH THIS DISH FEATURES various components, it is not difficult to make and the finished result is well worth the effort. Make sure you marinate the tofu for at least an hour to allow it to absorb the flavours of the ginger, garlic and tamari. Serve with a mixed leaf salad, dressed with a splash each of toasted sesame oil and lime juice.

INGREDIENTS

425g/15oz/3³/4 cups tofu, cut into
  1cm/¹/2in cubes
4 large potatoes, about 900g/2lb total
  weight, peeled
sunflower oil, for frying
salt and freshly ground black pepper
30ml/2 tbsp sesame seeds, toasted

For the marinade
30ml/2 tbsp tamari or dark soy sauce
15ml/1 tbsp clear honey
2 garlic cloves, crushed
4 cm/1¹/2 in piece fresh root ginger, grated
5ml/1 tsp toasted sesame oil

For the sauce
15ml/1 tbsp olive oil
8 tomatoes, halved, seeded and chopped
Serves 4

1 Mix together all the marinade ingredients in a shallow dish and add the tofu. Spoon the marinade over the tofu and leave to marinate in the fridge for at least 1 hour. Turn the tofu occasionally in the marinade to allow the flavours to infuse.

HEALTH BENEFITS

Made from processed soya beans, tofu is a highly nutritious protein food and is the richest non-dairy source of calcium. Tofu also contains valuable B complex vitamins and iron.

2 To make the rösti, par-boil the potatoes for 10–15 minutes until almost tender. Leave to cool, then grate coarsely. Season well. Preheat the oven to 200°C/400°F/Gas 6.

3 Using a slotted spoon, remove the tofu from the marinade and reserve the marinade. Spread out the tofu on a baking tray and bake for 20 minutes, turning occasionally, until golden and crisp on all sides.

4 Take a quarter of the potato mixture in your hands at a time and form into rough cakes. Dampen your hands if the mixture sticks.

5 Heat a frying pan with just enough oil to cover the base. Place the cakes in the frying pan and flatten the mixture, using your hands or a spatula to form rounds about 1cm/¹/2in thick.

6 Cook for about 6 minutes until golden and crisp underneath. Carefully turn over the rösti and cook for a further 6 minutes until golden.

7 Meanwhile, make the sauce. Heat the oil in a pan, add the reserved marinade and the tomatoes and cook for 2 minutes, stirring. Reduce the heat and simmer, covered, for about 10 minutes, stirring occasionally, until the tomatoes break down. Press through a sieve (strainer) to make a thick, smooth sauce.

8 To serve, place a rösti on each of four warm serving plates. Scatter the tofu on top, spoon over the tomato sauce and sprinkle with sesame seeds.

COOK'S TIP

Tamari is a thick, mellow-flavoured Japanese soy sauce, which unlike conventional Chinese soy sauce is wheat-free, and so is suitable for people who are on wheat- or gluten-free diets. It is sold in Japanese food stores and some larger health food stores.

Energy 453kcal/1897kJ; Protein 16g; Carbohydrate 47g, of which sugars 8g; Fat 24g, of which saturates 3g; Cholesterol 0mg; Calcium 609mg; Fibre 5g; Sodium 596mg.

Lemon, Thyme and Aduki Bean Stuffed Mushrooms with Pine Nut Tarator

FIELD MUSHROOMS have a rich flavour and a meaty texture that go well with this fragrant herb and lemon stuffing. The garlicky pine nut accompaniment is a traditional Middle Eastern dish with a smooth, creamy consistency similar to that of hummus. Green leafy vegetables, such as spinach or Swiss chard, and roast or baked potatoes are ideal side dishes.

INGREDIENTS

200g/7oz/1 cup dried or 400g/14oz/
  2 cups drained, canned aduki beans
45ml/3 tbsp olive oil, plus extra for brushing
1 onion, finely chopped
2 garlic cloves, crushed
30ml/2 tbsp fresh chopped or 5ml/1 tsp
  dried thyme
8 large field (portobello) mushrooms,
  stalks finely chopped
50g/2oz/1 cup fresh wholemeal
  (whole-wheat) breadcrumbs
juice of 1 lemon
185g/6¹/2oz/3/4 cup goat's cheese,
  crumbled
salt and freshly ground black pepper

For the pine nut tarator

50g/2oz/¹/2 cup pine nuts toasted
50g/2oz/1 cup cubed white bread
2 garlic cloves, chopped
200ml/7fl oz/1 cup semi-skimmed milk
45ml/3 tbsp olive oil
15ml/1 tbsp chopped fresh parsley,
  to garnish (optional)
Serves 4–6

1 If using dried beans, soak them overnight, then drain and rinse well. Place in a pan, add enough water to cover and bring to the boil. Boil rapidly for 10 minutes, then reduce the heat, cook for 30 minutes until tender, then drain. If using canned beans, rinse, drain well, then set aside.

2 Preheat the oven to 200°C/ 400°F/Gas 6. Heat the oil in a large, heavy frying pan, add the onion and garlic and sauté for 5 minutes until softened. Add the thyme and the mushroom stalks and cook for a further 3 minutes, stirring occasionally, until tender.

3 Stir in the beans, breadcrumbs and lemon juice, season well, then cook for 2 minutes until heated through. Mash two-thirds of the beans with a fork or potato masher, leaving the remaining beans whole.

4 Brush a baking dish and the base and sides of the mushrooms with oil, then top each one with a spoonful of the bean mixture. Place the mushrooms in the dish, cover with foil and bake for 20 minutes. Remove the foil. Top each mushroom with some of the goat's cheese and bake for a further 15 minutes, or until the cheese is melted and bubbly and the mushrooms are tender.

5 To make the pine nut tarator, place all the ingredients in a food processor or blender and blend until smooth and creamy. Add more milk if the mixture appears too thick. Sprinkle with parsley, if using, and serve with the stuffed mushrooms.

HEALTH BENEFITS

Aduki beans are high in protein and fibre and low in fat. They also contain some B vitamins and iron.

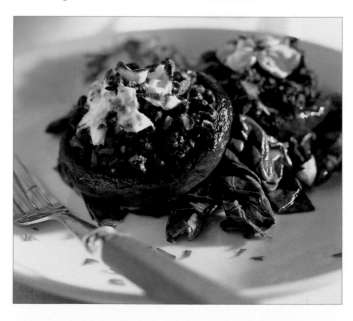

Energy 430kcal/1795kJ; Protein 16g; Carbohydrate 29g, of which sugars 5g; Fat 28g, of which saturates 7g; Cholesterol 24mg; Calcium 211mg; Fibre 2g; Sodium 547mg.

Spiced Couscous with Halloumi and Courgette Ribbons

A STAPLE FOOD IN North Africa, couscous is commonly served with meat or vegetable stews. Here, it forms the foundation of the dish and is topped with griddled sliced courgettes and halloumi, a mild cheese from Cyprus.

INGREDIENTS

275g/10oz/1²/3 cup couscous
1 bay leaf
1 cinnamon stick
30ml/2 tbsp olive oil, plus extra for brushing
1 large red onion, chopped
2 garlic cloves, chopped
5ml/1 tsp mild chilli powder
5ml/1 tsp ground cumin
5ml/1 tsp ground coriander
5 cardamom pods, bruised
50g/2oz/¹/4 cup whole almonds, toasted
1 peach, stoned and diced
25g/1oz/2 tbsp butter
3 courgettes (zucchini), sliced lengthways
   into ribbons
225g/8oz halloumi cheese, sliced
salt and freshly ground black pepper
chopped fresh flat leaf parsley,
   to garnish
Serves 4

1 Place the couscous in a bowl and pour over 500ml/17fl oz/2¹/4 cups boiling water. Add the bay leaf and cinnamon stick and season with salt. Leave the couscous for 10 minutes until the water is absorbed, then fluff up the grains with a fork.

HEALTH BENEFITS

Almonds have long been regarded as having special protective properties. Although they have a high fat content, the fat is monounsaturated and can help lower cholesterol levels. Best eaten whole, almonds are also a useful source of calcium and vitamin E.

2 Meanwhile, heat the oil in a large, heavy pan, add the onion and garlic and sauté gently for about 7 minutes until the onion has softened, stirring occasionally.

3 Stir in the chilli powder, cumin, coriander and cardamom pods, and cook for a further 3 minutes to allow the flavours to mingle. Add the couscous, almonds, diced peach and butter, and heat through for 2 minutes.

4 Brush a griddle pan with olive oil and heat until very hot. Turn down the heat to medium, then place the courgettes on the griddle and cook for 5 minutes until tender and slightly charred. Turn the courgettes over, add the halloumi and continue cooking for a further 5 minutes, turning the halloumi halfway through.

5 Remove the cinnamon stick, bay leaf and cardamom pods from the couscous, then arrange it on a plate and season well. Top with the halloumi and courgettes. Sprinkle the parsley over the top and serve.

COOK'S TIP

If you don't own a griddle pan, grill (broil) the courgettes (zucchini), which will give them a similar smoky flavour.

Energy 576kcal/2391kJ; Protein 25g; Carbohydrate 41g, of which sugars 5g; Fat 36g, of which saturates 14g; Cholesterol 53mg; Calcium 531mg; Fibre 2g; Sodium 602mg

Main Dishes

Rice and Beans with Avocado Salsa

MEXICAN-STYLE RICE AND BEANS make a delicious supper dish. Spoon on to tortillas and serve with a tangy salsa. Alternatively, serve as an accompaniment to a spicy stew.

INGREDIENTS

40g/1¹/₂oz/¹/₄ cup dried or 75g/3oz/
    ¹/₂ cup canned kidney beans, rinsed
    and drained
4 tomatoes, halved and seeded
2 garlic cloves, chopped
1 onion, sliced
45ml/3 tbsp olive oil
225g/8oz/generous 1 cup long grain
    brown rice, rinsed
600ml/1 pint/2¹/₂ cups vegetable stock
2 carrots, diced
75g/3oz/³/₄ cup green beans
salt and freshly ground black pepper
4 wheat tortillas and sour cream, to serve

For the avocado salsa
1 avocado
juice of 1 lime
1 small red onion, diced
1 small red chilli, seeded and chopped
15ml/1 tbsp chopped fresh
    coriander (cilantro)

Serves 4

1 If using dried kidney beans, place in a bowl, cover with cold water and leave to soak overnight, then drain and rinse well. Place in a pan with enough water to cover and bring to the boil. Boil rapidly for 10 minutes, then reduce the heat and simmer for 40–50 minutes until tender. Drain and set aside.

2 Heat the grill (broiler) to high. Place the tomatoes, garlic and onion on a baking tray. Pour over 15ml/1 tbsp of the olive oil and toss to coat. Grill (broil) for 10 minutes or until the tomatoes and onions are softened, turning once. Set aside to cool.

3 Heat the remaining oil in a pan, add the rice and cook for 2 minutes, stirring, until light golden.

HEALTH BENEFITS

Brown rice contains a good, healthy combination of valuable nutrients, including vitamin E, minerals and fibre.

4 Purée the cooled tomatoes and onion in a food processor or blender, then add the mixture to the rice and cook for a further 2 minutes, stirring frequently. Pour in the stock, then cover and cook gently, for 20 minutes, stirring occasionally.

5 Reserve 30ml/2 tbsp of the kidney beans for the salsa. Add the rest to the stock mixture with the carrots and green beans and cook for 10 minutes until the vegetables are tender. Season well. Remove the pan from the heat and leave to stand, covered, for 15 minutes.

6 To make the avocado salsa, cut the avocado in half and remove the stone (pit). Peel and dice the flesh, then toss in the lime juice. Add the onion, chilli, coriander and reserved kidney beans, then season with salt.

7 To serve, spoon the hot rice and beans on to warm tortillas. Hand round the salsa and sour cream.

Energy 609kcal/2562kJ; Protein 13g; Carbohydrate 97g, of which sugars 12g; Fat 22g, of which saturates 4g; Cholesterol 0mg; Calcium 124mg; Fibre 10g; Sodium 474mg.

Teriyaki Soba Noodles with Tofu and Asparagus

YOU CAN, OF COURSE, BUY ready-made teriyaki sauce, but it is easy to prepare at home using ingredients that are now readily available. Japanese soba noodles are made from buckwheat flour, which gives them a unique texture and colour.

INGREDIENTS

350g/12oz soba noodles
30ml/2 tbsp toasted sesame oil
200g/7oz/¹/₂ bunch asparagus tips
30ml/2 tbsp groundnut (peanut) or
    vegetable oil
225g/8oz block of tofu
2 spring onions (scallions), cut diagonally
1 carrot, cut into matchsticks
2.5ml/¹/₂ tsp chilli flakes
15ml/1 tbsp sesame seeds
salt and freshly ground black pepper

For the teriyaki sauce
60ml/4 tbsp dark soy sauce
60ml/4 tbsp Japanese sake or dry sherry
60ml/4 tbsp mirin
5ml/1 tsp caster (superfine) sugar
Serves 4

1 Cook the noodles according to the instructions on the packet, then drain and rinse under cold running water. Set aside.

2 Heat the sesame oil in a griddle pan or in a baking tray placed under the grill (broiler) until very hot. Turn down the heat to medium, then cook the asparagus for 8–10 minutes, turning frequently, until tender and browned. Set aside.

HEALTH BENEFITS

Sesame seeds are an excellent source of the antioxidant vitamin E, which acts as a natural preservative, preventing oxidation and strengthening the heart and nerves.

3 Meanwhile, heat the groundnut or vegetable oil in a wok or large frying pan until very hot. Add the tofu and fry for 8–10 minutes until golden, turning it occasionally to crisp all sides. Carefully remove from the wok or pan and leave to drain on kitchen paper. Cut the tofu into 1cm/¹/₂in slices.

VARIATION

Use dried egg or rice noodles instead of soba noodles, if you wish.

4 To prepare the teriyaki sauce, mix the soy sauce, sake or dry sherry, mirin and sugar together, then heat the mixture in the wok or frying pan.

5 Toss in the noodles and stir to coat them in the sauce. Heat through for 1–2 minutes, then spoon into warmed individual serving bowls with the tofu and asparagus. Scatter the spring onions and carrot on top and sprinkle with the chilli flakes and sesame seeds. Serve immediately.

Energy 519kcal/2162kJ; Protein 13g; Carbohydrate 77g, of which sugars 5g; Fat 16g, of which saturates 3g; Cholesterol 0mg; Calcium 397mg; Fibre 2g; Sodium 1093mg.

Broccoli, Chilli and Artichoke Pasta

CHILLI FLAKES ADD A FIERY TOUCH to this simple southern Italian dish.

INGREDIENTS

350g/12oz/3 cups dried
   gnocchi pasta
300g/11oz broccoli florets
90ml/6 tbsp olive oil
1 large garlic clove, crushed
2.5–5ml/¹/₂–1 tsp dried chilli flakes
185g/6¹/₂oz/1¹/₂ cups artichoke hearts
   in oil, drained
salt and freshly ground black pepper
15ml/1 tbsp chopped fresh flat
   leaf parsley, to garnish
grated Pecorino, for sprinkling (optional)
Serves 6

1 Cook the pasta in a large pan of boiling salted water according to the instructions on the packet until it is al dente. Add the broccoli for the last 3 minutes of cooking time. Drain, reserving a little of the cooking water in the pan.

2 Meanwhile, heat the olive oil in a large, heavy pan and sauté the garlic and chilli flakes for 1 minute.

HEALTH BENEFITS

The heart, blood and immune system will all benefit from the combination of garlic, chilli and broccoli in this dish.

3 Add the pasta, broccoli and artichoke hearts and cook for 2 minutes until hot. Add a little of the reserved pasta water if the mixture seems a little dry. Season and sprinkle with the parsley and Pecorino, if using.

Rustic Buckwheat Pasta and Fontina Cheese Bake

CHARACTERISTIC OF THE mountain regions of northern Italy, this bake is a spicy combination of nutty-flavoured buckwheat pasta, vegetables and Fontina cheese.

INGREDIENTS

2 potatoes, cubed
225g/8oz/2 cups buckwheat pasta shapes,
   such as spirals
275g/10oz/2¹/₂ cups Savoy cabbage,
   shredded
45ml/3 tbsp olive oil, plus extra for greasing
1 onion, chopped
2 leeks, sliced
2 garlic cloves, chopped
175g/6oz/2¹/₂ cups brown cap (cremini)
   mushrooms, sliced
5ml/1 tsp caraway seeds
5ml/1 tsp cumin seeds
150ml/¹/₄ pint/²/₃ cup vegetable stock
150g/5oz/1¹/₄ cups Fontina cheese, diced
25g/1oz/¹/₄ cup walnuts, roughly chopped
salt and freshly ground black pepper
Serves 6

1 Preheat the oven to 200°C/400°F/ Gas 6 and oil a deep baking dish. Cook the potatoes in boiling salted water for 8–10 minutes until tender, then drain and set aside.

2 Meanwhile, cook the pasta in boiling, salted water until it is only just cooked and is still very al dente. Add the cabbage in the last minute of cooking time. Drain, then rinse under cold running water.

3 Heat the olive oil in a large, heavy pan and fry the onion and leeks for 5 minutes until softened. Add the garlic and mushrooms and cook for a further 3 minutes until tender, stirring occasionally. Stir in the spices and cook for 1 minute, stirring.

4 Add the cooked potatoes, pasta and cabbage and stir to combine, then season well. Spoon the mixture into the baking dish. Pour the stock over the vegetables, then sprinkle with the cheese and walnuts. Bake for 15 minutes or until the cheese is melted and bubbling.

HEALTH BENEFITS

Numerous studies have shown that, if eaten once a week, cabbage can reduce the risk of cancer and heart disease. Ideally, it should be raw or lightly cooked. It is also known to cleanse the blood and to treat kidney and bladder disorders.

Broccoli: Energy 380kcal/1595kJ; Protein 10g; Carbohydrate 46g, of which sugars 2g; Fat 19g, of which saturates 3g; Cholesterol 0mg; Calcium 50mg; Fibre 3g; Sodium 16mg.
Buckwheat: Energy 366kcal/1524kJ; Protein 13g; Carbohydrate 40g, of which sugars 5g; Fat 18g, of which saturates 5g; Cholesterol 18mg; Calcium 252mg; Fibre 5g; Sodium 315mg.

Cheat's Lasagne with Mixed Mushrooms

THIS SIMPLE-TO-ASSEMBLE vegetarian version of lasagne requires neither baking nor the lengthy preparation of various sauces and fillings, but is no less delicious.

INGREDIENTS

40g/1 1/2oz/2/3 cup dried porcini
    mushrooms
50ml/2fl oz/1/4 cup olive oil
1 large garlic clove, chopped
375g/13oz/5 cups mixed mushrooms,
    including brown cap (cremini), field
    (portobello), shiitake and wild varieties,
    roughly sliced
175ml/6fl oz/3/4 cup dry white wine
90ml/6 tbsp canned chopped tomatoes
2.5ml/1/2 tsp sugar
8 fresh lasagne sheets
40g/1 1/2oz/1/2 cup grated Parmesan cheese
salt and freshly ground black pepper
fresh basil leaves, to garnish

Serves 4

1 Place the porcini mushrooms in a bowl and cover with boiling water. Leave to soak for 15 minutes, then drain and rinse.

2 Heat the olive oil in a large, heavy frying pan and sauté the soaked mushrooms over a high heat for 5 minutes until the edges are slightly crisp. Reduce the heat, then add the garlic and fresh mushrooms, and sauté for a further 5 minutes until tender, stirring occasionally.

3 Add the wine and cook for 5–7 minutes until reduced. Stir in the tomatoes, sugar and seasoning and cook over a medium heat for about 5 minutes until thickened.

4 Meanwhile, cook the lasagne according to the instructions on the packet until it is al dente. Drain lightly – the pasta should still be moist.

5 To serve, spoon a little of the sauce on to each of four warm serving plates. Place a sheet of lasagne on top and spoon a quarter of the remaining mushroom sauce over each serving. Sprinkle with some Parmesan and top with another pasta sheet. Sprinkle with black pepper and more Parmesan and garnish with basil leaves.

HEALTH BENEFITS

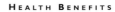

Shiitake mushrooms, a valuable source of zinc, iron and potassium, are reputed to help thin the blood and consequently reduce the risk of heart disease.

Energy 313kcal/1310kJ; Protein 11g; Carbohydrate 32g, of which sugars 3g; Fat 17g, of which saturates 4g; Cholesterol 9mg; Calcium 121mg; Fibre 5g; Sodium 94mg.

Tomato and Lentil Dahl with Toasted Almonds

RICHLY FLAVOURED WITH spices, coconut milk and tomatoes, this lentil dish makes a filling supper. Warm naan bread and natural yogurt are all that are needed as accompaniments. Split red lentils give the dish a vibrant colour, but you could use larger yellow split peas instead, if you wish.

INGREDIENTS

30ml/2 tbsp vegetable oil
1 large onion, finely chopped
3 garlic cloves, chopped
1 carrot, diced
10ml/2 tsp cumin seeds
10ml/2 tsp yellow mustard seeds
2.5cm/1in piece fresh root ginger, grated
10ml/2 tsp ground turmeric
5ml/1 tsp mild chilli powder
5ml/1 tsp garam masala
225g/8oz/1 cup split red lentils
400ml/14fl oz/1²/₃ cups water
400ml/14fl oz/1²/₃ cups coconut milk
5 tomatoes, peeled, seeded and chopped
juice of 2 limes
60ml/4 tbsp chopped fresh
    coriander (cilantro)
salt and freshly ground black pepper
25g/1oz/¹/₄ cup flaked (sliced) almonds,
    toasted, to serve
Serves 4

HEALTH BENEFITS

• *Spices have long been recognized for their medicinal qualities, from curing flatulence to warding off colds and flu.*
• *Lentils are a useful source of low-fat protein. They contain good amounts of B vitamins and provide a rich source of zinc and iron.*
• *You need to eat foods rich in vitamin C at the same meal to improve absorption of iron. Limes are a good source, but you could also serve a fresh fruit dessert containing apples, kiwi fruit and oranges.*

1 Heat the oil in a large, heavy pan. Sauté the onion for 5 minutes until softened, stirring occasionally to prevent it sticking. Add the garlic, carrot, cumin and mustard seeds, and ginger. Cook for 5 minutes, stirring, until the seeds begin to pop and the carrot softens slightly.

2 Stir in the ground turmeric, chilli powder and garam masala, and cook for 1 minute or until the flavours begin to mingle, stirring to prevent the spices burning.

3 Add the lentils, water, coconut milk and tomatoes, and season well. Bring to the boil, then reduce the heat and simmer, covered for about 45 minutes, stirring occasionally to prevent the lentils sticking.

4 Stir in the lime juice and 45ml/ 3 tbsp of the fresh coriander, then check the seasoning. Cook for a further 15 minutes until the lentils soften and become tender. To serve, sprinkle with the remaining coriander and the flaked almonds.

Energy 360kcal/1516kJ; Protein 17g; Carbohydrate 48g, of which sugars 15g; Fat 13g, of which saturates 2g; Cholesterol 0mg; Calcium 103mg; Fibre 10g; Sodium 148mg.

Roasted Vegetables with Salsa Verde

THERE ARE ENDLESS VARIATIONS of the Italian salsa verde, which means 'green sauce'. Usually a blend of fresh chopped herbs, garlic, olive oil, anchovies and capers, this is a simplified version. Here, it is served with roasted vegetables and a traditional rice and vermicelli dish from the island of Cyprus.

INGREDIENTS

3 courgettes (zucchini), sliced lengthways
1 large fennel bulb, cut into wedges
450g/1lb butternut squash, cut into
    2cm/³/4in chunks
12 shallots
2 red (bell) peppers, seeded and cut
    lengthways into thick slices
4 plum tomatoes, halved and seeded
45ml/3 tbsp olive oil
2 garlic cloves, crushed
5ml/1 tsp balsamic vinegar
salt and freshly ground black pepper

For the salsa verde
45ml/3 tbsp chopped fresh mint
90ml/6 tbsp chopped fresh flat leaf parsley
15ml/1 tbsp Dijon mustard
juice of ¹/2 lemon
30ml/2 tbsp olive oil

For the rice
15ml/1 tbsp vegetable or olive oil
75g/3oz/³/4 cup vermicelli, broken into
    short lengths
225g/8oz/generous 1 cup long grain rice
900ml/1¹/2 pints/3³/4 cups vegetable stock
Serves 4

COOK'S TIP

The salsa verde will keep for up to 1 week if stored in an airtight container in the refrigerator.

1 Preheat the oven to 220°C/425°F/ Gas 7. To make the salsa verde, place all the ingredients, with the exception of the olive oil, in a food processor or blender. Blend to a coarse paste, then add the oil, a little at a time, until the mixture forms a smooth purée. Season to taste.

2 To roast the vegetables, toss the courgettes, fennel, squash, shallots, peppers and tomatoes in the olive oil, garlic and balsamic vinegar. Leave for 10 minutes to allow the flavours to mingle.

3 Place all the vegetables – apart from the squash and tomatoes – on a baking sheet, brush with half the oil and vinegar mixture and season.

4 Roast for 25 minutes, then remove the tray from the oven. Turn the vegetables over and brush with the rest of the oil and vinegar mixture. Add the squash and tomatoes and cook for a further 20–25 minutes until all the vegetables are tender and lightly blackened around the edges.

5 Meanwhile, prepare the rice. Heat the oil in a heavy pan. Add the vermicelli and fry for about 3 minutes or until golden and crisp. Season with salt and pepper to taste.

6 Rinse the rice under cold running water, drain well, and add it to the vermicelli. Cook for 1 minute, stirring to coat it in the oil.

7 Add the vegetable stock, then cover the pan and cook for about 12 minutes until the water is absorbed. Stir the rice, then cover and leave to stand for 10 minutes. Serve the warm rice with the roasted vegetables and salsa verde.

HEALTH BENEFITS

• Brightly coloured vegetables, such as (bell) peppers, tomatoes and courgettes (zucchini), are packed with the antioxidant vitamins C and E, and beta carotene, which are thought to reduce the risk of cancer.
• Mint aids the digestion and can help people with irritable bowel syndrome.

Jamaican Black Bean Pot

MOLASSES IMPARTS A RICH flavour to the spicy sauce, which incorporates a stunning mix of black beans, red and yellow peppers and orange butternut squash. This dish is delicious served with cornbread or plain rice.

INGREDIENTS

225g/8oz/1¼ cups dried black beans
1 bay leaf
30ml/2 tbsp vegetable oil
1 large onion, chopped
1 garlic clove, chopped
5ml/1 tsp English mustard powder
15ml/1 tbsp blackstrap molasses
30ml/2 tbsp soft dark brown sugar
5ml/1 tsp dried thyme
2.5ml/½ tsp dried chilli flakes
5ml/1 tsp vegetable bouillon powder
1 red (bell) pepper, seeded and diced
1 yellow (bell) pepper, seeded and diced
675g/1½lb/5¼ cups butternut squash or
    pumpkin, seeded and cut into
    1cm/½in dice
salt and freshly ground black pepper
sprigs of thyme, to garnish
Serves 4

3 Heat the oil in the pan and sauté the onion and garlic for about 5 minutes until softened, stirring occasionally. Add the mustard powder, molasses, sugar, thyme and chilli and cook for 1 minute, stirring. Stir in the black beans and spoon the mixture into a flameproof casserole.

4 Add enough water to the reserved cooking liquid to make 400ml/14fl oz/1⅔ cups, then mix in the bouillon powder and pour into the casserole. Bake for 25 minutes.

5 Add the peppers and squash or pumpkin and mix well. Cover, then bake for 45 minutes until the vegetables are tender. Serve garnished with thyme.

HEALTH BENEFITS

Blackstrap molasses is a by-product of sugar processing and contains less sugar than treacle. It is a good source of iron, calcium, zinc, copper and chromium. Eating molasses regularly is said to help acne, arthritis, angina, constipation and anaemia.

1 Soak the beans overnight in plenty of water, then drain and rinse well. Place in a large pan, cover with fresh water and add the bay leaf. Bring to the boil, then boil rapidly for 10 minutes.

2 Reduce the heat, cover, and simmer for 30 minutes until tender. Drain, reserving the cooking water. Preheat the oven to 180°C/350°F/Gas 4.

Energy 297kcal/1252kJ; Protein 15.1g; Carbohydrate 45.9g, of which sugars 20.3g; Fat 7.1g, of which saturates 1g; Cholesterol 0mg; Calcium 129mg; Fibre 12.6g; Sodium 16mg.

Aubergine and Chickpea Tagine

Spiced with coriander, cumin, cinnamon, turmeric and a dash of chilli sauce, this Moroccan-style stew makes a sustaining supper dish.

INGREDIENTS

1 small aubergine (eggplant), diced
2 courgettes (zucchini), thickly sliced
60ml/4 tbsp olive oil
1 large onion, sliced
2 garlic cloves, chopped
150g/5oz/2 cups brown cap (cremini)
    mushrooms, halved
15ml/1 tbsp ground coriander
10ml/2 tsp cumin seeds
15ml/1 tbsp ground cinnamon
10ml/2 tsp ground turmeric
225g/8oz new potatoes, quartered
600ml/1 pint/2¹/2 cups passata (bottled
    strained tomatoes)
15ml/1 tbsp tomato purée (paste)
15ml/1 tbsp chilli sauce
75g/3oz/¹/3 cup ready-to-eat dried apricots
400g/14oz/3 cups canned chickpeas,
    drained and rinsed
salt and freshly ground black pepper
15ml/1 tbsp chopped fresh coriander
    (cilantro), to garnish

Serves 4

1 Sprinkle salt over the aubergine and courgettes and leave for 30 minutes. Rinse well under running water and pat dry with a dish towel. Heat the grill (broiler) to high. Arrange the courgettes and aubergine on a baking sheet and toss in 30ml/2 tbsp of the oil. Grill (broil) for 20 minutes, turning often, until tender and golden.

2 Meanwhile, heat the remaining oil in a large heavy pan and cook the onion and garlic for 5 minutes until softened, stirring occasionally. Add the mushrooms and sauté for 3 minutes until tender. Add the spices and cook for 1 minute more, stirring, to allow the flavours to mingle.

3 Add the potatoes and cook for 3 minutes, stirring. Pour in the passata, tomato purée and 150ml/ ¹/4 pint/²/3 cup water, cover, and cook for 10 minutes or until the sauce begins to thicken.

4 Add the aubergine, courgettes, chilli sauce, apricots and chickpeas to the pan. Season and cook, partially covered for 10–15 minutes until the potatoes are tender. Add a little extra water if the tagine becomes too dry. Sprinkle with chopped fresh coriander to serve immediately.

HEALTH BENEFITS

High in fibre and low in fat, chickpeas, like other pulses, have the ability to reduce blood cholesterol, regulate blood sugar and prevent constipation.

Energy 435kcal/1824kJ; Protein 17g; Carbohydrate 54g, of which sugars 31g; Fat 18g, of which saturates 3g; Cholesterol 0mg; Calcium 117mg; Fibre 10g; Sodium 353mg.

Tarts, Pies
and
Pizzas

Whether you are looking for a hearty winter pie or a light summer tart, you'll find a slice of something special in this chapter. For starters, try the individual treats, such as Red Onion and Goat's Cheese Pastries or Wild Mushroom and Fontina Tarts. Then there are the moveable feasts – dishes you'll delight in taking to picnics, pot-luck suppers or buffets. What could be more delicious than a warm Caramelized Onion Tart, served with a mixed leaf salad, or a Summer Herb Ricotta Flan with a spoonful of tapenade? Mushroom, Nut and Prune Jalousie makes a marvellous alternative to the traditional Sunday roast, as does the hearty Chestnut, Stilton and Ale Pie. Fed up with vegetarian lasagne? Try a tasty alternative – a bake that layers polenta with rich tomato sauce and the classy combination of spinach, cream and Gorgonzola cheese. Or if it's pizza that you'd like, try a quick-to-cook yeast-free polenta pan-pizza that's topped with red onions, garlic-flavoured mushrooms and mozzarella.

Caramelized Onion Tart

SERVED WARM WITH A MIXED leaf salad, this classic and elegant French tart makes a perfect light summer lunch.

INGREDIENTS

15ml/1 tbsp unsalted butter
15ml/1 tbsp olive oil
500g/1¼lb onions, sliced
large pinch of ground nutmeg
5ml/1 tsp soft dark brown sugar
2 eggs
150ml/¼ pint/⅔ cup single (light) cream
50g/2oz/½ cup Gruyère cheese, grated
salt and freshly ground black pepper

For the pastry

75g/3oz/⅔ cup plain (all-purpose) flour
75g/3oz/⅔ cup wholemeal
    (whole-wheat) flour
75g/3oz/6 tbsp unsalted butter
1 egg yolk
Serves 6

1 To make the pastry, rub together the plain and wholemeal flours and butter in a large bowl, until the mixture resembles fine breadcrumbs. Mix in the egg yolk and enough cold water to form a dough.

2 Turn out the dough on to a lightly floured work surface and form into a smooth ball, then wrap in clear film (plastic wrap) and chill for about 30 minutes.

3 Meanwhile, make the filling. Heat the butter and oil in a large, heavy frying pan. Cook the onions over a low heat for 30 minutes until very soft and translucent, stirring often. Stir in the nutmeg, sugar and seasoning, and cook for a further 5 minutes until the onions are golden and caramelized. Set aside and allow to cool slightly.

4 Preheat the oven to 220°C/ 425°F/Gas 7. Lightly grease a loose-based 35 x 12cm/14 x 4½in fluted tin (pan). Roll out the pastry and use to line the prepared tin. Trim the top, then chill for 20 minutes.

5 Prick the pastry base with a fork, then line with baking parchment and baking beans and bake blind for 10 minutes until lightly golden. Remove the paper and beans, then spoon the onions into the pastry case.

6 Beat the eggs with the cream, then add the cheese and season to taste. Pour the mixture over the onions and bake for 30 minutes until set and golden.

Energy 905kcal/3748kJ; Protein 15g; Carbohydrate 36.7g, of which sugars 3g; Fat 78.2g, of which saturates 47.1g; Cholesterol 384mg; Calcium 272mg; Fibre 1.6g; Sodium 383mg.

Mediterranean One-crust Pie

THIS FREE-FORM PIE ENCASES a rich vegetable and kidney bean filling. If your pastry cracks, just patch it up with offcuts – it adds to the pie's rustic character.

INGREDIENTS

500g/1¼lb aubergine (eggplant), cubed
1 red (bell) pepper
30ml/2 tbsp olive oil
1 large onion, finely chopped
1 courgette (zucchini), sliced
2 garlic cloves, crushed
15ml/1 tbsp fresh oregano or 5ml/1 tsp
    dried, plus extra fresh oregano to garnish
200g/7oz/1½ cups canned red kidney
    beans, drained and rinsed
115g/4oz/1 cup pitted black olives, rinsed
375g/13oz/2⁄3 cup passata (bottled
    strained tomatoes)
1 egg, beaten, or a little milk
30ml/2 tbsp semolina
salt and freshly ground black pepper

For the pastry

75g/3oz/2⁄3 cup plain (all-purpose) flour
75g/3oz/2⁄3 cup wholemeal
    (whole-wheat) flour
75g/3oz/6 tbsp vegetable margarine
50g/2oz/2⁄3 cup grated Parmesan cheese
Serves 4

1 Preheat the oven to 220°C/425°F/ Gas 7. To make the pastry, sift the flours into a large bowl. Rub in the vegetable margarine until the mixture resembles fine breadcrumbs, then stir in the grated Parmesan. Mix in enough cold water to form a firm dough.

2 Turn out the dough on to a lightly floured work surface and form into a smooth ball. Wrap the dough in clear film (plastic wrap) or a plastic bag and chill for about 30 minutes.

3 To make the filling, place the aubergine in a colander and sprinkle with salt, then leave for 30 minutes. Rinse and pat dry with kitchen paper. Meanwhile, place the pepper on a baking tray and roast in the oven for 20 minutes. Put the pepper in a plastic bag and leave until cool enough to handle. Peel and seed the pepper, then dice the flesh. Set aside.

4 Heat the oil in a large, heavy frying pan. Fry the onions for 5 minutes until softened, stirring occasionally. Add the aubergine and fry for 5 minutes until tender.

5 Add the courgettes, garlic and oregano, and cook for a further 5 minutes, stirring frequently. Add the kidney beans and olives, stir, then add the passata and pepper. Cook until heated through, and set aside to cool.

6 Roll out the pastry on a lightly floured board or work surface to form a rough 30cm/12in round. Place on a lightly oiled baking sheet. Brush with a little of the beaten egg, sprinkle over the semolina, leaving a 4cm/1½in border, then spoon over the filling.

7 Gather up the edges of the pastry to partly cover the filling – it should be open in the middle. Brush with the remaining egg and bake for 30–35 minutes until golden.

Energy 554kcal/2318kJ; Protein 17.7g; Carbohydrate 56.6g, of which sugars 15.7g; Fat 30.2g, of which saturates 4.2g; Cholesterol 13mg; Calcium 295mg; Fibre 11.6g; Sodium 1353mg.

Summer Herb Ricotta Flan

SIMPLE TO MAKE AND INFUSED with aromatic herbs, this delicate flan makes a delightful lunch dish.

INGREDIENTS

olive oil, for greasing and glazing
800g/1lb 11oz/3^1/2 cups ricotta cheese
75g/3oz/1 cup freshly grated
   Parmesan cheese
3 eggs, separated
60ml/4 tbsp torn fresh basil leaves
60ml/4 tbsp snipped fresh chives
45ml/3 tbsp fresh oregano leaves
2.5ml/^{1}/2 tsp salt
2.5ml/^{1}/2 tsp paprika
freshly ground black pepper
chopped herbs, to garnish

For the tapenade

400g/14oz/3^1/2 cups pitted black olives,
   rinsed and halved, reserving a few whole
   to garnish (optional)
5 garlic cloves, crushed
75ml/5 tbsp/^{1}/3 cup olive oil

Serves 4

1 Preheat the oven to 180°C/350°F/ Gas 4 and lightly grease a 23cm/9in springform cake tin (pan) with oil. Mix together the ricotta, Parmesan and egg yolks in a food processor or blender. Add the herbs and seasoning, and blend until smooth and creamy.

2 Whisk the egg whites in a large bowl until they form soft peaks. Gently fold the egg whites into the ricotta mixture, taking care not to knock out too much air. Spoon the ricotta mixture into the tin and smooth the top.

3 Bake for 1 hour 20 minutes or until the flan is risen and the top golden. Remove from the oven and brush lightly with olive oil, then sprinkle with paprika. Leave the flan to cool before removing from the tin.

4 Make the tapenade. Place the olives and garlic in a food processor or blender and process until finely chopped. Gradually add the olive oil and blend to a coarse paste, then transfer to a serving bowl. Garnish the flan with the basil leaves and olives and serve with the tapenade.

Red Onion and Goat's Cheese Pastries

THESE ATTRACTIVE little pastries couldn't be easier to make. Ring the changes by spreading the pastry base with pesto or tapenade before you add the filling.

INGREDIENTS

15ml/1 tbsp olive oil
450g/1lb/1^1/2 cups red onions, sliced
30ml/2 tbsp fresh thyme or
   10ml/2 tsp dried
15ml/1 tbsp balsamic vinegar
425g/15oz packet ready-rolled puff pastry
115g/4oz/^{1}/2 cup goat's cheese, cubed
1 egg, beaten
salt and freshly ground black pepper
fresh thyme sprigs, to garnish (optional)
mixed green salad leaves, to serve

Serves 4

1 Heat the oil in a large, heavy frying pan, add the onions and fry over a gentle heat for 10 minutes or until softened, stirring occasionally to prevent them browning. Add the thyme, seasoning and balsamic vinegar, and cook for a further 5 minutes. Remove the pan from the heat and leave to cool.

2 Preheat the oven to 220°C/ 425°F/Gas 7. Unroll the pastry and using a 15cm/6in plate as a guide, cut four rounds.

3 Place the four pastry rounds on a dampened baking sheet and, using the point of a knife, score a border, 2cm/^{3}/4in inside the edge of each round.

4 Divide the onions evenly among the pastry rounds, inside the border, and top with the goat's cheese. Brush the edge of each round with beaten egg and bake for 25–30 minutes until golden. Garnish with thyme, if using, before serving with salad leaves.

Flan: Energy 718kcal/2974kJ; Protein 33g; Carbohydrate 5g, of which sugars 4g; Fat 63g, of which saturates 23g; Cholesterol 291mg; Calcium 782mg; Fibre 4g; Sodium 719mg.
Pastries: Energy 623kcal/2590kJ; Protein 12g; Carbohydrate 46g, of which sugars 7g; Fat 44g, of which saturates 15g; Cholesterol 95mg; Calcium 209mg; Fibre 3g; Sodium 795mg.

Wild Mushroom and Fontina Tarts

ITALIAN FONTINA CHEESE gives these tarts a creamy, nutty flavour. Serve them warm with salad leaves.

INGREDIENTS

25g/1oz/¹/2 cup dried wild mushrooms
30ml/2 tbsp olive oil
1 red onion, chopped
2 garlic cloves, chopped
30ml/2 tbsp medium-dry sherry
1 egg
120ml/4fl oz/¹/2 cup single (light) cream
25g/1oz Fontina cheese, thinly sliced
salt and freshly ground black pepper
rocket (arugula) leaves, to serve

For the pastry

115g/4oz/1 cup wholemeal
    (whole-wheat) flour
50g/2oz/4 tbsp unsalted butter
25g/1oz/¹/4 cup walnuts, roasted
    and ground
1 egg, lightly beaten
Serves 4

2 Meanwhile, soak the dried mushrooms in 300ml/¹/2 pint/ 1¹/4 cups boiling water for 30 minutes. Drain and reserve the liquid. Heat the oil in a frying pan. Add the onion and fry for 5 minutes, then add the garlic and fry for 2 minutes, stirring.

3 Add the soaked mushrooms and cook for 7 minutes over a high heat until the edges become crisp. Add the sherry and the reserved liquid. Cook over a high heat for about 10 minutes until the liquid evaporates. Season and set aside to cool.

4 Preheat the oven to 200°C/ 400°F/Gas 6. Lightly grease four 10cm/4in tart tins (pans). Roll out the pastry on a lightly floured work surface and use to line the tart tins.

5 Prick the pastry, line with baking parchment and baking beans and bake blind for 10 minutes. Remove the paper and beans.

6 Whisk the egg and cream to mix, add to the mushroom mixture, then season to taste. Spoon into the pastry cases, top with cheese slices and bake for 18 minutes until the filling is set. Serve warm with rocket.

1 To make the pastry, rub the flour and butter together until it resembles fine breadcrumbs, then stir in the walnuts. Add the egg and mix to form a soft dough. Wrap the pastry in clear film (plastic wrap) and chill in the refrigerator for 30 minutes.

COOK'S TIP

You can prepare the pastry cases in advance, bake them blind for 10 minutes, then store in an airtight container for up to 2 days.

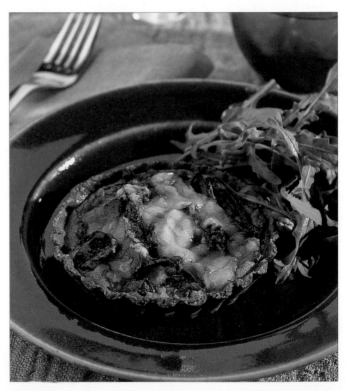

Energy 409kcal/1701kJ; Protein 10.2g; Carbohydrate 21.9g, of which sugars 2.3g; Fat 31g, of which saturates 13.4g; Cholesterol 143mg; Calcium 121mg; Fibre 2.3g; Sodium 199mg.

Mushroom, Nut and Prune Jalousie

JALOUSIE, THE FRENCH WORD for shutter, refers to this pie's slatted top. The pie has a rich, nutty filling and, served with crisp roast potatoes and steamed vegetables, makes a great alternative to the Sunday joint.

INGREDIENTS

75g/3oz/¹/3 cup green lentils, rinsed
5ml/1 tsp vegetable bouillon powder
15ml/1 tbsp sunflower oil
2 large leeks, sliced
2 garlic cloves, chopped
200g/7oz/3 cups field (portobello)
  mushrooms, finely chopped
10ml/2 tsp dried mixed herbs
75g/3oz/³/4 cup chopped mixed nuts
15ml/1 tbsp pine nuts (optional)
75g/3oz/¹/3 cup ready-to-eat pitted prunes
25g/1oz/¹/2 cup fresh breadcrumbs
2 eggs, beaten
2 sheets ready-rolled puff pastry, total
  weight about 425g/15oz
flour, for dusting
salt and freshly ground black pepper
Serves 6

1 Put the lentils in a pan and cover with cold water. Bring to the boil, then reduce the heat and add the vegetable bouillon powder. Partly cover the pan and simmer for 20 minutes or until the lentils are tender. Set aside.

2 Heat the oil in a large, heavy frying pan, add the leeks and garlic and fry for 5 minutes or until softened. Add the mushrooms and herbs and cook for a further 5 minutes. Transfer the mushroom mixture to a bowl using a slotted spoon. Stir in the nuts, pine nuts, if using, prunes, breadcrumbs and lentils.

COOK'S TIP

Try other combinations of vegetables, nuts and dried fruit.

3 Preheat the oven to 220°C/ 425°F/Gas 7. Add two-thirds of the beaten egg to the mushroom mixture and season well. Set aside and leave to cool.

4 Meanwhile, unroll one of the pastry sheets. Cut off 2.5cm/1 in from its width and length, then lay it on a dampened baking sheet. Unroll the second pastry sheet, dust lightly with flour, then fold in half lengthways. Make a series of cuts across the fold, 1cm/¹/2in apart, leaving a 2.5cm/1 in border around the edge of the pastry.

5 Spoon the mushroom mixture evenly over the pastry base, leaving a 2.5cm/1 in border. Dampen the edges of the pastry with water.

6 Open out the folded piece of pastry and lay it over the top of the filling. Trim the edges, if necessary, then press the edges of the pastry together to seal and crimp the edges.

7 Brush the top of the pastry with the remaining beaten egg and bake for 25–30 minutes until golden. Leave to cool slightly before serving.

Energy 523kcal/2179kJ; Protein 14g; Carbohydrate 38g, of which sugars 5g; Fat 36g, of which saturates 9g; Cholesterol 89mg; Calcium 101mg; Fibre 5g; Sodium 470mg.

Layered Polenta Bake

POLENTA, TOMATOES, SPINACH and
beans make a tasty supper dish.

INGREDIENTS
5ml/1 tsp salt
375g/13oz/3 cups fine polenta
olive oil, for greasing and brushing
25g/1oz/¹/3 cup freshly grated
    Parmesan cheese
salt and freshly ground black pepper

For the tomato sauce
15ml/1 tbsp olive oil
2 garlic cloves, chopped
400g/14oz/3 cups chopped tomatoes
15ml/1 tbsp chopped fresh sage
2.5ml/¹/2 tsp soft light brown sugar
200g/7oz/1 ¹/2 cups canned cannellini
    beans, rinsed and drained

For the spinach sauce
250g/9oz spinach, tough stalks removed
150ml/¹/4 pint/²/3 cup single (light) cream
115g/4oz/1 cup Gorgonzola cheese, cubed
large pinch of ground nutmeg
Serves 6

1 Make the polenta. Bring 2 litres/
3¹/2 pints/8 cups water to the boil
in a large, heavy pan and add the salt.
Remove the pan from the heat.
Gradually pour in the polenta,
whisking continuously.

2 Return the pan to the heat and
stir constantly for 15–20 minutes
until the polenta is thick and comes
away from the side of the pan. Remove
the pan from the heat.

3 Season well with pepper, then
spoon the polenta on to a wet
work surface or piece of marble. Using
a wet spatula, spread out the polenta
until it is 1cm/¹/2in thick. Leave to cool
for about 1 hour.

4 Preheat the oven to 190°C/
375°F/Gas 5. To make the tomato
sauce, heat the oil in a pan, then fry the
garlic for 1 minute. Add the tomatoes
and sage and bring to the boil. Reduce
the heat, add the sugar and seasoning,
and simmer for 10 minutes until
slightly reduced, stirring occasionally.
Stir in the beans and cook for a further
2 minutes.

5 Meanwhile, wash the spinach
thoroughly and place in a large
pan with only the water that clings to
the leaves. Cover the pan tightly and
cook over a medium heat for about
3 minutes or until tender, stirring
occasionally. Tip the spinach into a
colander and drain, then squeeze out
as much excess water as possible with
the back of a wooden spoon.

6 Heat the cream, cheese and
nutmeg in a small, heavy pan.
Bring to the boil, then reduce the heat.
Stir in the spinach and seasoning, then
cook gently until slightly thickened,
stirring frequently.

7 Cut the polenta into triangles,
then place a layer of polenta in an
oiled deep baking dish. Spoon over the
tomato sauce, then top with another
layer of polenta. Top with the spinach
sauce and cover with the remaining
polenta triangles. Brush with olive oil,
sprinkle with Parmesan and bake for
35–40 minutes. Heat the grill (broiler)
to high and grill (broil) until the top is
golden before serving.

Energy 457kcal/1904kJ; Protein 16g; Carbohydrate 54g, of which sugars 4g; Fat 19g, of which saturates 9g; Cholesterol 35mg; Calcium 261mg; Fibre 6g; Sodium 773mg.

Chestnut, Stilton and Ale Pie

THIS HEARTY WINTER DISH has a rich Guinness gravy and a herb pastry top. The Stilton adds a delicious creaminess but can be left out to make a less rich version of the pie.

INGREDIENTS

30ml/2 tbsp sunflower oil
2 large onions, chopped
500g/1¼lb/8 cups button (white)
   mushrooms, halved
3 carrots, sliced
1 parsnip, cut into thick slices
15ml/1 tbsp fresh thyme or
   5ml/1 tsp dried
2 bay leaves
250ml/8fl oz/1 cup Guinness
120ml/4fl oz/½ cup vegetable stock
5ml/1 tsp vegetarian Worcestershire sauce
5ml/1 tsp soft dark brown sugar
350g/12oz/3 cups canned chestnuts,
   drained and halved
30ml/2 tbsp plain (all-purpose) flour
150g/5oz/1¼ cups Stilton cheese, cubed
1 egg, beaten, or milk, to glaze
salt and freshly ground black pepper

For the pastry
115g/4oz/1 cup wholemeal
   (whole-wheat) flour
a pinch of salt
50g/2oz/4 tbsp unsalted butter or
   vegetable margarine
15ml/1 tbsp fresh thyme or
   5ml/1 tsp dried
Serves 4

1 To make the pastry, rub together the flour, salt and butter or margarine until the mixture resembles fine breadcrumbs. Add the thyme and enough water to form a soft dough.

HEALTH BENEFITS

Chestnuts contain useful amounts of B complex vitamins, potassium and calcium and, unlike other nuts, they are very low in fat.

2 Turn out the dough on to a floured board or work surface and knead for 1 minute until it forms a smooth dough. Wrap in clear film (plastic wrap) and chill for 30 minutes.

3 Meanwhile, to make the filling, heat the oil in a heavy pan and fry the onions for 5 minutes until softened, stirring occasionally. Add the mushrooms and cook for a further 3 minutes or until just tender. Add the carrots, parsnip and herbs, stir to combine and cover the pan. Cook for 3 minutes until slightly softened.

4 Pour in the Guinness, vegetable stock and Worcestershire sauce, then add the sugar and seasoning. Simmer, covered, for 5 minutes, stirring occasionally. Add the chestnuts.

5 Mix the flour to a paste with 30ml/ 2 tbsp water. Add to the Guinness mixture and cook, uncovered, for 5 minutes until the sauce thickens, stirring. Stir in the cheese and heat until melted, stirring constantly.

6 Preheat the oven to 220°C/ 425°F/Gas 7. Roll out the pastry to fit the top of a 1.5 litre/2½ pint/ 6¼ cup deep pie dish. Spoon the chestnut mixture into the dish. Dampen the edges of the dish and cover with the pastry. Seal, trim and crimp the edges. Cut a small slit in the top of the pie and use any surplus pastry to make pastry leaves. Brush with egg or milk and bake for 30 minutes until the pastry is golden.

Energy 666kcal/2782kJ; Protein 18.9g; Carbohydrate 70.3g, of which sugars 22.6g; Fat 32.7g, of which saturates 16.6g; Cholesterol 62mg; Calcium 238mg; Fibre 11g; Sodium 415mg.

Polenta Pan-pizza with Red Onions, Garlic Mushrooms and Mozzarella

THIS YEAST-FREE PIZZA IS COOKED in a frying pan rather than the oven. The slightly cakey texture of the base is complemented by the garlicky red onion and mushroom topping. Serve with a simple tomato and basil salad.

INGREDIENTS

30ml/2 tbsp olive oil
1 large red onion, sliced
3 garlic cloves, crushed
115g/4oz/1 1/2 cups brown cap (cremini)
    mushrooms, sliced
5ml/1 tsp dried oregano
115g/4oz mozzarella cheese, crumbled
15ml/1 tbsp pine nuts (optional)

For the pizza base

50g/2oz/1/2 cup unbleached plain
    (all-purpose) flour, sifted
2.5ml/1/2 tsp salt
115g/4oz/1 cup fine polenta
5ml/1 tsp baking powder
1 egg, beaten
150ml/1/4 pint/2/3 cup milk
25g/1oz/1/3 cup freshly grated
    Parmesan cheese
2.5ml/1/2 tsp dried chilli flakes
15ml/1 tbsp olive oil
Serves 2

1 To make the topping, heat half the olive oil in a heavy frying pan, add the sliced red onion and fry for gently 10 minutes until tender, stirring occasionally. Remove the onion from the pan and set aside.

2 Add the remaining oil to the pan and fry the garlic for 1 minute until slightly coloured. Add the sliced mushrooms and oregano and cook for 5 minutes more until the mushrooms are tender.

3 To make the pizza base, mix together the flour, salt, polenta and baking powder in a bowl. Make a well in the centre and add the egg. Gradually add the milk, and mix well with a fork to make into a thick, smooth batter. Stir in the Parmesan and chilli flakes.

4 Heat the olive oil in a 25cm/10in heavy flameproof frying pan until very hot. Spoon in the batter and spread evenly. Cook over a moderate heat for about 3 minutes or until the base is set. Remove the pan from the heat and run a knife around the edge of the pizza base.

5 Place a plate over the pan and, holding them tightly together, flip over. Slide the pizza base back into the pan on its uncooked side and cook for 2 minutes until golden.

6 Preheat the grill (broiler) to high. Spoon the onions over the base, then top with the mushroom mixture. Scatter the mozzarella on top, then grill (broil) for about 6 minutes until the mozzarella has melted. Sprinkle over the pine nuts (if using) and grill until golden. Serve cut into wedges.

Energy 782kcal/3262kJ; Protein 31.9g; Carbohydrate 77.1g, of which sugars 12.4g; Fat 39.1g, of which saturates 14.5g; Cholesterol 145mg; Calcium 540mg; Fibre 4.8g; Sodium 439mg.

Rocket and Tomato Pizza

PEPPERY ROCKET and fresh basil add colour and flavour to this crisp pizza.

INGREDIENTS

1 garlic clove, crushed
10ml/2 tsp olive oil, plus extra for drizzling
150g/5oz/1 cup canned chopped tomatoes
2.5ml/^{1}/2 tsp sugar
30ml/2 tbsp torn fresh basil leaves
2 tomatoes, seeded and chopped
150g/5oz/^{2}/3 cup mozzarella cheese, sliced
20g/^{3}/4oz/1 cup rocket (arugula) leaves
salt and freshly ground black pepper

For the pizza base

225g/8oz/2 cups strong white bread flour
5ml/1 tsp salt
2.5ml/^{1}/2 tsp easy-blend (rapid-rise)
   dried yeast
15ml/1 tbsp olive oil
Serves 2

1 To make the pizza base, place the flour, salt and yeast in a bowl. Make a well in the centre and add the oil and 150ml/^{1}/4 pint/^{2}/3 cup warm water. Mix with a round-bladed knife to form a soft dough.

2 Turn out the dough on to a lightly floured work surface and knead for 5 minutes. Cover with the upturned bowl or a dish towel and leave to rest for about 5 minutes, then knead for a further 5 minutes until the dough is smooth and elastic. Place in a lightly oiled bowl and cover. Leave in a warm place for about 45 minutes until doubled in bulk.

3 Preheat the oven to 220°C/ 425°F/Gas 7. Make the topping. Fry the garlic in the oil for 1 minute. Add the tomatoes and sugar, and cook for 5–7 minutes until reduced and thickened. Stir in the basil. Season.

VARIATION

To make a Roquefort and walnut pizza, replace half the strong white bread flour with wholemeal (whole-wheat) flour. Use 75g/3oz/^{3}/4 cup crumbled Roquefort cheese instead of the mozzarella. Omit the rocket (arugula) and use 30ml/2 tbsp chopped walnuts.

4 Knead the risen dough lightly, then roll out to form a rough 30cm/12in round. Place on a lightly oiled baking sheet and push up the edges of the dough to form a shallow, even rim.

5 Spoon the tomato mixture over the pizza base, then top with the chopped fresh tomatoes. Arrange the mozzarella on top. Season with salt and pepper and drizzle with a little olive oil. Bake in the top of the oven for 10–12 minutes until crisp and golden. Scatter the rocket over the pizza just before serving.

Energy 713kcal/3000kJ; Protein 28g; Carbohydrate 90g, of which sugars 6g; Fat 29g, of which saturates 12g; Cholesterol 44mg; Calcium 442mg; Fibre 5g; Sodium 1312mg.

Salads

Salads stepped off the sidelines long ago. For the past few decades they have been steadily growing in popularity and variety, as the proliferation of packs of fresh leaves in supermarkets proves. In addition to numerous different types of lettuce, shoppers can now choose rocket (arugula), chicory, baby spinach and fresh herbs, as well as an astonishing array of additional ingredients. Mix and match is the name of the game, and rice, lentils, beans, peas, nuts, seeds, couscous and seaweed can be added for bulk and extra nutrition. When shopping for saladstuffs, it is worth investigating small local growers, many of whom offer box schemes, and whose produce is often so fresh that you have to wait while they cut or lift it. It's never been easier to eat the recommended daily quota of five fresh vegetables and fruit, as these delicious recipes prove. Try Avocado, Red Onion and Spinach Salad with Polenta Croûtons, Feta and Mint Potato Salad, or Sesame Noodle Salad. Every one an original – and absolutely delicious.

Warm Vegetable Salad with Peanut Sauce

BASED ON THE CLASSIC Indonesian salad, gado-gado, this salad features raw red pepper and sprouted beans, which make a crunchy contrast to the warm steamed broccoli, green beans and carrots. Topped with slices of hard-boiled egg. this salad is substantial enough to serve as a main course.

INGREDIENTS

8 new potatoes
225g/8oz broccoli, cut into small florets
200g/7oz/1 1/2 cups fine green beans
2 carrots, cut into thin ribbons with a
    vegetable peeler
1 red (bell) pepper, seeded and cut into strips
50g/2oz/1/2 cup sprouted beans
sprigs of watercress, to garnish

For the peanut sauce
15ml/1 tbsp sunflower oil
1 bird's eye chilli, seeded and sliced
1 garlic clove, crushed
5ml/1 tsp ground coriander
5ml/1 tsp ground cumin
60ml/4 tbsp crunchy peanut butter
75ml/5 tbsp water
15ml/1 tbsp dark soy sauce
1cm/1/2in piece fresh root ginger,
    finely grated
5ml/1 tsp soft dark brown sugar
15ml/1 tbsp lime juice
60ml/4 tbsp coconut milk
Serves 2–4

HEALTH BENEFITS

Sprouted beans, which are available from health food stores and some supermarkets, are easily digestible and packed with concentrated goodness. When fresh, their vitamin and enzyme content is at its peak and they are believed to stimulate the body's ability to cleanse itself. They provide valuable amounts of vitamin E, which is said to improve fertility.

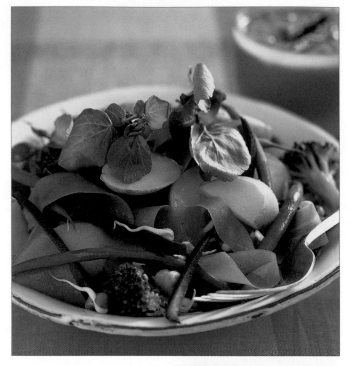

1 First make the peanut sauce. Heat the oil in a pan, add the chilli and garlic, and cook for 1 minute or until softened. Add the spices and cook for 1 minute. Stir in the peanut butter and water, then cook for 2 minutes until combined, stirring constantly.

2 Add the soy sauce, ginger, sugar, lime juice and coconut milk, then cook over a low heat until smooth and heated through, stirring frequently. Transfer to a bowl.

3 Bring a pan of lightly salted water to the boil, add the potatoes and cook for 10–15 minutes, until tender. Drain, then halve or thickly slice the potatoes, depending on their size.

4 Meanwhile, steam the broccoli and green beans for 4–5 minutes until tender but still crisp. Add the carrots 2 minutes before the end of the cooking time.

5 Arrange the cooked vegetables on a serving platter with the red pepper and sprouted beans. Garnish with watercress and serve with the peanut sauce.

Energy 257kcal/1058kJ; Protein 10g; Carbohydrate 19g, of which sugars 8g; Fat 16g, of which saturates 3g; Cholesterol 0mg; Calcium 81mg; Fibre 5g; Sodium 380mg.

Avocado, Red Onion and Spinach Salad with Polenta Croûtons

THE SIMPLE LEMON DRESSING gives a sharp tang to the creamy avocado, sweet red onions and crisp spinach. Golden polenta croûtons, with their crunchy golden exterior and soft centre, add a delicious contrast.

INGREDIENTS

1 large red onion, cut into wedges
300g/11oz ready-made polenta,
*   cut into 1cm/1⁄2in cubes*
olive oil, for brushing
225g/8oz baby spinach leaves
1 avocado, peeled, stoned (pitted) and sliced
5ml/1 tsp lemon juice

For the dressing
60ml/4 tbsp extra virgin olive oil
juice of 1⁄2 lemon
salt and freshly ground black pepper
Serves 4

1 Preheat the oven to 200°C/400°F/ Gas 6. Place the onion wedges and polenta cubes on a lightly oiled baking sheet and bake for 25 minutes or until the onion is tender and the polenta is crisp and golden, turning them regularly to prevent them sticking. Leave to cool slightly.

2 Meanwhile, make the dressing. Place the olive oil, lemon juice and seasoning to taste in a bowl or screw-top jar. Stir or shake thoroughly to combine.

3 Place the spinach leaves in a serving bowl. Toss the avocado in the lemon juice to prevent it browning, then add to the spinach with the roasted onions.

4 Pour the dressing over the salad and toss gently to combine. Sprinkle the polenta croûtons on top or hand them round separately and serve immediately.

HEALTH BENEFITS

Avocados have been traditionally regarded as a high fat food that should be avoided. However, although they do contain high amounts of fat, it is beneficial monounsaturated fat, and new research has revealed that regularly eating avocados can actually decrease the level of cholesterol in the body. Avocados also have a valuable mineral content and eating them can improve the condition of your skin and hair.

COOK'S TIP

If you can't find ready-made polenta, you can make your own using instant polenta grains. Simply cook according to the packet instructions, then pour into a tray and leave to cool and set.

Energy 519kcal/2155kJ; Protein 9g; Carbohydrate 52g, of which sugars 5g; Fat 30g, of which saturates 4g; Cholesterol 0mg; Calcium 117mg; Fibre 6g; Sodium 83mg.

Roasted Tomato and Mozzarella Salad with Basil Dressing

ROASTING THE TOMATOES adds a new dimension to this salad. Make the basil oil just before serving to retain its fresh flavour and vivid colour.

INGREDIENTS

6 large plum tomatoes
olive oil, for brushing
2 balls fresh mozzarella cheese,
    cut into 8–12 slices
salt and freshly ground black pepper
basil leaves, to garnish

For the basil oil
25 basil leaves
60ml/4 tbsp extra virgin olive oil
1 garlic clove, crushed
Serves 4

Preheat the oven to 200°C/400°F/ Gas 6 and oil a baking tray. Cut the tomatoes in half lengthways and remove the seeds. Place the tomatoes skin-side down on the baking tray and roast for 20 minutes or until the tomatoes are tender but still retain their shape.

2 Meanwhile, make the basil oil. Place the basil leaves, olive oil and garlic in a food processor or blender and process until smooth. Transfer to a bowl and chill until required.

3 For each serving, place the tomato halves on top of 2 or 3 slices of mozzarella and drizzle over the oil. Season well. Garnish with basil leaves and serve at once.

HEALTH BENEFITS

Basil is a natural tranquillizer and calms the nervous system. It can also stimulate the appetite and is good for the digestion, easing cramps and nausea.

Mixed Herb Salad with Toasted Mixed Seeds

THIS SIMPLE SALAD is the perfect antidote to a rich, heavy meal as it contains fresh herbs that can ease the digestion. Balsamic vinegar adds a rich, sweet taste to the dressing, but red or white wine vinegar could be used instead.

INGREDIENTS

90g/3¹/₂oz/4 cups mixed salad leaves
50g/2oz/2 cups mixed salad herbs, such as
    coriander (cilantro), parsley, basil and
    rocket (arugula)
25g/1oz/3 tbsp pumpkin seeds
25g/1oz/3 tbsp sunflower seeds

For the dressing
60ml/4 tbsp extra virgin olive oil
15ml/1 tbsp balsamic vinegar
2.5 ml/¹/₂ tsp Dijon mustard
salt and freshly ground black pepper
Serves 4

To make the dressing, combine the ingredients in a bowl or screw-top jar, shake or mix with a small whisk or fork until combined.

HEALTH BENEFITS

• *Parsley contains useful amounts of vitamin C and iron.*
• *Pumpkin and sunflower seeds, although high in calories, are full of useful vitamins, minerals and fibre, including iron, vitamin E and zinc.*

2 Put the salad and herb leaves in a large bowl.

3 Toast the pumpkin and sunflower seeds in a dry frying pan over a medium heat for 2 minutes until golden, tossing frequently to prevent them burning. Allow the seeds to cool slightly before sprinkling them over the salad.

4 Pour the dressing over the salad and toss with your hands until the leaves are well coated, then serve.

Tomato: Energy 303kcal/1257kJ; Protein 9g; Carbohydrate 7g, of which sugars 7g; Fat 27g, of which saturates 8g; Cholesterol 23mg; Calcium 170mg; Fibre 3g; Sodium 179mg.
Herb: Energy 214kcal/882kJ; Protein 3g; Carbohydrate 3g, of which sugars 1g; Fat 21g, of which saturates 3g; Cholesterol 0mg; Calcium 20mg; Fibre 3g; Sodium 32mg.

Feta and Mint Potato Salad

FETA CHEESE, YOGURT AND fresh mint combine with potatoes in this salad.

INGREDIENTS

500g/1¼lb salad potatoes, such as
    Pink Fir Apple potatoes
90g/3½oz feta cheese, crumbled

For the dressing
225g/8oz/1 cup live natural (plain) yogurt
15g/½oz/½ cup fresh mint leaves
30ml/2 tbsp mayonnaise
salt and freshly ground black pepper
Serves 4

I Steam the potatoes over a pan of boiling water for about 20 minutes until tender, then drain well and tip into a large bowl.

2 Meanwhile, make the dressing. Place the yogurt and mint in a food processor and process for a few minutes until the mint leaves are finely chopped. Transfer to a small bowl.

3 Stir in the mayonnaise and season with salt and pepper to taste. Spoon the dressing over the warm potatoes and scatter with the feta cheese. Serve immediately or cover and leave to cool.

COOK'S TIPS

Pink Fir Apple potatoes have a smooth waxy texture and retain their shape when cooked, making them ideal for salads. Charlotte and other special salad potatoes could be used instead.

HEALTH BENEFITS

Potatoes are often considered to be fattening, but it is usually the method of preparation that is to be blamed. Steaming adds no calories and preserves the vitamin C content.

Apple and Beetroot Salad with Red Leaves

BITTER LEAVES ARE COMPLEMENTED by sweet-flavoured apples and beetroot in this summer salad.

INGREDIENTS

50g/2oz/⅓ cup whole
    unblanched almonds
2 red apples, cored and diced
juice of ½ lemon
115g/4oz/4 cups red salad leaves, such as
    lollo rosso, oak leaf and radicchio
200g/7oz cooked beetroot (beets) in
    natural juice, sliced

For the dressing
30ml/2 tbsp olive oil
15ml/1 tbsp walnut oil
15ml/1 tbsp red or white wine vinegar
salt and freshly ground black pepper
Serves 4

I Toast the almonds in a dry frying pan for 2–3 minutes until golden brown, tossing frequently to prevent them burning.

2 Meanwhile, make the dressing. Put the olive and walnut oils, vinegar and seasoning in a bowl or screw-top jar. Stir or shake thoroughly to combine and make a thick dressing.

3 Toss the apples in lemon juice to prevent them browning, then place in a large bowl and add the salad leaves, beetroot and almonds. Pour over the dressing and toss gently.

HEALTH BENEFITS

Red fruits and vegetables have high levels of vitamins C and E and beta carotene.

Feta: Energy 246kcal/1031kJ; Protein 9g; Carbohydrate 26g, of which sugars 6g; Fat 12g, of which saturates 5g; Cholesterol 28mg; Calcium 200mg; Fibre 2g; Sodium 412mg.
Apple: Energy 225kcal/932kJ; Protein 4g; Carbohydrate 11g, of which sugars 11g; Fat 18g, of which saturates 2g; Cholesterol 0mg; Calcium 51mg; Fibre 4g; Sodium 37mg.

Sesame Noodle Salad

TOASTED SESAME OIL ADDS a nutty flavour to this Asian-style salad. Best served warm, it is substantial enough to serve as a main meal.

INGREDIENTS

250g/9oz medium egg noodles
200g/7oz/1 cup sugar snap peas or
    mangetouts (snow peas), sliced diagonally
2 carrots, cut into julienne
2 tomatoes, seeded and diced
30ml/2 tbsp chopped fresh
    coriander (cilantro)
15ml/1 tbsp sesame seeds
3 spring onions (scallions), shredded
fresh coriander, to garnish

For the dressing

10ml/2 tsp light soy sauce
30ml/2 tbsp toasted sesame seed oil
15ml/1 tbsp sunflower oil
4cm/1¹/₂in piece fresh root ginger, grated
1 garlic clove, crushed
Serves 2–4

1 Place the noodles in a pan of lightly salted boiling water and bring back to the boil. Cook for 2 minutes, then add the sugar snap peas or mangetouts and cook for a further 2 minutes. Drain and rinse under cold running water to halt the cooking.

HEALTH BENEFITS

Garlic is highly antiseptic, particularly in its raw form, and, like ginger, can help the body to ward off colds and flu and stimulate circulation.

2 Meanwhile, make the dressing. Combine the soy sauce, sesame and sunflower oils, ginger and garlic in a screw-top jar or bowl. Shake or mix to combine thoroughly.

3 Place the noodles and the peas or mangetouts in a bowl and add the carrots, tomatoes and coriander. Pour the dressing over the top, and toss with your hands to combine. Sprinkle with the sesame seeds and top with the spring onions and coriander.

Japanese Salad

HIJIKI IS A MILD-TASTING seaweed, and combined with radishes, cucumber and beansprouts, it makes a delicate, refreshing salad.

INGREDIENTS

15g/¹/₂oz/¹/₂ cup hijiki
250g/9oz/1¹/₄ cups radishes, sliced into
    very thin rounds
1 small cucumber, cut into thin sticks
75g/3oz/¹/₂ cup beansprouts

For the dressing

15ml/1 tbsp sunflower oil
15ml/1 tbsp toasted sesame oil
5ml/1 tsp light soy sauce
30ml/2 tbsp rice vinegar or 15ml/1 tbsp
    wine vinegar
15ml/1 tbsp mirin
Serves 4

1 Soak the hijiki in a bowl of cold water for 10–15 minutes until rehydrated, drain, rinse under cold running water and drain again. It should almost triple in volume.

2 Place the hijiki in a pan of water. Bring to the boil, then reduce the heat and simmer for about 30 minutes or until tender. Drain.

3 Meanwhile, make the dressing. Place the sunflower and sesame oils, soy sauce, vinegar and mirin in a bowl or screw-top jar. Stir or shake thoroughly to combine.

4 Arrange the hijiki in a shallow bowl or platter with the radishes, cucumber and beansprouts. Pour over the dressing and toss lightly. Serve immediately.

HEALTH BENEFITS

Hijiki is treasured as one of nature's richest sources of minerals, the balance of which is said to counteract high blood pressure. The seaweed has a distinguished reputation in Japan for enhancing beauty and adding lustre to hair.

Sesame: Energy 409kcal/1719kJ; Protein 11g; Carbohydrate 53g, of which sugars 8g; Fat 19g, of which saturates 3g; Cholesterol 19mg; Calcium 86mg; Fibre 7g; Sodium 308mg.
Japanese: Energy 99kcal/400kJ; Protein 3g; Carbohydrate 3g, of which sugars 3g; Fat 8g, of which saturates 1g; Cholesterol 0mg; Calcium 44mg; Fibre 2g; Sodium 129mg.

White Bean Salad with Roasted Red Pepper Dressing

THE SPECKLED HERB AND RED pepper dressing adds a wonderful colour contrast to this salad, which is best served warm. Canned beans are used for convenience – substitute cooked, dried beans, if you prefer.

INGREDIENTS

1 large red (bell) pepper
60ml/4 tbsp olive oil
1 large garlic clove, crushed
25g/1oz/1 cup fresh oregano leaves or
*   flat leaf parsley*
15ml/1 tbsp balsamic vinegar
400g/14oz/3 cups canned flageolet or
*   small cannellini beans, drained and rinsed*
200g/7oz/1 1/2 cups canned cannellini
*   beans, drained and rinsed*
salt and freshly ground black pepper
Serves 4

1 Preheat the oven to 200°C/400°F/ Gas 6. Place the red pepper on a baking sheet, brush with oil and roast for 30 minutes or until the skin wrinkles and the flesh is soft.

2 Remove the pepper from the oven and place in a plastic bag. Seal and leave to cool. (This makes the skin easier to remove.)

3 When the pepper is cool enough to handle, remove it from the bag and peel off the skin. Rinse under cold running water. Slice the pepper in half, remove the seeds and dice. Set aside.

4 Heat the remaining oil in a pan and cook the garlic for 1 minute until softened. Remove from the heat, then add the oregano or parsley, the red pepper and any juices, and the balsamic vinegar.

5 Put the beans in a large bowl and pour over the dressing. Season to taste, then stir gently until combined. Serve warm.

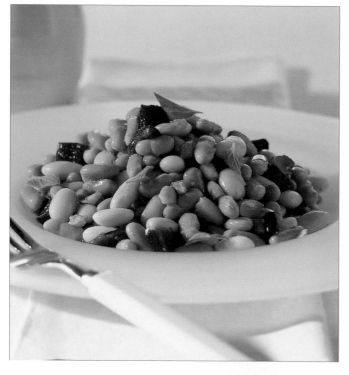

HEALTH BENEFITS

Low in fat and high in fibre and protein, pulses such as cannellini beans should be a regular part of a healthy balanced diet. They are also a good source of many minerals, including iron, potassium, phosphorus and magnesium, as well as B complex vitamins.

Energy 208kcal/864kJ; Protein 4g; Carbohydrate 13g, of which sugars 4g; Fat 16g, of which saturates 2g; Cholesterol 0mg; Calcium 33mg; Fibre 3g; Sodium 7mg.

Roasted Beetroot with Horseradish Dressing

FRESH BEETROOT IS ENJOYING a well-deserved renaissance. Roasting gives it a delicious sweet flavour, which contrasts wonderfully with this sharp, tangy dressing.

INGREDIENTS

450g/1lb baby beetroot (beets), preferably with leaves
15ml/1 tbsp olive oil

For the dressing

30ml/2 tbsp lemon juice
30ml/2 tbsp mirin
120ml/8 tbsp olive oil
30ml/2 tbsp creamed horseradish
salt and freshly ground black pepper

Serves 4

1 Cook the beetroot in boiling salted water for 30 minutes. Drain, add the olive oil and toss gently. Preheat the oven to 200°C/400°F/Gas 6.

2 Place the beetroot on a baking sheet and roast for 40 minutes or until tender when pierced with a knife.

3 Meanwhile, make the dressing. Whisk together the lemon juice, mirin, olive oil and horseradish until smooth and creamy. Season.

4 Cut the beetroot in half, place in a bowl and add the dressing. Toss gently and serve immediately.

HEALTH BENEFITS

Beetroot (beet) has a reputation for containing cancer-fighting compounds and is thought to enhance the immune system. It is a powerful blood-purifier and is rich in iron, vitamins C and A, and folates, which are essential for maintaining healthy cells.

COOK'S TIP

This salad is probably at its best served warm, but you can cook the beetroots (beet) in advance, if more convenient, and serve the dish at room temperature. Add the dressing to the beetroot just before serving.

Energy 365kcal/1507kJ; Protein 2g; Carbohydrate 10g, of which sugars 9g; Fat 34g, of which saturates 5g; Cholesterol 1mg; Calcium 27mg; Fibre 3g; Sodium 143mg.

Watercress, Pear, Walnut and Roquefort Salad

SHARP-TASTING BLUE ROQUEFORT and peppery watercress leaves are complemented in this salad by sweet pears and crunchy walnuts.

INGREDIENTS

75g/3oz/1/2 cup shelled walnuts, halved
2 red Williams pears, cored and sliced
15ml/1 tbsp lemon juice
150g/5oz/1 large bunch watercress, tough
   stalks removed
200g/7oz/scant 2 cups Roquefort cheese,
   cut into chunks

For the dressing
45ml/3 tbsp extra virgin olive oil
30ml/2 tbsp lemon juice
2.5ml/1/2 tsp clear honey
5ml/1 tsp Dijon mustard
salt and freshly ground black pepper
Serves 4

1 Toast the walnuts in a dry frying pan for 2 minutes until golden, tossing frequently to prevent them burning.

HEALTH BENEFITS

Watercress is reputed to energize the liver, kidney and bladder. It provides vitamins A and C, thought to play a role in combating cancer. It also contains natural antibiotic compounds.

2 Meanwhile, make the dressing. Place the olive oil, lemon juice, honey, mustard and seasoning in a bowl or screw-top jar. Stir or shake thoroughly to combine.

3 Toss the pear slices in the lemon juice, then place them in a bowl and add the watercress, walnuts and Roquefort. Pour the dressing over the salad, toss well and serve immediately.

Panzanella

OPEN-TEXTURED, ITALIAN-STYLE bread is essential for this colourful, classic Tuscan salad.

INGREDIENTS

275g/10oz/10 slices day-old Italian-style
   bread, thickly sliced
1 cucumber, peeled and cut into chunks
5 tomatoes, seeded and diced
1 large red onion, chopped
200g/7oz/11/3 cups good-quality olives
20 basil leaves, torn

For the dressing
60ml/4 tbsp extra virgin olive oil
15ml/1 tbsp red or white wine vinegar
salt and freshly ground black pepper
Serves 6

1 Soak the bread in water for about 2 minutes, then lift out and squeeze gently, first with your hands and then in a dish towel to remove any excess water. Chill for 1 hour.

HEALTH BENEFITS

Rich in healthy monounsaturated fat, olives act as a gentle laxative and have a soothing effect on the digestive system.

2 Meanwhile, to make the dressing, place the oil, vinegar and seasoning in a bowl or screw-top jar. Shake or mix thoroughly to combine. Place the cucumber, tomatoes, onion and olives in a bowl.

3 Break the bread into chunks and add to the bowl with the basil. Pour the dressing over the salad, and toss before serving.

Watercress: Energy 461kcal/1909kJ; Protein 14g; Carbohydrate 9g, of which sugars 9g; Fat 41g, of which saturates 13g; Cholesterol 45mg; Calcium 356mg; Fibre 4g; Sodium 894mg.
Panzanella: Energy 282kcal/1179kJ; Protein 6g; Carbohydrate 30g, of which sugars 7g; Fat 16g, of which saturates 2g; Cholesterol 0mg; Calcium 101mg; Fibre 3g; Sodium 1007mg.

Side Dishes

Put as much thought into your selection of side dishes as you do when choosing your main course and you'll find it easy to turn out healthy, well-balanced meals. This eclectic selection of recipes is based largely on vegetables, which are valued for the cancer-thwarting phytochemicals, antioxidants, vitamins, minerals and fibre they contribute to our diet. Brightly coloured orange and green vegetables are particularly rich in nutrients, but they must be cooked carefully. Baking, steaming and stir-frying are better than boiling, for instance, when vitamins and minerals are lost to the cooking water. Baked Fennel with a Crumb Crust, Courgettes in Rich Tomato Sauce and Garlic Sweet Potato Mash are as delicious as they are nutritious, and Spring Vegetable Stir-fry is a positive power-house of goodness, including baby carrots, spring greens, asparagus and broccoli. Ordinary potatoes shouldn't be forgotten as they are a major source of vitamin C – try them sliced and baked with mustard-flavoured butter, or roast new potatoes with fresh rosemary and plenty of garlic.

Potato Pan Gratin

POTATOES, LAYERED WITH mustard butter and baked until golden, are perfect to serve with a green salad for supper, or as an accompaniment to a vegetable or nut roast.

INGREDIENTS

4 large potatoes, total weight about 900g/2lb
25g/1oz/2 tbsp butter
15ml/1 tbsp olive oil
2 large garlic cloves, crushed
30ml/2 tbsp Dijon mustard
15ml/1 tbsp lemon juice
15ml/1 tbsp fresh thyme leaves,
 plus extra to garnish
50ml/2fl oz/1/4 cup vegetable stock
salt and freshly ground black pepper
Serves 4

VARIATION

Any root vegetables can be used: try celeriac, parsnips, swede (rutabaga) or turnips.

1 Thinly slice the potatoes using a knife or a slicing attachment on a food processor. Place in a bowl of cold water to prevent them discolouring.

2 Preheat the oven to 200°C/400°F/Gas 6. Heat the butter and oil in a deep, flameproof frying pan or skillet. Add the garlic and cook gently for 3 minutes until light golden, stirring constantly. Stir in the mustard, lemon juice and thyme. Remove from the heat and pour into a jug (pitcher).

3 Drain the potatoes and pat dry with kitchen paper. Place a layer of potatoes in the frying pan or skillet, season and pour over one-third of the butter mixture. Place another layer of potatoes on top, season, and pour over another third of the butter mixture. Arrange a final layer of potatoes on top, pour over the rest of the butter mixture and then the stock. Season and sprinkle with the reserved thyme.

4 Cover the top with baking parchment and bake for 1 hour, then remove the paper and cook for a further 15 minutes or until golden.

HEALTH BENEFITS

Potatoes are a high-carbohydrate food that provide sustained energy. Baking them rather than boiling helps to retain their vitamin C content.

Garlic Sweet Potato Mash

DELICIOUS MASHED WITH garlicky butter, orange-fleshed sweet potatoes not only look good, they're packed with vitamins and make a welcome change to potatoes.

INGREDIENTS

4 large sweet potatoes, total weight about
 900g/2lb, cubed
40g/1 1/2oz/3 tbsp unsalted butter
3 garlic cloves, crushed
salt and freshly ground black pepper
Serves 4

HEALTH BENEFITS

Orange-fleshed sweet potatoes are rich in beta carotene and vitamins C and E, which are believed to be linked with lowering the risk of cancer, heart disease and strokes.

1 Cook the sweet potatoes in a large pan of boiling salted water for about 15 minutes or until tender, then drain and return to the pan.

COOK'S TIPS

• *If the sweet potatoes seem to be on the dry side when you are mashing them, add a little milk.*
• *Add some chopped herbs, if you wish.*

2 Melt the butter in a heavy pan, then sauté the garlic over a low to medium heat for 1–2 minutes until light golden, stirring to prevent the garlic burning.

3 Pour the garlic butter over the sweet potatoes, season with salt and plenty of black pepper, and mash thoroughly until smooth and creamy. Serve immediately.

Gratin: Energy 238kcal/1002kJ; Protein 3.9g; Carbohydrate 36.3g, of which sugars 3g; Fat 9.6g, of which saturates 4.5g; Cholesterol 16mg; Calcium 15mg; Fibre 2.3g; Sodium 70mg.
Mash: Energy 586kcal/2477kJ; Protein 16.3g; Carbohydrate 101.4g, of which sugars 52.1g; Fat 15.8g, of which saturates 7.1g; Cholesterol 240mg; Calcium 182mg; Fibre 2.8g; Sodium 968mg.

Split Pea and Shallot Mash

GREATLY UNDERRATED and under-used, split peas can make a fantastic purée. When this is enlivened with herbs and spices, the purée makes an excellent alternative to mashed potatoes, and is particularly good with winter pies and nut roasts. It can also be served with warmed pitta bread, accompanied by diced tomatoes and a splash of olive oil.

INGREDIENTS

225g/8oz/1 cup yellow split peas
1 bay leaf
8 sage leaves, roughly chopped
15ml/1 tbsp olive oil
3 shallots, finely chopped
8ml/heaped 1 tsp cumin seeds
1 large garlic clove, chopped
50g/2oz/4 tbsp butter, softened
salt and freshly ground black pepper

Serves 4–6

1 Place the split peas in a bowl and cover with cold water. Leave to soak overnight, then rinse and drain.

2 Place the peas in a pan, cover with fresh cold water and bring to the boil. Skim off any foam that rises to the surface, then reduce the heat. Add the bay leaf and sage, and simmer for 30–40 minutes until the peas are tender. Add more water during cooking, if necessary.

3 Meanwhile, heat the oil in a frying pan and cook the shallots, cumin seeds and garlic for 3 minutes or until the shallots soften, stirring occasionally. Add the mixture to the split peas while they are still cooking.

4 Drain the split peas, reserving the cooking water. Remove the bay leaf, then place the split peas in a food processor or blender with the butter and season well.

5 Add 105ml/7 tbsp of the reserved cooking water and blend until the mixture forms a coarse purée. Add more water if the mash seems to be too dry. Adjust the seasoning and serve warm.

HEALTH BENEFITS

Split peas, like other pulses, are an excellent source of protein, fibre, minerals and B vitamins. They are particularly good for diabetics as they can help to control blood sugar levels.

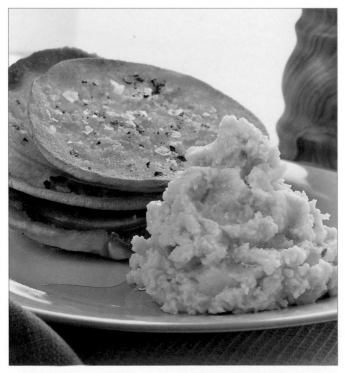

Energy 213kcal/895kJ; Protein 9g; Carbohydrate 23g, of which sugars 2g; Fat 10g, of which saturates 5g; Cholesterol 18mg; Calcium 18mg; Fibre 4g; Sodium 65mg.

Root Vegetable Gratin with Indian Spices

SUBTLY SPICED WITH CURRY powder, turmeric, coriander, this rich gratin is substantial enough to serve on its own for lunch or supper. It also makes a good accompaniment to a vegetable or bean curry.

INGREDIENTS

2 large potatoes, total weight about
     450g/1lb
2 sweet potatoes, total weight about
     275g/10oz
175g/6oz celeriac
15ml/1 tbsp unsalted butter
5ml/1 tsp curry powder
5ml/1 tsp ground turmeric
2.5ml/^{1}/2 tsp ground coriander
5ml/1 tsp mild chilli powder
3 shallots, chopped
salt and freshly ground black pepper
150ml/^{1}/4 pint/^{2}/3 cup single (light) cream
150ml/^{1}/4 pint/^{2}/3 cup milk
chopped fresh flat leaf parsley,
     to garnish

Serves 4

I Thinly slice the potatoes, sweet potatoes and celeriac, using a sharp knife or the slicing attachment on a food processor. Immediately place the vegetables in a bowl of cold water to prevent them discolouring.

VARIATION

Use semi-skimmed (low-fat) milk, if you prefer a less rich gratin.

2 Preheat the oven to 180°C/ 350°F/Gas 4. Heat half the butter in a heavy pan, add the curry powder, turmeric and coriander and half the chilli powder. Cook for 2 minutes, then leave to cool slightly.

3 Drain the vegetables, then pat dry. Place in a bowl, add the spice mixture and the shallots and mix well.

HEALTH BENEFITS

This gratin contains ground spices, which boost a sluggish digestion and have a beneficial effect on the circulation.

4 Arrange the vegetables in a gratin dish, seasoning between the layers. Mix together the cream and milk, pour the mixture over the vegetables, then sprinkle the remaining chilli powder on top.

5 Cover with greaseproof (waxed) paper and bake for about 45 minutes. Remove the greaseproof paper, dot with the remaining butter and bake for a further 50 minutes until the top is golden.

6 Serve immediately, garnished with chopped fresh parsley.

Energy 278kcal/1169kJ; Protein 7g; Carbohydrate 39g, of which sugars 9g; Fat 12g, of which saturates 7g; Cholesterol 31mg; Calcium 124mg; Fibre 6g; Sodium 103mg.

Rosemary and Garlic Roasted New Potatoes

THESE NEW POTATOES, FLAVOURED with fresh rosemary and lots of garlic, are good with vegetable stews.

INGREDIENTS

800g/1³/4lb small new potatoes
5 garlic cloves, peeled and bruised
3 sprigs of rosemary
30ml/2 tbsp olive oil
sea salt and freshly ground black pepper
Serves 4

HEALTH BENEFITS

So much can be said about the healing power of garlic. It is particularly valued for its ability to boost the immune system. As a result, it has been found to be helpful in treating AIDS patients.

1 Preheat the oven to 200°C/400°F/ Gas 6. Put the potatoes, garlic and rosemary in a roasting pan. Add the oil and toss to coat. Season well.

VARIATION

Shallots can be roasted in the same way. Cook for 35 minutes or until tender.

2 Bake for 40–45 minutes until the potatoes are crisp on the outside and soft in the centre.

3 Remove the pan from the oven halfway through cooking and shake the pan to turn the potatoes and coat them in oil. Discard the rosemary and garlic, if you wish, and serve hot.

Honey-glazed Carrots

NATURALLY SWEET CARROTS, sautéed in a glossy honey and mustard glaze, make a delicious accompaniment to all sorts of vegetarian main courses.

INGREDIENTS

450g/1lb/2¹/2 cups carrots, cut into
    thick matchsticks
25g/1oz/2 tbsp butter
15ml/1 tbsp olive oil
1 garlic clove, crushed
15ml/1 tbsp chopped fresh rosemary leaves
5ml/1 tsp Dijon mustard
10ml/2 tsp clear honey
Serves 4

COOK'S TIP

Other root vegetables, such as parsnips, celeriac, baby turnips and swede (rutabaga) can be cooked in this glaze. Buy organic vegetables whenever possible and simply scrub, or peel very thinly.

1 Steam the carrots over a pan of boiling water for 2–4 minutes until just tender.

HEALTH BENEFITS

Carrots are a rich source of beta carotene, the plant form of vitamin A (just one carrot supplies enough of this vitamin for an entire day). A deficiency of vitamin A leads to night blindness, so the old saying that carrots help you see in the dark may be based on fact.

2 Heat the butter and oil in a heavy pan, add the garlic and rosemary and cook, stirring, for 1 minute or until the garlic is golden brown.

3 Add the carrots, mustard and honey to the pan, and cook, stirring constantly, for 2 minutes or until the carrots are only just tender. Serve immediately.

Potatoes: Energy 171kcal/721kJ; Protein 3.9g; Carbohydrate 31.8g, of which sugars 2.9g; Fat 3.9g, of which saturates 0.7g; Cholesterol 0mg; Calcium 41mg; Fibre 2.8g; Sodium 26mg.
Carrots: Energy 122kcal/507kJ; Protein 1g; Carbohydrate 11.1g, of which sugars 10.4g; Fat 8.6g, of which saturates 2.8g; Cholesterol 1mg; Calcium 32mg; Fibre 2.7g; Sodium 85mg.

Courgettes in Rich Tomato Sauce

THIS RICH-FLAVOURED Mediterranean dish can be served hot or cold, either as a side dish or as part of a tapas meal. Cut the courgettes into fairly thick slices, so that they stay slightly crunchy.

INGREDIENTS

15ml/1 tbsp olive oil
1 onion, chopped
1 garlic clove, chopped
4 courgettes (zucchini), thickly sliced
400g/14oz/3 cups canned chopped
   tomatoes, strained
2 tomatoes, peeled, seeded
   and chopped
5ml/1 tsp vegetable bouillon powder
15ml/1 tbsp tomato purée (paste)
salt and freshly ground black pepper
Serves 4

1 Heat the oil in a heavy pan, add the onion and garlic and sauté for 5 minutes or until the onion is softened, stirring occasionally. Add the courgettes and cook for a further 5 minutes.

VARIATION

Add 1 or 2 sliced and seeded red (bell) peppers with the courgettes (zucchini) in step 1.

2 Add the canned and fresh tomatoes, bouillon powder and tomato purée. Stir well, then simmer for 10–15 minutes until the sauce is thickened and the courgettes are just tender. Season to taste and serve.

HEALTH BENEFITS

Like carrots, courgettes (zucchini) are a source of beta carotene and vitamin C.

Baked Fennel with a Crumb Crust

THE DELICATE ANISEED FLAVOUR of baked fennel makes it a very good accompaniment to all sorts of pasta dishes and risottos.

INGREDIENTS

3 fennel bulbs, cut lengthways into quarters
30ml/2 tbsp olive oil
1 garlic clove, chopped
50g/2oz/1 cup day-old wholemeal
   (whole-wheat) breadcrumbs
30ml/2 tbsp chopped fresh flat leaf parsley
salt and freshly ground black pepper
fennel leaves, to garnish (optional)
Serves 4

VARIATION

To make a cheese-topped version of this dish, add 60ml/4 tbsp finely grated strong-flavoured cheese, such as mature (sharp) Cheddar, Red Leicester or Parmesan, to the mixture in step 3.

1 Cook the fennel in a pan of boiling salted water for 10 minutes or until just tender.

2 Drain the fennel and place in a baking dish or roasting pan, then brush with half of the olive oil. Preheat the oven to 190°C/375°F/Gas 5.

HEALTH BENEFITS

A natural diuretic, fennel is also known for its ability to relieve wind and flatulence.

3 In a small bowl, mix together the garlic, breadcrumbs and parsley with the rest of the oil. Sprinkle the mixture evenly over the fennel, then season well.

4 Bake for 30 minutes or until the fennel is tender and the breadcrumbs are crisp and golden. Serve hot, garnished with a few fennel leaves, if you wish.

Courgettes: Energy 104kcal/433kJ; Protein 5g; Carbohydrate 11g, of which sugars 10g; Fat 5g, of which saturates 1g; Cholesterol 0mg; Calcium 64mg; Fibre 2g; Sodium 183mg.
Fennel: Energy 113kcal/471kJ; Protein 3g; Carbohydrate 8g, of which sugars 3g; Fat 8g, of which saturates 1g; Cholesterol 0mg; Calcium 49mg; Fibre 1g; Sodium 77mg.

Spring Vegetable Stir-fry

FAST, FRESH AND PACKED WITH healthy vegetables, this stir-fry is delicious served with marinated tofu and rice or noodles.

INGREDIENTS

15ml/1 tbsp vegetable oil
5ml/1 tsp toasted sesame oil
1 garlic clove, chopped
2.5cm/1in piece fresh root ginger,
    finely chopped
225g/8oz baby carrots
350g/12oz/3 cups broccoli florets
175g/6oz/1/3 cup asparagus tips
2 spring onions (scallions), cut on the diagonal
175g/6oz/1 1/2 cups spring greens
    (collards), finely shredded
30ml/2 tbsp light soy sauce
15ml/1 tbsp apple juice
15ml/1 tbsp sesame seeds, toasted
Serves 4

1 Heat a frying pan or wok over a high heat. Add the vegetable oil and the sesame oil, and reduce the heat. Add the garlic and sauté gently for 2 minutes.

2 Add the chopped ginger, carrots, broccoli and asparagus tips to the pan and stir-fry for 4 minutes. Add the spring onions and spring greens and stir-fry for a further 2 minutes.

3 Add the soy sauce and apple juice and cook for 1–2 minutes until the vegetables are tender; add a little water if they appear dry. Sprinkle the sesame seeds on top and serve.

HEALTH BENEFITS

Green and orange vegetables are an excellent source of beta carotene, as well as vitamins C and E.

Oriental Green Beans

THIS IS A SIMPLE and delicious way of enlivening green beans. The dish can be served hot or cold and, accompanied by an omelette and some crusty bread, makes a perfect light lunch or supper.

INGREDIENTS

450g/1lb/3 cups green beans
15ml/1 tbsp olive oil
5ml/1 tsp sesame oil
2 garlic cloves, crushed
2.5cm/1in piece fresh root ginger,
    finely chopped
30ml/2 tbsp dark soy sauce
Serves 4

VARIATION

Substitute other green beans, if you wish. Runner (green) beans and other flat varieties should be cut diagonally into thick slices before steaming.

1 Steam the beans over a pan of boiling salted water for 4 minutes or until just tender.

HEALTH BENEFITS

• *This dish contains good amounts of garlic and fresh root ginger, both of which are said to give the immune system a significant boost.*
• *Recent studies confirm that ginger may be more effective in preventing nausea than prescribed drugs.*

2 Meanwhile, heat the olive and sesame oils in a heavy pan, add the garlic and sauté for 2 minutes.

3 Stir in the ginger and soy sauce and cook, stirring constantly, for a further 2–3 minutes until the liquid has reduced, then pour this mixture over the warm beans. Leave for a few minutes to allow all the flavours to mingle before serving.

Stir-fry: Energy 143kcal/594kJ; Protein 7g; Carbohydrate 11g, of which sugars 10g; Fat 8g, of which saturates 1g; Cholesterol 0mg; Calcium 164mg; Fibre 3g; Sodium 571mg.
Beans: Energy 78kcal/320kJ; Protein 2g; Carbohydrate 5g, of which sugars 3g; Fat 6g, of which saturates 1g; Cholesterol 0mg; Calcium 43mg; Fibre 3g; Sodium 535mg.

Desserts

Sumptuous desserts do not have to be laden with fat and sugar, nor need they be nutritional no-hopers. Many of the recipes in this chapter are as luscious as you like, but won't add to your waistline or leave you feeling unsatisfied. Delicately flavoured Mango and Orange Sorbet, and Rhubarb and Ginger Yogurt Ice are stunning examples, as is the Raspberry Fromage Frais and Amaretti Scrunch. This creamy concoction of fromage frais or thick natural yogurt, fresh raspberries and crisp amaretti crumbs is what spoons were made for. Another speedy dessert, which tastes simply wonderful, is Pan-fried Apple Slices with Walnut Shortbread, while Date, Fig and Orange Pudding and Winter Fruit Poached in Mulled Wine are two desserts that make the most of dried fruit, which contributes valuable minerals, including iron, potassium and calcium, as well as B complex vitamins and fibre. You'll also find inspiring variations on rice pudding in the form of the saffron-scented Indian Rice Pudding and the South-east Asian Coconut Rice Puddings with Grilled Oranges.

Mango and Orange Sorbet

FRESH AND TANGY, and gloriously vibrant in colour, this sorbet is the perfect finale to a spicy meal.

INGREDIENTS

115g/4oz/¹/₂ cup caster (superfine) sugar
2 large mangoes
juice of 1 orange
1 egg white (optional)
thinly pared strips of fresh unwaxed orange
    rind, to decorate

Serves 2–4

1 Gently heat the sugar and 300ml/ ¹/₂ pint/1¹/₄ cups water in a pan until the sugar has dissolved. Bring to the boil, then reduce the heat and simmer for 5 minutes. Leave to cool.

2 Cut away the two sides of the mangoes close to the stones (pits). Peel, then cut the flesh from the stones. Dice the fruit.

3 Process the mango flesh and orange juice in a food processor with the sugar syrup until smooth.

4 Pour the mixture into a freezer-proof container and freeze for 2 hours until semi-frozen. Whisk the egg white, if using, until it forms stiff peaks, then stir it into the sorbet. Whisk well to remove any ice crystals and freeze until solid.

5 Transfer the sorbet to the refrigerator 10 minutes before serving. Serve garnished with orange rind.

HEALTH BENEFITS

Mangoes and oranges aid the digestion, boost the immune system and are said to cleanse the blood. They are also an excellent source of vitamins A and C.

Rhubarb and Ginger Yogurt Ice

THIS DELICATE PINK YOGURT ice is flavoured with honey and ginger.

INGREDIENTS

300g/11oz/scant 1¹/₂ cups set natural
    (plain) live yogurt
200g/7oz/scant 1 cup fromage frais or
    extra set natural live yogurt
375g/13oz/3 cups rhubarb, chopped
45ml/3 tbsp stem ginger syrup
30ml/2 tbsp clear honey
3 pieces stem ginger, finely chopped

Serves 6

1 In a bowl, whisk together the yogurt and fromage frais.

2 Pour the yogurt mixture into a shallow freezer-proof container and freeze for 1 hour.

3 Meanwhile, put the rhubarb, stem ginger syrup and honey in a large pan and cook over a low heat for 15 minutes, or until the rhubarb is soft. Leave to cool, then purée in a food processor or blender.

4 Remove the semi-frozen yogurt mixture from the freezer and fold in the rhubarb and stem ginger purée. Beat well until smooth. Add the chopped stem ginger.

5 Return the yogurt ice to the freezer and freeze for a further 2 hours. Remove from the freezer and beat again, then freeze until solid. Serve scoops of the yogurt ice on individual plates or in bowls.

HEALTH BENEFITS

• *Rhubarb is rich in potassium and is an effective laxative. However, it is also high in oxalic acid, which is reputed to inhibit the absorption of iron and calcium and can exasperate joint problems, such as arthritis. The leaves are poisonous and should never be eaten.*
• *Stem ginger retains many of the health-giving qualities of fresh ginger. It aids digestion and is effective in treating gastrointestinal disorders.*

COOK'S TIP

Take the yogurt ice out of the freezer and transfer it to the refrigerator 15 minutes before serving to allow it to soften.

Sorbet: Energy 175kcal/747kJ; Protein 1g; Carbohydrate 45g, of which sugars 45g; Fat 0g, of which saturates 0g; Cholesterol 0mg; Calcium 17mg; Fibre 3g; Sodium 4mg.
Ice: Energy 118kcal/500kJ; Protein 5g; Carbohydrate 16g, of which sugars 16g; Fat 4g, of which saturates 3g; Cholesterol 8mg; Calcium 190mg; Fibre 1g; Sodium 75mg.

Raspberry Fromage Frais and Amaretti Scrunch

THIS DESSERT LOOKS STUNNING, but it is actually very simple to make. The raspberries give a luscious swirl of colour and the amaretti make a crunchy contrast to the creamy fromage frais or yogurt.

INGREDIENTS

250g/9oz/1½ cups frozen or
    fresh raspberries
500g/1¼lb/2½ cups fromage frais or
    thick natural (plain) live yogurt
30ml/2 tbsp clear honey
finely grated rind of 1 small lemon
75g/3oz/1½ cups amaretti,
    broken into pieces
crystallized rose petals,
    for decoration (optional)

Serves 4–6

| If using frozen raspberries, allow them to partly defrost. If using fresh ones, partly freeze them.

2 Place the fromage frais or yogurt in a bowl and stir in the honey and lemon rind. Add the raspberries and fold in gently, being careful not to over mix. Chill for 1 hour.

3 Stir in the amaretti just before serving. Decorate with crystallized rose petals, if you wish.

HEALTH BENEFITS

Raspberries are extremely cleansing for the body and can relieve menstrual cramps and cystitis.

Tropical Fruit with Hot Rum and Cinnamon Sauce

DARK RUM AND CINNAMON give this hot fruit dessert a distinctly Caribbean flavour. It is best eaten as soon as it is ready, so prepare the fruit ahead of time, then cook between courses – this will only take a few minutes.

INGREDIENTS

25g/1oz/2 tbsp unsalted butter
1 medium pineapple, peeled, cored and sliced
1 mango, peeled, stoned and cut into
    1cm/½in cubes
1 papaya, peeled, halved, seeded and sliced
2 bananas, thickly sliced
30ml/2 tbsp clear honey or maple syrup
5ml/1 tsp ground cinnamon
60ml/4 tbsp dark rum
natural (plain) live yogurt or yogurt ice,
    to serve

Serves 4

| Melt the butter in a large, heavy frying pan. Add the sliced pineapple and cook for 3 minutes or until it starts to brown, turning it occasionally.

HEALTH BENEFITS

Papaya contains the enzyme, papain, which can help to stimulate the digestion. Like pineapple and mango, papaya is rich in both vitamin C and beta carotene.

2 Add the prepared mango, papaya and bananas to the pan and cook for 1 minute, turning occasionally.

3 Stir in the honey or maple syrup, cinnamon and rum, and cook for a further 2 minutes or until the sauce thickens and the fruit is tender. Serve immediately with yogurt or yogurt ice.

Raspberry: Energy 175kcal/735kJ; Protein 7g; Carbohydrate 17g, of which sugars 17g; Fat 9g, of which saturates 5g; Cholesterol 7mg; Calcium 115mg; Fibre 3g; Sodium 38mg.
Tropical: Energy 229kcal/970kJ; Protein 2g; Carbohydrate 37g, of which sugars 36g; Fat 6g, of which saturates 3g; Cholesterol 14mg; Calcium 37mg; Fibre 5g; Sodium 7mg.

Pan-fried Apple Slices with Walnut Shortbread

SOFT, CARAMELIZED APPLES AND crisp nutty shortbread make a perfect combination. Serve warm with a spoonful of yogurt or fromage frais or a scoop of vanilla ice cream.

INGREDIENTS

25g/1oz/2 tbsp unsalted butter
4 dessert apples, cored and thinly sliced
30ml/2 tbsp soft light brown sugar
10ml/2 tsp ground ginger
5ml/1 tsp ground cinnamon
2.5ml/¹/2 tsp ground nutmeg

For the walnut shortbread
75g/3oz/²/3 cup wholemeal
  (whole-wheat) flour
75g/3oz/²/3 cup plain (all-purpose) flour
25g/1oz/¹/4 cup oatmeal
5ml/1 tsp baking powder
1.5ml/¹/4 tsp salt
50g/2oz/¹/4 cup caster (superfine) sugar
115g/4oz/8 tbsp unsalted butter
40g/1¹/2oz/¹/4 cup walnuts, finely chopped
15ml/1 tbsp milk, plus extra for brushing
demerara (raw) sugar, for sprinkling
Serves 4

1 Preheat the oven to 180°C/350°F/ Gas 4 and grease one or two baking sheets. To make the walnut shortbread, sift together the flours, adding any bran left in the sieve (strainer), and mix with the oatmeal, baking powder, salt and sugar. Rub in the butter with your fingers until the mixture resembles fine breadcrumbs.

2 Add the chopped walnuts, then stir in enough of the milk to form a soft dough.

3 Gently knead the dough on a floured work surface. Form into a round, then roll out to a 5mm/¹/4in thickness. Using a 7.5cm/3in fluted cutter, stamp out eight rounds – you may have some dough left over.

4 Place the shortbread rounds on the prepared baking sheets. Brush the tops with milk and sprinkle with sugar. Bake for 12–15 minutes until golden, then transfer to a wire rack and leave to cool.

5 To prepare the apples, melt the butter in a heavy frying pan. Add the apples and cook for 3–4 minutes over a gentle heat until softened. Increase the heat to medium, add the sugar and spices, and stir well. Cook for a few minutes, stirring frequently, until the sauce turns golden brown and caramelizes.

6 Place two shortbread rounds on each of four individual serving plates and spoon over the warm apples and sauce. Serve immediately.

HEALTH BENEFITS

• *Recent studies have shown that eating walnuts regularly can greatly reduce the risk of heart disease and lower the level of blood cholesterol in the body.*
• *There is much truth in the adage: 'an apple a day keeps the doctor away.' Apples have many health-giving properties. They help cleanse the blood, remove impurities in the liver and inhibit the growth of harmful bacteria in the digestive tract. Apples are also known to treat skin diseases and arthritis.*

COOK'S TIP

To prevent the apples browning after they are sliced, place them in a large bowl of water mixed with about 15ml/1 tbsp lemon juice.

Energy 605kcal/2544kJ; Protein 7g; Carbohydrate 64g, of which sugars 34g; Fat 37g, of which saturates 20g; Cholesterol 81mg; Calcium 77mg; Fibre 5g; Sodium 232mg.

Coconut Rice Puddings with Oranges

STICKY RICE PUDDING is a speciality of many South-east Asian countries. In these little desserts Thai jasmine rice is cooked with rich and creamy coconut milk.

INGREDIENTS

175g/6oz/scant 1 cup jasmine rice
400ml/14fl oz/1²/3 cup coconut milk
2.5ml/¹/2 tsp grated nutmeg, plus extra
   for sprinkling
large pinch of salt
60ml/4 tbsp golden caster (superfine) sugar
oil, for greasing
2 oranges, skin and pith removed and cut
   into thin rounds
orange peel twists, to decorate

Serves 4

1 Rinse and drain the rice. Place in a pan, cover with water, and bring to the boil. Cook for 5 minutes until the grains are just beginning to soften. Drain well.

2 Place the rice in a steamer lined with muslin (cheesecloth), then make a few holes in the muslin to allow the steam to get through. Steam the rice for 15 minutes or until tender.

HEALTH BENEFITS

Rice is gluten-free and therefore can be eaten by coeliacs. Although, more refined than brown rice, jasmine rice is a useful source of energy.

3 Put the steamed rice in a heavy pan with the coconut milk, nutmeg, salt and sugar, and cook over gentle heat until the mixture begins to simmer. Simmer for about 5 minutes until the mixture is thick and creamy, stirring frequently to prevent the rice sticking to the bottom of the pan.

4 Spoon the rice mixture into four lightly oiled 175ml/6fl oz/³/4 cup moulds or ramekins and leave to cool.

5 When ready to serve, heat the grill (broiler) to high. Line a baking tray or the grill rack with foil and place the orange slices on top. Sprinkle the oranges with a little grated nutmeg, then grill (broil) for 6 minutes until lightly golden, turning the slices halfway through cooking.

6 When the rice mixture is cold, run a knife around the edge of the moulds or ramekins and turn out the rice. Decorate with orange peel twists and serve with the warm orange slices.

Energy 268kcal/1145kJ; Protein 4g; Carbohydrate 65g, of which sugars 27g; Fat 1g, of which saturates 0g; Cholesterol 0mg; Calcium 69mg; Fibre 2g; Sodium 215mg.

Date, Fig and Orange Pudding

THIS LIGHT STEAMED SPONGE avoids the use of suet, which is usually made from hydrogenated fat, often animal in origin. The addition of fresh orange juice and rind, and orange liqueur, gives an intense citrus tang.

INGREDIENTS

juice and rind of 2 oranges
115g/4oz/²/3 cup stoned (pitted),
    ready-to-eat dried dates, chopped
115g/4oz/²/3 cup ready-to-eat dried
    figs, chopped
30ml/2 tbsp orange liqueur (optional)
175g/6oz/³/4 cup unsalted butter,
    plus extra for greasing
175g/6oz/³/4 cup soft light brown sugar
3 eggs
75g/3oz/²/3 cup self-raising wholemeal
    (self-rising whole-wheat) flour
115g/4oz/1 cup unbleached self-raising
    (self-rising) flour
30ml/2 tbsp golden (light corn) syrup
    (optional)

Serves 6

1 Reserve a few strips of orange rind for the decoration and put the rest in a pan with the orange juice. Add the chopped dates and figs and orange liqueur, if using. Cook, covered, over a gentle heat for 8–10 minutes, until the fruit is soft.

2 Leave the fruit mixture to cool, then transfer to a food processor or blender and process until smooth. Press through a sieve (strainer) to remove the fig seeds, if you wish.

3 Cream the butter and sugar until pale and fluffy, then beat in the fig purée. Beat in the eggs, then fold in the flours and mix until combined.

HEALTH BENEFITS

The healing qualities of figs have been recognized for thousands of years and, as a result, the fruit has been used to treat almost every known disease. Widely known as a gentle laxative, figs also contain vitamins B_6 and C, calcium and iron. Dates contain their fair share of vitamin B_6 and iron and feature a useful amount of potassium.

4 Grease a 1.2 litre/2 pint/5 cup heatproof bowl, and pour in the golden syrup, if using. Tilt the bowl to cover the inside with a layer of syrup. Spoon in the cake mixture. Cover the top with greaseproof (waxed) paper, with a pleat down the centre, and then with pleated foil, and tie with string.

5 Place the bowl in a large pan, and pour in enough water to come halfway up the sides of the bowl. Cover with a tight-fitting lid and steam for 2 hours. Check the water occasionally and top up if necessary. Turn out and decorate with the reserved orange rind.

Energy 556kcal/2351kJ; Protein 9g; Carbohydrate 73g, of which sugars 51g; Fat 28g, of which saturates 17g; Cholesterol 183mg; Calcium 145mg; Fibre 4g; Sodium 142mg.

Lemon and Almond Tart

THIS REFRESHING, TANGY TART has a rich, creamy lemon filling set off by a caramelized sugar top. Serve warm or cold with a dollop of crème fraîche or yogurt.

INGREDIENTS

2 eggs
50g/2oz/¼ cup golden caster
    (superfine) sugar
finely grated rind and juice of
    4 unwaxed lemons
2.5ml/½ tsp vanilla extract
50g/2oz/½ cup ground almonds
120ml/4fl oz/½ cup single (light) cream

For the pastry

225g/8oz/2 cups unbleached spelt flour
75g/3oz/¾ cup icing (confectioners')
    sugar, plus extra for dusting
130g/4½oz/9 tbsp butter
1 egg, beaten
a pinch of salt
Serves 8–10

1 Preheat the oven to 180°C/350°F/ Gas 4. To make the pastry, sift together the flour and sugar in a large bowl. Rub in the butter with your fingertips until the mixture resembles fine breadcrumbs. Add the egg and salt, then mix to a smooth dough with the blade of a table knife.

2 Knead the dough lightly on a floured work surface and form into a smooth flat round. Wrap the dough in clear film (plastic wrap) and chill for 15 minutes.

3 Roll out the dough on a floured work surface and use to line a 23cm/9 in loose-bottomed flan tin (pan). Prick the base and chill for 15 minutes.

4 Line the pastry case with baking parchment. Tip in some baking beans and bake blind for 10 minutes. Remove the paper and beans and return the pastry case to the oven for a further 10 minutes or until it is light golden.

5 Meanwhile, make the filling. Beat the eggs with the sugar in a large bowl until the mixture leaves a thin ribbon trail. Gently stir in the lemon rind and juice, vanilla extract, almonds and cream.

6 Carefully pour the filling into the pastry case and level the surface. Bake for about 25 minutes or until the filling is set.

7 Heat the grill (broiler) to high. Sift a thick layer of icing sugar over the tart and grill (broil) until the sugar caramelizes. Decorate the tart with a little extra sifted icing sugar before serving warm or cold with crème fraîche.

HEALTH BENEFITS

• *The high level of vitamin C in lemons is widely known but they also contain good amounts of calcium, iron and potassium.*
• *Lemons are a natural antiseptic and have been used for centuries to treat skin problems. They are also used to cleanse the body of toxins.*

COOK'S TIP

Spelt flour is a type of wheat flour that is available in supermarkets and health food stores. If you can't find it, use unbleached plain (all-purpose) flour instead.

Energy 303kcal/1268kJ; Protein 6g; Carbohydrate 31g, of which sugars 14g; Fat 18g, of which saturates 9g; Cholesterol 104mg; Calcium 68mg; Fibre 1g; Sodium 110mg.

Desserts

Baked Ricotta Cakes with Red Sauce

THESE HONEY AND vanilla-flavoured desserts take only minutes to make. The fragrant fruity sauce provides a contrast of both colour and flavour.

INGREDIENTS

250g/9oz/generous 1 cup ricotta cheese
2 egg whites, beaten
60ml/4 tbsp clear honey, plus extra to taste
5ml/1 tsp vanilla extract
450g/1lb/4 cups mixed fresh or frozen
    fruit, such as strawberries, raspberries,
    blackberries and cherries
fresh mint leaves, to decorate (optional)

Serves 4

1 Preheat the oven to 180°C/350°F/ Gas 4. Place the ricotta cheese in a bowl and break it up with a wooden spoon. Add the beaten egg whites, honey and vanilla extract and mix thoroughly until the mixture is smooth and well combined.

2 Lightly grease four ramekins. Spoon the ricotta mixture into the prepared ramekins and level the tops. Bake for 20 minutes or until the ricotta cakes are risen and golden.

3 Meanwhile, make the fruit sauce. Reserve about a quarter of the fruit for decoration. Place the rest of the fruit in a pan, with a little water if the fruit is fresh, and heat gently until softened. Leave to cool slightly, remove any cherry stones, if using cherries.

COOK'S TIP

The red berry sauce can be made a day in advance. Chill until ready to use. Frozen fruit doesn't need extra water, as there are usually plenty of ice crystals clinging to the berries.

4 Press the fruit through a sieve (strainer), then taste and sweeten with honey if it is too tart. Serve the sauce, warm or cold, with the ricotta cakes. Decorate with the reserved berries and mint leaves, if using.

HEALTH BENEFITS

• Ricotta contains about 4 per cent fat, compared with 35 per cent in a hard cheese like Cheddar. It is a good source of vitamin B_{12}, calcium and protein.
• All berries are rich in the anti-cancer compound, ellagic acid, which is a powerful antioxidant.

Energy 168kcal/705kJ; Protein 9g; Carbohydrate 19g, of which sugars 19g; Fat 7g, of which saturates 4g; Cholesterol 31mg; Calcium 182mg; Fibre 6g; Sodium 99mg.

Apricot Panettone Pudding

PANETTONE makes a rich addition to this traditional dessert.

INGREDIENTS

unsalted butter, for greasing
350g/12oz panettone, sliced into triangles
25g/1oz/¹/4 cup pecan nuts
75g/3oz/¹/3 cup ready-to-eat unsulphured
   dried apricots, chopped
500ml/17fl oz/2¹/4 cups semi-skimmed
   (low-fat) milk
5ml/1 tsp vanilla extract
1 large egg, beaten
30ml/2 tbsp maple syrup
grated nutmeg
demerara (raw) sugar, for sprinkling

Serves 6

1 Butter a 1 litre/1³/4 pint/4 cup baking dish. Arrange half the panettone in the dish, scatter over half the pecan nuts and all the apricots, then add another layer of panettone on top.

2 Heat the milk and vanilla extract in a small pan until it just simmers. Put the egg and maple syrup in a large bowl, grate in 2.5ml/¹/2 nutmeg, then whisk in the hot milk.

3 Preheat the oven to 200°C/400°F/ Gas 6. Pour the egg mixture over the panettone, lightly pressing down the bread so it is submerged. Leave the dessert to stand for 10 minutes.

4 Scatter over the reserved pecan nuts and sprinkle with the demerara sugar and nutmeg. Bake for 40–45 minutes until risen and golden. Serve immediately or leave to cool to warm.

HEALTH BENEFITS

Dried apricots have an even higher concentration of beta carotene than fresh ones. This powerful antioxidant is known to lower the risk of cataracts, heart disease and some forms of cancer. They are also an excellent source of iron.

Energy 305kcal/1282kJ; Protein 10g; Carbohydrate 44g, of which sugars 23g; Fat 11g, of which saturates 3g; Cholesterol 50mg; Calcium 175mg; Fibre 4.5g; Sodium 223mg.

Indian Rice Pudding

THIS CREAMY DESSERT is scented with saffron, cardamom and freshly grated nutmeg. Shelled pistachio nuts give a subtle contrast in colour and add a delicious crunch to the dessert.

INGREDIENTS

115g/4oz/³/4 cup brown short grain rice
350ml/12fl oz/1¹/2 cups boiling water
600ml/1 pint/2¹/2 cups semi-skimmed
  (low-fat) milk
6 cardamom pods, bruised
2.5ml/¹/2tsp freshly grated nutmeg
pinch of saffron strands
60ml/4 tbsp maize malt syrup
15ml/1 tbsp clear honey
50g/2oz/¹/2 cup pistachio nuts, chopped

Serves 4

1 Wash the rice under cold running water and place in a pan with the boiling water. Bring to the boil and boil, uncovered, for 15 minutes.

2 Pour in the milk, then reduce the heat and simmer, partially covered, for 15 minutes.

COOK'S TIP

Maize malt syrup is a natural alternative to refined sugar and can be found in health food stores.

3 Add the cardamom pods, grated nutmeg, saffron, maize malt syrup and honey, and cook for a further 15 minutes, or until the rice is tender, stirring occasionally.

4 Spoon the rice into small serving bowls and sprinkle with pistachio nuts before serving hot or cold.

HEALTH BENEFITS

• Brown rice is unrefined and therefore, unlike white polished rice, retains most of its fibre and nutrients. It is a source of some B complex vitamins and vitamin E.
• Pistachio nuts are densely packed with nourishment, being rich in protein, vitamins and minerals. However, because of their high fat content, they go rancid quickly, so buy them in a store with a high turnover of stock and store them in a cool dry place. Due to their high fat content, pistachio nuts should be eaten in moderation.

Energy 274kcal/1153kJ; Protein 9g; Carbohydrate 42g, of which sugars 17g; Fat 9g, of which saturates 3g; Cholesterol 9mg; Calcium 226mg; Fibre 1g; Sodium 125mg.

Winter Fruit Poached in Mulled Wine

FRESH APPLES AND PEARS are combined with dried apricots and figs, and cooked in a fragrant, spicy wine until tender and intensely flavoured.

INGREDIENTS

300ml/¹/₂ pint/1¹/₄ cups red wine
300ml/¹/₂ pint/1¹/₄ cups fresh orange juice
finely grated rind and juice of 1 orange
45ml/3 tbsp clear honey or barley
  malt syrup
3 small cinnamon sticks
4 cloves
4 cardamom pods, split
2 pears, such as Comice or William, peeled,
  cored and halved
8 ready-to-eat dried figs
12 ready-to-eat dried unsulphured apricots
2 eating apples, peeled, cored and
  thickly sliced

Serves 4

1 Put the wine, the fresh and squeezed orange juice and half the orange rind in a pan with the honey or syrup and spices. Bring to the boil, then reduce the heat and simmer for 2 minutes, stirring occasionally.

HEALTH BENEFITS

• *The combination of fresh and dried fruit ensures a healthy amount of vitamins and minerals, particularly vitamins C, beta carotene, potassium and iron. The fruit is also rich in fibre.*

• *Cardamom and cinnamon soothe indigestion and, along with cloves, can offer relief from colds and coughs.*

2 Add the pears, figs and apricots to the pan and cook, covered, for 25 minutes, occasionally turning the fruit in the wine mixture. Add the apples and cook for a further 12–15 minutes until the fruit is tender.

3 Remove the fruit from the pan and discard the spices. Cook the wine mixture over a high heat until reduced and syrupy, then pour it over the fruit. Serve decorated with the reserved orange rind, if wished.

Energy 257kcal/1089kJ; Protein 2g; Carbohydrate 51g, of which sugars 5g; Fat 1g, of which saturates 0g; Cholesterol 0mg; Calcium 112mg; Fibre 7g; Sodium 42mg.

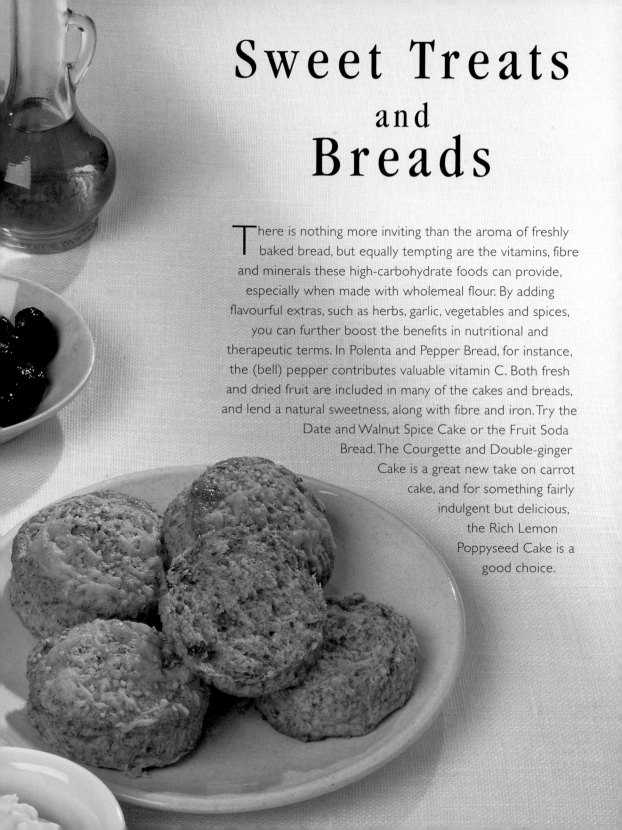

Sweet Treats
and
Breads

There is nothing more inviting than the aroma of freshly baked bread, but equally tempting are the vitamins, fibre and minerals these high-carbohydrate foods can provide, especially when made with wholemeal flour. By adding flavourful extras, such as herbs, garlic, vegetables and spices, you can further boost the benefits in nutritional and therapeutic terms. In Polenta and Pepper Bread, for instance, the (bell) pepper contributes valuable vitamin C. Both fresh and dried fruit are included in many of the cakes and breads, and lend a natural sweetness, along with fibre and iron. Try the Date and Walnut Spice Cake or the Fruit Soda Bread. The Courgette and Double-ginger Cake is a great new take on carrot cake, and for something fairly indulgent but delicious, the Rich Lemon Poppyseed Cake is a good choice.

Plum Crumble Pie

POLENTA ADDS A WONDERFUL golden hue and crunchiness to the crumble topping for this fruit-filled pie.

INGREDIENTS

115g/4oz/1 cup plain (all-purpose) flour, sifted
115g/4oz/1 cup wholemeal
    (whole-wheat) flour
150g/5oz/³/4 cup caster (superfine) sugar
115g/4oz/1 cup polenta
5ml/1 tsp baking powder
pinch of salt
150g/5oz/10 tbsp unsalted butter,
    plus extra for greasing
1 egg
15ml/1 tbsp olive oil
25g/1oz/¹/4 cup rolled oats
15ml/1 tbsp demerara (raw) sugar
custard or cream, to serve

For the filling
10ml/2 tsp caster (superfine) sugar
15ml/1 tbsp polenta
450g/1lb dark plums
Serves 6–8

1 Mix together the flours, sugar, polenta, baking powder and salt in a bowl. Rub in the butter until the mixture resembles fine breadcrumbs. Stir in the egg and olive oil and enough cold water to form a smooth dough.

2 Grease a 23cm/9in spring-form cake tin (pan). Press two-thirds of the dough evenly over the base and up the sides of the tin. Wrap the remaining dough in clear film (plastic wrap) and chill while you make the filling.

3 Preheat the oven to 180°C/ 350°F/Gas 4. Sprinkle the sugar and polenta into the pastry case.

4 Cut the plums in half. Remove the stones (pits), then place the plums, cut-side down, on top of the polenta.

HEALTH BENEFITS

Plums are an excellent source of the antioxidant vitamin E.

5 Remove the remaining dough from the refrigerator and crumble it between your fingers, then combine with the oats. Sprinkle evenly over the the plums, then sprinkle the demerara sugar on top.

6 Bake for 50 minutes or until golden. Leave for 15 minutes before removing the cake from the tin. Leave to to cool on a wire rack. Serve with custard or cream.

Energy 398kcal/1682kJ; Protein 6g; Carbohydrate 61g, of which sugars 29g; Fat 16g, of which saturates 8g; Cholesterol 62mg; Calcium 48mg; Fibre 3.8g; Sodium 74mg.

Courgette and Double-ginger Cake

BOTH FRESH AND PRESERVED ginger are used to flavour this unusual tea bread. It is delicious served warm, cut into thick slices and spread with butter or margarine.

INGREDIENTS

3 eggs

225g/8oz/generous 1 cup caster (superfine) sugar

250ml/8fl oz/1 cup sunflower oil

5ml/1 tsp vanilla extract

15ml/1 tbsp syrup from a jar of stem ginger

225g/8oz courgettes (zucchini), grated

2.5cm/1in piece fresh root ginger, grated

350g/12oz/3 cups plain (all-purpose) flour

5ml/1 tsp baking powder

pinch of salt

5ml/1 tsp ground cinnamon

2 pieces stem ginger, chopped

15ml/1 tbsp demerara (raw) sugar

Serves 8–10

2 Sift together the flour, baking powder and salt into a large bowl. Add the cinnamon and mix well, then stir the dried ingredients into the courgette mixture.

VARIATION

Grated carrots – and even parsnips – can be used in place of courgettes (zucchini) in this tea bread.

3 Lightly grease a 900g/2lb loaf tin (pan) and pour in the courgette mixture. Smooth and level the top, then sprinkle the chopped ginger and demerara sugar over the surface.

4 Bake for 1 hour until a skewer inserted into the centre comes out clean. Leave the cake in the tin to cool for about 20 minutes, then turn out on to a wire rack.

1 Preheat the oven to 190°C/325°F/ Gas 5. Beat together the eggs and sugar until light and fluffy. Slowly beat in the oil until the mixture forms a batter. Mix in the vanilla extract and ginger syrup, then stir in the courgettes and fresh ginger.

HEALTH BENEFITS

Ginger has many attributes, not least its ability to help alleviate travel sickness and vertigo. Courgettes (zucchini) are a good source of vitamin C, beta carotene and folate.

Energy 502kcal/2107kJ; Protein 7.1g; Carbohydrate 67.3g, of which sugars 34g; Fat 24.6g, of which saturates 3.3g; Cholesterol 71mg; Calcium 95mg; Fibre 1.6g; Sodium 35mg.

Date and Walnut Spice Cake

THIS DELICIOUSLY MOIST AND richly spiced cake is topped with a sticky honey and orange glaze. Serve it as a dessert with a generous spoonful of natural yogurt or crème fraîche, flavoured with grated orange rind.

INGREDIENTS

115g/4oz/¹/₂ cup unsalted butter,
   plus extra for greasing
175g/6oz/³/₄ cup soft dark brown sugar
2 eggs
175g/6oz/1¹/₂ cups unbleached self-raising
   (self-rising) flour, plus extra for dusting
5ml/1 tsp bicarbonate of soda (baking soda)
2.5ml/¹/₂ tsp freshly grated nutmeg
5ml/1 tsp mixed (apple pie) spice
pinch of salt
175ml/6fl oz/³/₄ cup buttermilk
50g/2oz/¹/₃ cup ready-to-eat stoned
   (pitted) dates, chopped
25g/1oz/¹/₄ cup walnuts, chopped

For the topping

60ml/4 tbsp clear honey
45ml/3 tbsp fresh orange juice
15ml/1 tbsp coarsely grated orange rind,
   plus extra to decorate

Serves 8

1 Grease and lightly flour a 23cm/9in spring-form cake tin (pan). Preheat the oven to 180°C/350°F/Gas 4.

HEALTH BENEFITS

• Dried dates offer a more concentrated source of nutrients than fresh ones, including iron, potassium, niacin and magnesium. They also provide soluble fibre, making them a gentle laxative.
• According to a recent American study, a handful of walnuts a day has been found to lower blood cholesterol and therefore helps reduce the risk of heart disease.

2 Cream together the butter and sugar with a wooden spoon until fluffy and creamy. Add the eggs, one at a time, and beat well to combine.

3 Sift together the flour, bicarbonate of soda, spices and salt. Gradually add this to the creamed mixture, alternating with the buttermilk. Add the dates and walnuts, and stir well.

COOK'S TIP

To make your own buttermilk substitute, mix 15ml/1 tbsp lemon juice with 250ml/ 8fl oz/1 cup semi-skimmed (low-fat) milk.

4 Spoon the mixture into the prepared cake tin and level the top. Bake for 50 minutes or until a skewer inserted into the centre of the cake comes out clean. Leave to cool for 5 minutes, then turn out on to a wire rack to cool completely.

5 To make the topping, heat the honey, orange juice and rind in a small, heavy pan. Bring to the boil and boil rapidly for 3 minutes, without stirring, until syrupy. Make small holes, over the top of the warm cake using the skewer, and pour over the hot syrup. Decorate with the orange rind.

Energy 2666kcal/11243kJ; Protein 61.2g; Carbohydrate 429.6g, of which sugars 243.9g; Fat 90.2g, of which saturates 12.3g; Cholesterol 18mg; Calcium 650mg; Fibre 34.8g; Sodium 163mg.

Rich Lemon Poppyseed Cake

THE CLASSIC COMBINATION of poppy seeds and lemon is used for this light cake.

INGREDIENTS

350g/12oz/1½ cups unsalted butter, plus extra for greasing
350g/12oz/1¾ cups caster (superfine) sugar
45ml/3 tbsp poppy seeds
20ml/4 tsp finely grated lemon rind
75ml/5 tbsp luxury lemon curd
6 eggs, separated
120ml/4fl oz/½ cup semi-skimmed (low-fat) milk
350g/12oz/3 cups unbleached self-raising (self-rising) flour, plus extra for flouring
icing (confectioners') sugar, to decorate

For the filling
150g/5oz/½ cup luxury lemon curd
150ml/5fl oz/⅔ cup double (heavy) cream, whipped
Serves 8

1 Butter and lightly flour two 23cm/9in spring-form cake tins (pans). Preheat the oven to 180°C/350°F/Gas 4.

VARIATION

Replace the lemon curd and fromage frais filling with a tangy lemon syrup. Boil 45ml/3 tbsp lemon juice, 15ml/1 tbsp lemon rind and 30ml/2 tbsp sugar for 3 minutes until the mixture becomes syrupy and glossy. Make a single cake using half the ingredients. Pour the syrup over the warm cake and leave to cool before cutting into wedges to serve.

2 Cream together the butter and sugar with a wooden spoon until light and fluffy. Add the poppy seeds, lemon rind, lemon curd and egg yolks and beat well, then add the milk and mix well. Gently fold in the flour until combined.

3 Whisk the egg whites using a hand-held electric mixer until they form soft peaks. Carefully fold the egg whites into the cake mixture until just combined. Divide the cake mixture between the prepared tins.

4 Bake for 40–45 minutes until a skewer inserted into the centre of the cakes comes out clean and the tops are golden.

5 Leave the cakes to cool in the tins for 5 minutes, then remove from the tins and leave to cool completely on wire racks. To finish, spread one cake with the lemon curd and spoon the fromage frais evenly over the lemon curd. Put the second cake on top, press down gently, then dust with icing sugar before serving.

Energy 891kcal/3753kJ; Protein 12g; Carbohydrate 98g, of which sugars 59g; Fat 55g, of which saturates 32g; Cholesterol 307mg; Calcium 292mg; Fibre 2g; Sodium 259mg.

Chunky Chocolate and Banana Muffins

LUXURIOUS BUT NOT overly sweet, these muffins are simple and quick to make. Serve warm while the chocolate is still gooey.

INGREDIENTS

90ml/6 tbsp semi-skimmed
 (low-fat) milk
2 eggs
150g/5oz/10 tbsp unsalted
 butter, melted
225g/8oz/2 cups unbleached plain
 (all-purpose) flour
pinch of salt
5ml/1 tsp baking powder
150g/5oz/³/4 cup golden caster
 (superfine) sugar
150g/5oz plain (semisweet) chocolate,
 cut into large chunks
2 small bananas, mashed
Makes 12

1 Place 12 paper cases in a deep muffin tin (pan). Preheat the oven to 200°C/400°F/Gas 6. Place the milk, eggs and butter in a bowl and whisk until combined.

HEALTH BENEFITS

Bananas are rich in potassium, which is vital for muscle and nerve function. They are also a good source of energy.

2 Sift together the flour, salt and baking powder into a separate bowl. Add the sugar and chocolate to the flour mixture and then stir to combine. Slowly stir in the milk mixture, but do not beat it. Fold in the mashed bananas.

3 Spoon the mixture into the paper cases. Bake for 20 minutes until golden. Cool on a wire rack.

Apricot and Hazelnut Oat Cookies

THESE COOKIE-CUM-FLAPJACKS have a crumbly texture. These are sprinkled with apricots and hazelnuts, but use any combination of fruit and nuts.

INGREDIENTS

115g/4oz/¹/2 cup unsalted butter,
 plus extra for greasing
75g/3oz/scant ¹/2 cup golden caster
 (superfine) sugar
15ml/1 tbsp clear honey
115g/4oz/1 cup self-raising (self-rising)
 flour, sifted
115g/4oz/1 cup rolled oats
75g/3oz/scant ¹/2 cup ready-to-eat dried
 unsulphured apricots, chopped

For the topping
25g/1oz/2 tbsp ready-to-eat dried unsulphured apricots, chopped
25g/1oz/¹/4 cup hazelnuts, toasted
 and chopped
Makes 9

1 Lightly grease a baking sheet. Preheat the oven to 170°C/325°F/Gas 3. Put the butter, sugar and honey in a small, heavy pan and cook over a gentle heat, until the butter melts and the sugar dissolves, stirring occasionally. Remove the pan from the heat.

HEALTH BENEFITS

Oats provide soluble fibre, which is believed to lower blood cholesterol levels, and also makes the cookies sustaining.

2 Put the flour, oats and apricots in a bowl, add the honey mixture and mix with a wooden spoon to form a sticky dough. Divide the dough into nine pieces and place on the baking sheet. Press into 1cm/¹/2in thick rounds. Scatter over the apricots and hazelnuts and press into the dough.

3 Bake for 15 minutes until golden and slightly crisp. Leave to cool on the baking sheet for 5 minutes, then transfer to a wire rack.

Muffins: Energy 305kcal/1286kJ; Protein 4g; Carbohydrate 40g, of which sugars 25g; Fat 15g, of which saturates 9g; Cholesterol 69mg; Calcium 53mg; Fibre 1g; Sodium 60mg.
Cookies: Energy 262kcal/1106kJ; Protein 4g; Carbohydrate 33g, of which sugars 14g; Fat 14g, of which saturates 7g; Cholesterol 29mg; Calcium 67mg; Fibre 4g; Sodium 54mg.

Cheese and Potato Scones

THE UNUSUAL ADDITION OF creamy mashed potato gives these wholemeal scones a light moist crumb and a crisp crust. A sprinkling of mature Cheddar and sesame seeds adds the finishing touch.

INGREDIENTS

115g/4oz/1 cup wholemeal
  (whole-wheat) flour
2.5ml/^{1}/2 tsp salt
20ml/4 tsp baking powder
40g/1^1/2oz/3 tbsp unsalted butter,
  plus extra for greasing
2 eggs, beaten
50ml/2fl oz/^{1}/4 cup milk or buttermilk
115g/4oz/1^1/3 cups cooked, mashed potato
45ml/3 tbsp chopped fresh sage
50g/2oz/^{1}/2 cup grated mature (sharp)
  vegetarian Cheddar
sesame seeds, for sprinkling
Makes 9

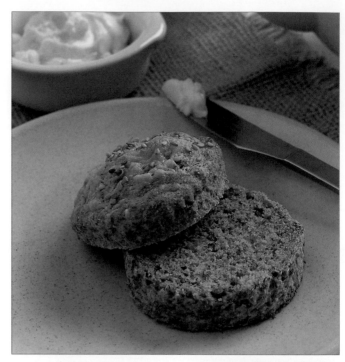

| Preheat the oven to 220°C/425°F/ Gas 7. Grease a baking sheet.

2 Sift the flour, salt and baking powder into a bowl. Rub in the butter using your fingers until the mixture resembles fine breadcrumbs, then mix in half the beaten eggs and all the milk or buttermilk. Add the mashed potato, sage and half the Cheddar, and mix to a soft dough with your hands.

3 Turn out the dough on to a floured work surface and knead lightly until smooth. Roll out the dough to 2cm/^{3}/4in thick, then stamp out nine scones using a 6cm/2^1/2in fluted cutter.

VARIATIONS

• Use unbleached self-raising (self-rising) flour instead of wholemeal (whole-wheat) flour and baking powder, if you wish.
• Fresh rosemary, basil or thyme can be used in place of the sage.

4 Place the scones on the prepared baking sheet and brush the tops with the remaining beaten egg. Sprinkle the rest of the cheese and the sesame seeds on top and bake for 15 minutes until golden. Transfer to a wire rack and leave to cool.

HEALTH BENEFITS

Fresh sage is thought to assist the digestion of rich food and also acts as a stimulant to the central nervous system.

Energy 149kcal/625kJ; Protein 6g; Carbohydrate 15g, of which sugars 1g; Fat 7g, of which saturates 4g; Cholesterol 67mg; Calcium 208mg; Fibre 1g; Sodium 1584mg.

Wholemeal Sunflower Bread

SUNFLOWER SEEDS GIVE A nutty crunchiness to this wholemeal loaf. Serve with a chunk of cheese and rich tomato chutney.

INGREDIENTS

450g/1lb/4 cups strong wholemeal (whole-wheat) bread flour
2.5ml/½ tsp easy-blend (rapid-rise) dried yeast
2.5ml/½ tsp salt
50g/2oz/½ cup sunflower seeds, plus extra for sprinkling

Makes 1 loaf

1 Grease and flour a 450g/1lb loaf tin (pan). Mix together the flour, yeast, salt and sunflower seeds in a bowl. Make a well in the centre and gradually stir in 300ml/½ pint/1¼ cups warm water. Mix to form a soft, sticky dough. The dough should be quite wet and sticky, so don't be tempted to add any extra flour.

2 Cover the bowl with a damp dish towel and leave the dough to rise in a warm place for 45–50 minutes or until doubled in bulk.

3 Preheat the oven to 200°C/ 400°F/Gas 6. Turn out the dough on to a floured work surface and knead for 10 minutes – the dough will still be quite sticky.

HEALTH BENEFITS

High in protein, sesame seeds also provide calcium as well as vitamin E and the B complex vitamins.

4 Form the dough into a rectangle and place in the loaf tin. Sprinkle the top with sunflower seeds. Cover with a damp dish towel and leave to rise again for a further 15 minutes.

5 Bake for 40–45 minutes until golden – the loaf should sound hollow when tapped underneath. Leave for 5 minutes, then turn out of the tin and leave to cool on a wire rack.

Energy 1686kcal/7136kJ; Protein 67g; Carbohydrate 297g, of which sugars 10g; Fat 34g, of which saturates 4g; Cholesterol 0mg; Calcium 226mg; Fibre 43g; Sodium 998mg.

Spicy Millet Bread

THIS IS A DELICIOUS SPICY BREAD with a golden crust. Cut into wedges, as you would a cake, and serve warm with a thick vegetable soup.

INGREDIENTS

90g/3¹/2oz/¹/2 cup millet
550g/1lb 6oz/5¹/2 cups unbleached strong white bread flour
10ml/2 tsp salt
5ml/1 tsp sugar
5ml/1 tsp dried chilli flakes (optional)
7g/¹/4oz sachet easy-blend (rapid-rise) dried yeast
25g/1oz/2 tbsp unsalted butter
1 onion, roughly chopped
15ml/1 tbsp cumin seeds
5ml/1 tsp ground turmeric
Makes 1 loaf

1 Bring 200ml/7fl oz/scant 1 cup water to the boil, add the millet, cover and simmer for 20 minutes until the grains are soft and the water is absorbed. Leave to cool until just warm.

2 Mix together the flour, salt, sugar, chilli flakes, if using, and yeast in a large bowl. Stir in the millet, then add 350ml/12fl oz/1¹/2 cups warm water and mix to form a soft dough.

HEALTH BENEFITS

Millet is a versatile – and much under-rated – grain. If eaten on a regular basis as part of a varied healthy diet, it can help lower the risk of heart disease and certain cancers.

3 Turn out the dough on to a floured work surface and knead for 10 minutes. If the dough seems a little dry, knead well until the dough is smooth and elastic.

4 Place the dough in an oiled bowl and cover with oiled clear film (plastic wrap). Leave to rise in a warm place for 1 hour until doubled in bulk.

5 Meanwhile, melt the butter in a heavy frying pan, add the onion and fry for 10 minutes until softened, stirring occasionally. Add the cumin seeds and turmeric, and fry for a further 5–8 minutes, stirring constantly, until the cumin seeds begin to pop. Set aside.

COOK'S TIP

To test if a dough has risen properly, make a small indentation in the top with your index finger. If the indentation does not spring back entirely, then rising is complete; if it springs back at once, the dough is not ready and should be left for another 15 minutes before retesting.

6 Knock back the dough by pressing down with your knuckles to deflate the dough, then shape into a round. Place the onion mixture in the middle of the dough and bring the sides over the filling to make a parcel, then seal well.

7 Place the loaf on an oiled baking sheet, seam-side down, cover with oiled clear film and leave in a warm place for 45 minutes until it has doubled in bulk. Preheat the oven to 220°C/425°F/Gas 7.

8 Bake the bread for 30 minutes until golden. It should sound hollow when tapped underneath. Leave to cool on a wire rack.

Energy 2464kcal/10426kJ; Protein 59.7g; Carbohydrate 509.5g, of which sugars 15.9g; Fat 31.5g, of which saturates 14.1g; Cholesterol 53mg; Calcium 957mg; Fibre 22.5g; Sodium 4209mg.

Polenta and Pepper Bread

Full of Mediterranean flavour, this satisfying, sunshine-coloured bread is best eaten while still warm, drizzled with olive oil and served with soup.

INGREDIENTS

175g/6oz/1½ cups polenta
5ml/1 tsp salt
350g/12oz/3 cups unbleached strong white
 bread flour, plus extra for dusting
5ml/1 tsp sugar
7g/¼oz sachet easy-blend (rapid-rise)
 dried yeast
1 red (bell) pepper, roasted, peeled and diced
15ml/1 tbsp olive oil

Makes 2 loaves

HEALTH BENEFITS

Weight for weight, red (bell) peppers contain about three times as much vitamin C as fresh oranges.

1 Mix together the polenta, salt, flour, sugar and yeast in a bowl. Stir in the red pepper until it is evenly distributed, then make a well in the centre of the mixture. Grease two loaf tins (pans).

COOK'S TIP

Cook the (bell) pepper in the oven or under a grill (broiler) until charred, then place in a plastic bag and leave until cool enough to peel.

2 Add 300ml/½ pint/1¼ cups warm water and the oil and mix to a soft dough. Knead for 10 minutes until smooth and elastic. Place in an oiled bowl, cover with oiled clear film (plastic wrap) and leave to rise for 1 hour or until doubled in bulk.

3 Knock back the dough, knead lightly, then divide in two. Shape each piece into an oblong and place in the tins. Cover with oiled clear film and leave to rise for 45 minutes. Preheat the oven to 220°C/425°F/Gas 7.

4 Bake for 30 minutes until golden – the loaves should sound hollow when tapped underneath. Leave for 5 minutes, then cool on a wire rack.

Energy 1994kcal/8427kJ; Protein 50.5g; Carbohydrate 366.9g, of which sugars 7.1g; Fat 44.7g, of which saturates 15.1g; Cholesterol 53mg; Calcium 1085mg; Fibre 14.9g; Sodium 2337mg.

Fruit Soda Bread

THIS TRADITIONAL IRISH bread is quick to make as it does not require prolonged kneading or rising. It is best eaten while still warm on the day of baking.

INGREDIENTS

225g/8oz/2 cups plain (all-purpose) flour
225g/8oz/2 cups wholemeal
   (whole-wheat) flour
5ml/1 tsp salt
5ml/1 tsp bicarbonate of soda (baking soda)
20ml/heaped 1 tbsp sugar
75g/3oz/³/4 cup raisins
50g/2oz/¹/4 cup ready-to-eat pitted
   prunes, chopped
1 egg, lightly beaten
300ml/¹/2 pint/1¹/4 cups buttermilk

Serves 4

1 Preheat the oven to 200°C/400°F/ Gas 6. Sift together the plain and wholemeal flours, salt and bicarbonate of soda into a bowl, adding any bran left in the sieve (strainer). Add the sugar and dried fruit, and mix well.

2 Make a well in the centre and add the egg and buttermilk. Mix first with a wooden spoon and then with your hands until it forms a soft, slightly sticky dough. If the dough is too dry, add a little more buttermilk.

HEALTH BENEFITS

Dried fruit is recognized as a good source of fibre as well as minerals, such as potassium and iron.

3 Turn out the dough on to a lightly floured work surface and knead lightly until smooth. Form into a flat round, about 4cm/1¹/2in thick.

4 Place on a greased baking sheet and dust the loaf with plain flour.

5 Cut a large deep cross, almost through to the bottom of the dough round. Bake for 30–35 minutes until risen and golden. The bread should sound hollow when tapped underneath. Transfer to a wire rack and leave to cool.

Energy 500kcal/2124kJ; Protein 18g; Carbohydrate 105g, of which sugars 27g; Fat 4g, of which saturates 1g; Cholesterol 59mg; Calcium 212mg; Fibre 10g; Sodium 845mg.

Rosemary and Rock Salt Focaccia

ENRICHED WITH OLIVE oil and flavoured with rosemary, garlic and black olives, this popular Italian bread takes its name from the Italian word for hearth – which is where it was traditionally baked.

INGREDIENTS

225g/8oz/2 cups unbleached plain
    (all-purpose) flour, sifted
2.5ml/1/2 tsp salt
7g/1/4oz sachet easy-blend (rapid-rise)
    dried yeast
4 garlic cloves, finely chopped
2 sprigs of rosemary, leaves removed
    and chopped
10 black olives, pitted and roughly
    chopped (optional)
15ml/1 tbsp olive oil

For the topping
90ml/6 tbsp olive oil
10ml/2 tsp rock salt
1 sprig of rosemary, leaves removed

Makes 1 loaf

1 Mix together the flour, salt, yeast, garlic, rosemary and olives, if using, in a bowl. Make a well in the centre and add the olive oil and 150ml/1/4 pint/2/3 cup warm water. Mix to form a soft dough.

HEALTH BENEFITS

The oil in olives is monounsaturated and this type of oil is believed to reduce blood cholesterol levels. Olives also provide good amounts of iron and the antioxidant, vitamin E.

2 Turn out the dough on to a floured work surface and knead for 10–15 minutes. Put the dough in an oiled bowl and cover with oiled clear film (plastic wrap) or a dish towel. Leave to rise in a warm place for 45 minutes, until the dough has doubled in bulk.

3 Turn out the dough on to the floured surface and knead lightly again. Roll out to an oval shape, about 1cm/1/2in thick.

4 Place the dough on a greased baking sheet, cover loosely with oiled clear film or a dish towel and leave in a warm place to rise again for 25–30 minutes.

5 Preheat the oven to 200°C/ 400°F/Gas 6. Make indentations with your fingertips all over the top of the bread. Drizzle two-thirds of the olive oil over the top, then sprinkle with the rock salt and rosemary.

6 Bake for 25 minutes until golden. The bread should sound hollow when tapped underneath. Transfer to a wire rack and spoon the remaining olive oil over the top.

VARIATIONS

• To make sun-dried tomato focaccia, omit the rosemary leaves and olives, and add 75g/3oz/1 1/2 cups chopped and drained sun-dried tomatoes in oil to the dry ingredients. Add 15ml/1 tbsp sun-dried tomato purée (paste) and 15ml/ 1 tbsp of the oil from the sun-dried tomatoes to the dough when adding the oil and water, then mix well.

• To make saffron focaccia, add a few strands of saffron to the warm water and leave to stand for 5 minutes before adding to the flour. Alternatively, add a pinch of saffron powder to the flour.

Energy 1607kcal/6716kJ; Protein 21g; Carbohydrate 175g, of which sugars 3g; Fat 96g, of which saturates 14g; Cholesterol 0mg; Calcium 333mg; Fibre 9g; Sodium 682mg.

Index

Author's Acknowledgements

For their help, patience and support, I'd like to give special thanks
to Jo Younger, James Fisher and Fatima for their inspiring and
delicious ideas and suggestions; and Linda Fraser for giving me the
opportunity to write this book and for her continued support and
guidance. Thanks, too, to Alan Long for his advice. Finally, special
thanks to my husband Silvio for his everlasting patience, support
and help with testing and sampling countless recipes.

I would also like to acknowledge the following books and
organisations, which were helpful in my research: Food Your
Miracle Medicine, Jean Carper, Simon & Schuster, 1993;
Delicatessen Food Handbook, Glynn Christian, Macdonald and Co,
1982; The Realeat Encyclopedia of Vegetarian Living, Peter Cox,
Bloomsbury 1994; Sophie Grigson's Ingredients Book, Mitchell
Beazley, 1991; Wholefoods Companion, Dianne Onstad, Chelsea
Green Publishing Co. US., 1996; Foods That Harm, Foods That
Heal, Reader's Digest, 1996; Healing Foods, Miriam Polunin,
Dorling Kindersley, 1997; The Food Pharmacy, Jean Carper, Simon
& Schuster, 1989; Solgar Vitamins; Health and Diet Co., and
Quest Vitamins.

NOTES

NOTES

NOTES

NOTES